The Open University

THE CORE OF LIFE
VOLUME I

EDITED BY JILL SAFFREY

Kylie-ann Johnson.
Access to HE: Science

PHOTOS ON COVER   ① ②
③ ④ ⑤

① DNA

Computer artwork showing a fragment of the molecule deoxyribonucleic acid (DNA). DNA contains the inherited instructions necessary for the development of a living organism. It consists of two strands twisted into a helical shape, with bases (coloured bars) projecting inwards. These bases pair in a complementary fashion to form a code of genetic instructions. Gene therapy uses DNA manipulation to treat genetic diseases. Courtesy of Mehau Kulyk/Science Photo Library.

② Brain cells: astrocytes and neurons (nerve cells)

Immunofluorescent light micrograph of brain cells from the cortex of a mammalian brain. The nucleus of both cell types is stained blue and cytoplasm of the astrocytes is stained green. Astrocytes have numerous branches which provide support and nutrition to the neurons and may also play a role in information storage. Courtesy of Nancy Kedersha/Science Photo Library.

③ Sea horse

X-ray (in false colours) of a sea horse, *Hippocampus* sp. A sea horse is a type of teleost fish. Sea horses swim slowly using fins (not seen here) and can use their tails to attach to seaweed or coral. The male sea horse incubates the fertilized eggs in a brood pouch on his abdomen. Courtesy of D. Roberts/Science Photo Library.

④ Sunflowers

A group of blooming sunflowers, *Helianthus* sp., against the sky. The plant produces composite flowers: the small, true flowers are clustered into a compact, round head which resembles a single flower. The plant is widely cultivated for its seeds which are used to make cooking oil and as food for livestock. Courtesy of David Nunuk/Science Photo Library.

⑤ Viruses

Illustration based on a transmission electron micrograph of human immunodeficiency viruses (HIV) (shown in yellow) budding out of a human T cell. HIV causes AIDS (Acquired Immune Deficiency Syndrome) by damaging T cells — the white blood cells that play a crucial role in the immune system. Courtesy of Chris Bjornberg/Science Photo Library.

The Open University, Walton Hall, Milton Keynes, MK7 6AA

First published 2001

Edited, designed and typeset by The Open University.

Printed in the United Kingdom by The Alden Group, Oxford.

ISBN 0 7492 97492

This publication forms part of an Open University course, S204 *Biology: Uniformity and Diversity*. The complete list of texts which make up this course can be found at the back. Details of this and other Open University courses can be obtained from the Call Centre, PO Box 724, The Open University, Milton Keynes MK7 6ZS, United Kingdom: tel. +44 (0)1908 653231, e-mail ces-gen@open.ac.uk

Alternatively, you may visit the Open University website at http://www.open.ac.uk where you can learn more about the wide range of courses and packs offered at all levels by The Open University.

To purchase this publication or other components of Open University courses, contact Open University Worldwide Ltd, The Berrill Building, Walton Hall, Milton Keynes MK7 6AA, United Kingdom: tel. +44 (0)1908 858785; fax +44 (0)1908 858787; e-mail ouwenq@open.ac.uk; website http://www.ouw.co.uk

1.1

s204book 3volIi1.1

The S204 Course Team

Course Team Chair
Hilary MacQueen

Academic Editor
Caroline Pond

Course Managers
Vivien Bacigalupo
Chris Edwards
Christine Gorman

Course Secretary
Dawn Partner

Authors
Mary Bell (Book 5)
Eric Bowers (Book 6)
John Burnett (Book 4)
Alan Cann (Book 4)
Mel Clements (Book 3)
Basiro Davey (Book 2)
Hilary Denny (Book 5)
Sue Downs (Book 5)
Mandy Dyson (Books 2 and 6)
Anna Furth (Books 3 and 4)
Michael Gillman (Book 2)
Tim Halliday (Book 2)
Jane Loughlin (Book 3)
David Male (Book 4)
Hilary MacQueen (Book 4)
Judith Metcalfe (Book 3)
Paul O'Shea (Book 3)
Phil Parker (Book 5)
Caroline Pond (Books 1, 2 and 6)
Irene Ridge (Books 1, 4 and 5)
Jerry Roberts (Book 5)
David Robinson (Book 6)
Jill Saffrey (Book 3)
Robert Saunders (Book 6)
Ayona Silva-Fletcher (Book 3)
Valda Stevens (Book 2)
Margaret Swithenby (Books 3 and 4)
Colin Walker (Books 3 and 4)

GLO Editor
Peggy Varley

Editors
Ian Nuttall
Gillian Riley
Bina Sharma
Margaret Swithenby

OU Graphic Design
Sue Dobson
Ruth Drage
Jenny Nockles
Pam Owen
Howard Twiner
Andrew Whitehead

Library
Lydia Eaton
Judy Thomas

Picture Research
Lydia Eaton

Book Assessors
Gianfranco Novarino (Book 1)
Aubrey Manning (Book 2)
Karl Swann and David Harris (Book 3)
Peter White (Book 4)
David Clarkson and Rachel Leech (Book 5)
John Currey and Brian James (Book 6)

External Course Assessor
Professor Sir David Smith

Consultants
Patricia Ash
Sue Downs
Christine Gorman
Jean MacQueen
Terry Whatson

Skills
Patricia Ash
Hilary Denny

CD-ROM and Video Production

MARY BELL
GAIL BLOCK
JACKI BROWN
PHIL BUTCHER
HILARY DENNY
MIKE DODD
ANNA FURTH
PHIL GAURON
MICHAEL GILLMAN
TIM HALLIDAY
NICKY HEATH
CARYL HOOPER
G. D. JAYALAKSHMI
JULIET KAUFFMANN
MARTIN KEMP
HILARY MacQUEEN
DEREK MARTIN
MARK MURPHY
PHIL PARKER
CAROLINE POND
IRENE RIDGE
JERRY ROBERTS
DAVID ROBINSON
JILL SAFFREY
LIZ SUGDEN
ANDREW SUTTON
MARGARET SWITHENBY
GARY TUCKNOTT
VERINA WAIGHTS
DARREN WYCHERLEY

CONTENTS

CELLS AND TISSUES

1.1   THE NATURE OF CELLS: AN OVERVIEW

Cells are the fundamental units of life; that is, they are the simplest units capable of independent existence. All living things are composed of one or more cells, and the molecular components of all cells are remarkably similar. How does the overwhelming diversity of living organisms arise from what would appear to be such uniform starting material? In order to begin to answer this fundamental question, in this chapter we examine cells, their components, and their interactions.

We begin with a brief resumé of the nature of cells; then we go on to study the organization of cells in more detail.

1.1.1   CELL UNIFORMITY

All cells are composed of the same kinds of molecular building blocks (Table 1.1) and share a similar basic plan, with which you may already be familiar. Although all cells possess a *cell membrane* enclosing the cell contents and are composed of similar molecules, the internal organization of prokaryote and eukaryote cells differs. Eukaryote cells contain structures known as **organelles**, which are large molecular assemblies predominantly composed of lipids together with associated proteins and which form internal membrane systems. Organelles serve to compartmentalize some of the different biochemical reactions that take place in eukaryote cells. Eukaryotes also contain specialized proteins that form a

Table 1.1   Simple summary of the chemical components of cells.

Chemical	Constituent molecule/ion	Functions
proteins	amino acids	many different functional roles, e.g. enzymes, structural proteins, contractile proteins, transporters, receptors
polysaccharides	monosaccharides	energy production and storage, and in plants and some invertebrate animals, support (cell walls)
glycoproteins	combinations of protein and carbohydrate, e.g. proteoglycans (peptidoglycans)	cell adhesion and recognition molecules, lubricants (e.g. mucus) bacterial cell wall
lipids	phospholipids cholesterol glycolipids neutral triacylglycerols	membrane structure (cell membrane and eukaryote organelles), signalling molecules energy storage
nucleic acids (DNA and RNA)	nucleotides	genetic information
ions	e.g. Na^+, K^+, Ca^{2+}, Cl^- (and others)	many, including fluid balance and signalling
minerals	e.g. calcium, phosphate	strength and support, e.g. bone

cytoskeleton, while prokaryotes do not. The *total* contents of the cell (apart from the nucleus) are known as the **cytoplasm**. The cellular contents excluding the organelles are known as the **cytosol,** which consists largely of water in which organic molecules and ions are dissolved. The cytoplasm of prokaryotes therefore consists entirely of cytosol, while that of eukaryotes consists of the cytosol plus the organelles and cytoskeleton.

○ Name three cell organelles that you are already familiar with, and state their main functions.

● You are likely to have thought of nuclei, mitochondria and chloroplasts. The nucleus separates the genetic information from the rest of the cell and is where transcription (the synthesis of RNA from DNA) takes place. The mitochondria are the sites at which energy, in the form of ATP, is generated. Chloroplasts are the sites of photosynthesis. You might also have thought of lysosomes, which are small membrane-bound structures that contain degradative enzymes that break down ingested pathogens, amongst other things.

Eukaryote cells contain a number of other organelles, some or all of which you may also be familiar with. The organelles found in animal and plant cells are shown in diagrams of 'typical' cells in Figure 1.1. You will become familiar with the content of Figure 1.1 since you will refer to it often as you learn about the different organelles later in this chapter.

1.1.2   CELL COMMUNITIES

Few cells exist as isolated entities; most are part of a cellular community. The nature of these communities varies. Single-celled organisms, such as bacteria, frequently live in colonies. Simple multicellular animals such as sponges are essentially aggregates of cells, while in the more complex multicellular organisms different cells tend to be organized into distinct groups or **tissues**, according to function. The most complex animals have evolved highly organized arrangements of different types of cells into **organs** and even **systems** that perform specific functions. An example of an organ with which you are familiar is the intestine, which forms part of the digestive system. Other examples include the nervous, circulatory, respiratory and excretory systems. In this book, we will focus mostly on examples of mammalian tissues.

The study of tissue structure is known as **histology** (from the Greek 'histo', meaning tissue or web). At first, histologists categorized tissues according to their function; so the major types were classified as nerve (communication), muscle (movement), epithelial (barrier) and connective (support and storage) tissues. Additional categories were blood or lymphoid cells, and glandular tissue, which is essentially a very complex type of epithelial tissue. In vertebrates, however, most tissues are compound in nature, that is, they contain a mixture of these six major cell types (for example, muscle contains blood vessels, nerves and connective tissue), so there is now a somewhat less rigid classification of tissues. Nevertheless, it is a useful skill to be able to recognize some of the different cell types typically present in a tissue or organ.

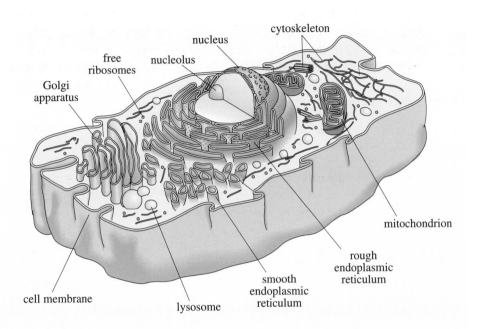

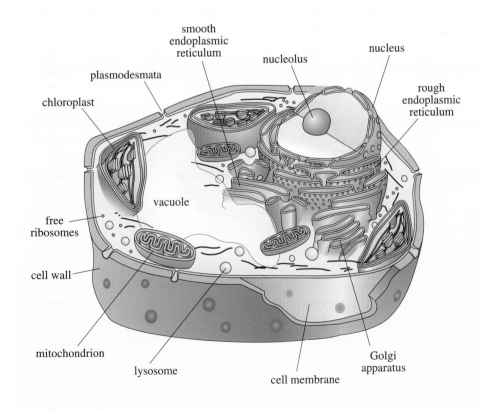

Figure 1.1 (a) Schematic diagram of a 'typical' animal cell, showing cell organelles and cytoskeleton; (b) schematic diagram of a 'typical' plant cell, showing cell organelles and cytoskeleton.

○ Why might such a skill be useful in medicine?

● A knowledge of the typical or 'normal' arrangement and relative abundance of cells in a tissue allows detection of 'abnormal' cells or arrangements of cells, such as those that may occur in certain diseases.

Identification of cells in a tissue specimen also allows deduction about the function of the tissue, as might be of interest in working out the physiology of a newly discovered animal. Cells with similar functions often (but not always) have a similar appearance even in animals that are only distantly related. A summary of different cell types is given in Table 1.2 which is intended as a point of reference.

1.1.3 A NOTE ON SIZE AND NUMBERS

You already have an idea of the range of sizes of many different organisms. However, when we get to the level of tissues, cells and cell organelles, it is difficult to comprehend just how small these structures are! Cells are also diverse in size; the giant nerve cells of squids have processes that can be up to nearly 1 mm in diameter while those of a large vertebrate are much thinner, at around 2 μm in diameter, although they may be several metres in length. Most animal cells, however are more regular in shape and typically measure about 10–50 μm in diameter. The diameter of mature plant cells is typically around 50–100 μm. The smallest cells are bacteria, but their size again varies widely; typically they are a few micrometres across.

○ Mitochondria are thought to have evolved from bacteria. What would you expect the size of a mitochondrion to be?

● Mitochondria are about the size of typical large bacteria; in animals they are usually about 2–8 μm in length.

A schematic illustration showing the relative sizes of some organisms, cells, organelles, molecules and atoms is shown in Figure 1.2.

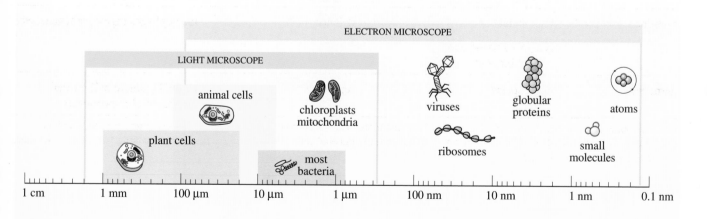

Figure 1.2   The relative sizes of organisms, cells, organelles, molecules and atoms, arranged on a logarithmic scale. The range of structures that are visible with the light and electron microscope (Sections 1.2.1 and 1.2.2) are also shown. (Note that the illustrations are not drawn to scale.)

Table 1.2 Summary of the principal types of mammalian cells.

Cell type	Examples	Functions	Special features
epithelial cells	epidermis (outer layer of skin); lining of intestine, blood vessels and lungs; cells of glands (e.g. salivary, mammary glands)	protection, barrier, absorption, secretion	form sheets of closely linked, polarized cells
hormone-producing (endocrine) cells	pancreas; adrenal gland	widespread communication	produce and secrete chemical messengers into the circulation
muscle cells	smooth muscle of internal organs, such as intestine and blood vessels	movement, e.g. peristalsis	contain contractile proteins; linked by gap junctions
	skeletal muscle of limbs	movement of limbs	contain contractile proteins; form syncytium of long multinucleate fibre-like cells
	cardiac (heart) muscle	contraction of heart	contain contractile proteins
nerve cells (neurons)	neurons of brain, spinal cord, small groups of neurons (ganglia) in body	rapid and specific communication	polarized cells with long processes; special membrane properties allow electrical signalling
support cells (often known as connective tissue cells)	bone cartilage fibroblasts	provide support and help organize tissue structure	produce much extracellular material
adipocytes	adipose tissue around certain organs and under skin	energy storage, protection	contain little cytoplasm apart from triacylglycerols
blood cells	red blood cells (rbcs)	oxygen transport	rbcs contain haemoglobin which binds oxygen; mammalian rbcs lose their nucleus
	leukocytes	defence	plasma cells produce antibodies
immune system cells	leukocytes lymphoid tissue and circulating leukocytes	defence	macrophages ingest pathogens, etc.
germ cells	eggs, sperm	reproduction	haploid (contain half normal number of chromosomes)

Note that some cells, such as leukocytes, can be classified into more than one group (blood and immune system). Endocrine cells and other glandular cells are frequently considered to be a specialized type of epithelial cell. Adipose tissue cells are often classified as connective tissue. For detailed explanations, see text.

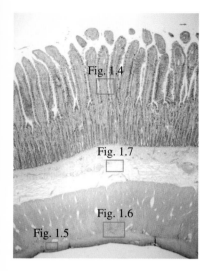

Figure 1.3 Light micrograph of a section of rat small intestine, stained with Alcian blue, haematoxylin and eosin. Magnification × 16. The labelled boxes indicate areas of different cell types and these are illustrated in more detail in Figures 1.4–1.8.

It is also worth noting the wide range of cell numbers in multicellular organisms. The much-studied nematode worm *C. elegans*, has exactly 959 somatic cells in its adult form, while vertebrates, especially mammals, have many more; there are more than 10^{13} cells in the human body.

1.1.4 CELL DIVERSITY: AN EXAMPLE

You have already seen that all cells conform to a basic structural plan, but that the form and functions of cells can be diverse. As an example of the diversity of animal cells, we shall consider the different types of cell found in the mammalian small intestine. Figure 1.3 is a photomicrograph that shows a section through the gut wall in which different layers of cells can be identified.

Each of the different cell types within the gut has a role to play in gut functions. Smooth muscle cells contract, causing a wave of constriction of the gut wall (known as peristalsis), which moves food along the intestine. Connective tissue cells provide support. Epithelial cells are a varied group; most are involved in the absorption of nutrients, but some produce digestive enzymes and yet others are specialized to secrete hormones into the blood. Blood vessels, the larger of which are actually composed of several cell types, transport absorbed nutrients to the rest of the organism. Cells of the immune system (not visible in Figure 1.3) defend against damage by ingested pathogens. Nerve cells (also known as neurons) coordinate the activities of the other cell types.

Now we will look more closely at the structural and functional differences between some of these cells. First, the epithelial cells, which form a barrier, or interface, across which some substances are secreted and most nutrients are selectively absorbed. What structural and molecular properties of the epithelial cells confer these particular functional characteristics? The barrier properties arise because the epithelial cells are tightly packed next to each other as a distinct cell layer. This packing occurs because of the type and arrangement of structural molecules within the cells, that results in the formation of special close contacts between them. You will learn more about these contacts in Section 1.5.2. A layer of epithelial cells is known as an **epithelium**.

The absorptive properties arise because of the presence and arrangement of specific proteins called *transporters*. There are many kinds of transporters, which you will learn about in Chapter 3; those involved in absorption of nutrients are located only in the part of the cell membrane that comes into contact with food (known as the apical surface; the other boundaries are known as the basolateral surfaces). So, the membrane of these epithelial cells is *polarized*, that is, its properties are different on one side of the cell than on the other. Absorption is facilitated by the presence of finger-like projections known as *microvilli*, which increase the surface area that is in contact with the ingested nutrients. These features of intestinal epithelial cells are shown in Figure 1.4b. They illustrate that the properties of a tissue or cell are determined not only by the particular molecules that they contain, but also by the *arrangement* of these molecules within the cell. We shall consider some of the other properties of intestinal epithelial cells later.

Next look at the smooth muscle cells. These cells are *contractile*, that is, their shape can change, either shortening (contraction) or lengthening (relaxation;

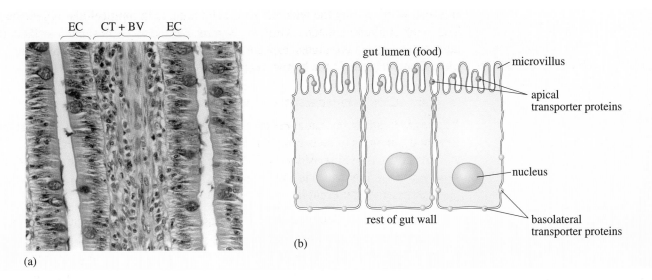

(a)

(b)

Figure 1.4 (a) Light micrograph showing epithelium from rat intestine stained with Alcian blue, haematoxylin and eosin. Cytoplasm is pale pink, nuclei dark purple/black. The bright blue areas are mucus present in some of the epithelial cells. EC = endothelial cells; CT = connective tissue; BV = blood vessel. Magnification × 215. (b) Simplified schematic diagram showing some properties of intestinal epithelium. The epithelial cells are rectangular in shape, and form a barrier because they are closely packed together, and linked by specialized proteins (Section 1.5.2). The cells are polarized; the surface of absorptive cells that is in contact with the nutrients in the gut possesses microvilli, which increase the surface area available for absorption, while the other surfaces do not. Also shown (*not* to scale) is the uneven distribution of transporter proteins in the membrane. Different types of transporter are present in the apical and basolateral membranes.

smooth muscle cells are different from other muscle cells, they have an intrinsic basal level of contraction, and can hence be stimulated to relax). Coordinated contraction and relaxation of many smooth muscle cells together results in the intestinal movements known as peristalsis. How are the movements of the separate muscle cells coordinated, and what is the nature of the molecules that produce this movement? Again, specific proteins are involved in these processes, some, known as gap junctions, allowing connectivity between the cells, and others that cause a change in shape. You will learn about these proteins in more detail in Chapter 7. The features of smooth muscle cells are shown in Figure 1.5.

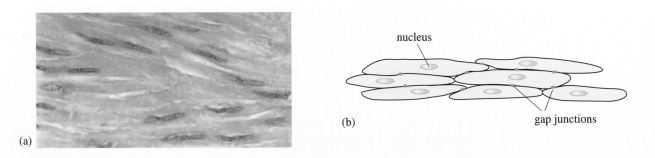

(a)

(b)

Figure 1.5 (a) Light micrograph showing smooth muscle from intestine stained with Alcian blue, haematoxylin and eosin. Magnification × 370. (b) Simplified schematic diagram showing some properties of smooth muscle cells. Smooth muscle cells are closely packed, and linked by gap junctions (Section 1.5.2). They contain specialized proteins that mediate contraction (not shown).

Next, consider the nerve cell, or neuron. Small groups of neurons are situated within the gut wall, in small linked clumps known as ganglia (Figure 1.6b). The neurons are not identical; they are diverse and have a number of different functions in the gut. All, however, are involved in conveying information to other cells. Some extend long processes into the surrounding smooth muscle, where they activate the smooth muscle cells, stimulating them either to contract or relax. These functional properties of neurons are reflected in structural specializations which are, again, the result of the presence and arrangement of specific proteins within these cells. Neurons, like intestinal epithelial cells, are polarized. Some of the properties of neurons are shown in Figure 1.6a.

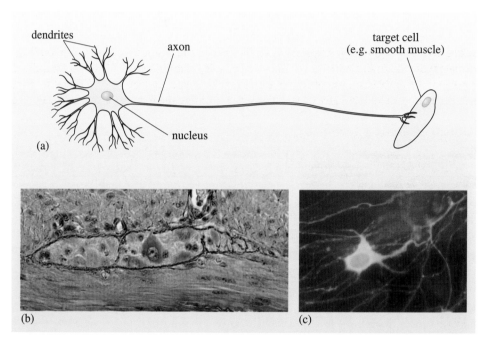

Figure 1.6 (a) Simplified diagram showing some of the properties of neurons. Neurons are specialized to transmit electrical signals rapidly, often over long distances. Typically they receive information at processes known as dendrites, and transmit information to their target cell, which may be a smooth muscle cell, an epithelial or another cell type, along a long cellular process known as an axon. Different membrane proteins are found in different regions of the neuronal membrane. Neurons are polarized cells (*not* to scale). (b) Light micrograph showing a small group of neurons in the rat intestine stained with Alcian blue, haematoxylin and eosin. (Note that the processes of the neurons are not visible in this preparation.) Magnification × 300. (c) Fluorescence micrograph of a labelled neuron from a similar sample. Magnification × 350.

Other cell types present in the gut are connective tissue cells, or fibroblasts, and leukocytes. These cells also have specific functions: fibroblasts provide support and secrete molecules that form the extracellular connective tissue; leukocytes are involved in defence. At a first glance, these two cell types perhaps do not have such interesting structural specializations as some of the other cells that we have described, but they each contain and secrete special proteins that determine their functions. Some of the properties of fibroblasts and leukocytes are shown in Figures 1.7 and 1.8.

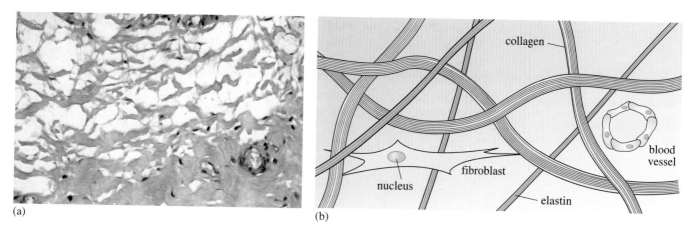

(a)

(b)

Figure 1.7 (a) Light micrograph showing fibroblasts and connective tissue from rat intestine stained with Alcian blue, haematoxylin and eosin. A blood vessel is also visible. Magnification × 200. (b) Simplified diagram showing some of the properties of fibroblasts. Fibroblasts have an irregular shape, and are often difficult to discern by light microcopy. They produce and secrete molecules into the extracellular space, forming the extracellular matrix, and connective tissue (Section 1.5.1).

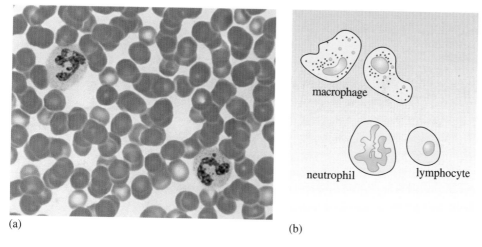

(a)

(b)

Figure 1.8 (a) Light micrograph showing two leukocytes among red blood cells from human blood stained with Alcian blue, haematoxylin and eosin. Magnification × 660. (b) Simplified diagram showing three types of leukocytes. Leukocytes are migratory cells of the immune system, that are carried in the circulation, and migrate into the tissues. Their role is in defence; they 'patrol' the body and congregate at sites of infection and tissue damage. Neutrophils and macrophages ingest material; lymphocytes have various roles in the immune response.

We have used these five cell types (epithelial, smooth muscle, neuron, fibroblast and leukocyte) as examples of cellular diversity and we will refer often to these cells during the course of this chapter and the rest of the book. There are of course other types of cell in the gut, and many more in other organs.

Before we go on, there are a few terms that need to be defined. Cells, such as the different types of intestinal cells that we have described above, that are specialized, are known as *differentiated* cells. During the development of an organism, these specialized cells are formed from unspecialized cells, by a process known as **differentiation**. The question of *how* the different cells of an organism, which of course arise from a single zygote, become differentiated is one which has always intrigued cell biologists and is still the subject of intense study. You will learn about differentiation in Chapter 10.

Aside from the inherent interest in how all the different cell types present in an adult individual arise from a single cell, there is a practical reason for studying these developmental processes. A number of human and animal diseases arise when things 'go wrong' during development (for example, spina bifida). Understanding the molecules and mechanisms involved in normal development may provide information that could lead to ways of preventing or remedying such conditions.

As you have seen, different types of cells differ not only in shape, but importantly, in some of the molecules that they contain. As well as the many structural molecules and enzymes involved in core metabolic reactions that are common to all the cells of a particular organism, they contain additional molecules which enable them to perform specialized functions. For example, many intestinal epithelial cells have special transporter proteins that allow absorption of nutrients. Smooth muscle cells, neurons, connective tissue cells and leukocytes, however, do not contain these particular types of transporters, but do contain other specialized molecules, many of which are proteins. You will remember that proteins are coded for by the genetic material of the cell (DNA, situated in the chromosomes). The DNA sequences that encode different proteins are known as genes; however, not all the genes that an organism contains are transcribed and translated into protein; those that are, are said to be *expressed*. It is this *differential* **gene expression** which gives rise to the presence of different proteins in different cells, and hence to cell differentiation. How gene expression is controlled is an important topic that we shall return to in Chapter 9.

1.1.5 CELLS ARE DYNAMIC

Apart from dormant cells such as those found in seeds and spores, all living cells are active (note that dead cells contribute to important structural tissues such as hair, horn and wood). In addition to the obvious examples of physical activity exhibited by muscle cells and by motile cells such as sperm cells, at the molecular level all cells are highly dynamic. Cells take up nutrients from their environment and convert them into energy and new molecules; they also eliminate waste molecules, and if conditions are right, many cells grow and divide. All these processes are the result of many coordinated biochemical events. As well as these 'housekeeping' processes that take place in all cells, specialized reactions occur in many cells, and all cells must interact with other members of the cellular community.

○ Give two examples of cellular interactions that occur in the gut.

● (i) Coordinated smooth muscle contraction involves interactions between individual smooth muscle cells. (ii) Smooth muscle cells are stimulated to contract or relax by the action of neurons.

These examples are just two of the many cell interactions that take place in the gut. If you consider that the gut also contains several other types of cells, and that it interacts with other organs and systems, you will appreciate the complexity of cell dynamics and interactions in just this part of an animal alone. Communication between cells is an essential biological process, and all cells interact with their neighbours. In structurally more complex animals, in addition to this universal interaction between adjacent and nearby cells, specialized cells that provide communication over larger distances, such as neurons and hormone-secreting cells, have evolved.

Once a cell has received a signal from another cell, it usually responds in some way. The response may, in some cases, be readily detected, as the shape or appearance of the cell may be affected. One example that we have considered is that of smooth muscle contraction in response to nerve stimulation. Another example is that of cell division, which, as you will learn in Chapter 10, often occurs in response to molecules secreted by other cells. Many cellular responses, however, involve changes in the biochemistry of cells that cannot be detected unless sensitive biochemical assays are used. It is important to realize that biochemical changes underlie *all* cellular responses. In our examples, muscle contraction is brought about by changes in specific proteins within the smooth muscle cells; cell division involves coordinated changes in a large number of proteins in the cell. Cellular responses also often involve a chain, or a cascade of biochemical events within the cell, and may culminate in changes in gene expression. Cell interactions can thus also play an essential role in the regulation of gene expression, and so in determining the very nature of cells, as you will see.

In this introductory section, we have illustrated the diversity and the complexity of cells. We have also begun to consider how this diversity can arise from an underlying uniformity of organization. In order to understand this further, and learn about how cells perform their many functions, we need to delve more deeply into the organization of cells. First we will consider the types of biological investigation that have been and still are used to find out about the nature of cells, and about how cells function.

SUMMARY OF SECTION 1.1

1   All cells are composed of similar kinds of molecules, and are enclosed by a cell membrane. Prokaryote and eukaryote cells differ; eukaryote cells (with occasional exceptions) have a nucleus, membrane-based organelles and a cytoskeleton; prokaryote cells do not.

2   Despite their underlying uniformity of molecular and intracellular organization, eukaryote cells are extremely diverse in overall structure and in function.

3   Cells form communities. Some unicellular organisms form colonies. In structurally complex organisms, cells that perform similar functions are often grouped together into tissues. In the most complex animals, different cells and tissues are often grouped together into an organ, or system, which is specialized to perform a specific function(s).

4   Animal tissues are usually composed of a mixture of cell types, which are classified as epithelial, muscle, nervous, connective, blood and immune system, hormone-secreting and germ cells, although some cells, such as the hormone-secreting cells of the intestinal epithelium, fall into more than one of these categories.

5   Cells become specialized, or differentiate, as a result of differential gene expression, leading to the synthesis of specific proteins.

6   Except when in a dormant state (e.g. spores), all living cells are dynamic. They interact with their environment in order to obtain a source of energy and molecular building blocks, and respond to biochemical environmental changes. Individual cells, particularly in multicellular organisms, receive and respond to 'signals' from other cells. Many cells move within their environment. All these processes require a myriad of biochemical events within the cell.

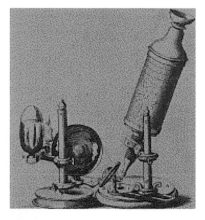

Figure 1.9 Robert Hooke's light microscope. Robert Hooke (1635–1703) has been called the greatest scientist of the 17th century. Alongside significant contributions to a range of science and technology disciplines, including biology, chemistry, physics, geology, architecture and astronomy, he devised the compound microscope and illumination system shown here, one of the best such microscopes of the time. With it he observed a diversity of objects, including insects and sponges, etc., and he recorded them with accurate drawings and beautifully detailed notes. Probably his most famous microscopical observation was his study of thin slices of cork. He wrote:

…I could exceedingly plainly perceive it all to be perforated and porous…these pores, or cells, … were indeed the first *microscopical* pores I ever saw, and perhaps, that were ever seen, for I had not met with any Writer or Person, that had made any mention of them before this.

1.2 HOW CELLS ARE STUDIED: A BRIEF ACCOUNT

In the first part of the chapter, we saw that vertebrate tissues, especially those of mammals, are complex, and are composed of diverse cells. This diversity arises because of differential gene expression, i.e. different types of cells express different proteins. But how have these facts been established; what methods are used to study the properties of cells?

We do not have space here to detail all the methods that are used in the study of cells and tissues. We will begin by giving a brief background with a historical perspective, but focusing on methods that still are used widely today. Details of some key techniques are shown in boxes. You will learn more of other important methods, including some of the molecular techniques that have revolutionized the study of cell biology, in later parts of this book. First we will consider how the *structure* of cells and tissues is studied.

1.2.1 LIGHT MICROSCOPY: THE STUDY OF TISSUE ORGANIZATION

Almost all cells are too small to be seen by the naked eye. It was only when lenses and microscopes were developed that the study of the detail of the cellular organization of organisms could begin. The first simple microscopes were little more than glass lenses; the first compound microscopes were made early in the 17th century (Figure 1.9). When Robert Hooke examined thin slices of cork under a compound microscope in 1655, he noticed small rectangular-shaped structures (Figure 1.10). Because they reminded him of monks' cells, he named these structures 'cells'. They were, in fact, not living cells, but the outer walls of dead plant cells. A brief history of the study of cells and cell structure by light microscopy (often abbreviated to LM) is shown in Table 1.3.

Although what Hooke was observing were the cell walls in dead cork tissue, he had effectively discovered plant cells and gained a first understanding of the basic structure of plant tissue.

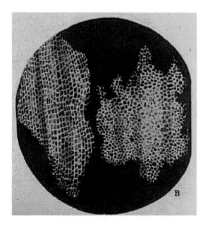

Figure 1.10 The cell walls of cork drawn by Hooke.

Table 1.3 Summary of 'landmark' events in the history of early light microscopy.

Year	Event
1655	Robert Hooke made the first observations of cells using light microscopy of mature plant tissue
1674	Living protoctists observed by van Leeuwenhoek
1838/9	Cell theory proposed by Schleiden and Schwann – that the unit of structure and function in animals and plants is the nucleated cell
1855	Virchow proposed that cells arise only by the division of pre-existing cells
1857	Kolliker discovered mitochondria
1898	Golgi first described what became known as the 'Golgi apparatus'

A problem faced by the early microscopists was that most living animal tissues are translucent, making it difficult to discern structural detail. During the 19th century the use of chemicals to fix and stain samples was developed; stains were found that bound to different cellular components or to particular types of cell. The study of stained preparations allowed a wide range of cells to be studied, leading to the formulation of the cell theory. Haematoxylin, for example, binds to negatively charged molecules such as those with phosphate groups, and so stains nucleic acids and is used to visualize nuclei, while eosin binds to positively charged molecules, such as many cytosolic proteins, and so is used to stain the cytosol. These and similar stains have been used with great effect for many years to study the organization of tissues, both in normal and in diseased specimens.

A particularly striking example of a method that labelled whole cells selectively was a silver impregnation technique developed by the Italian scientist, Camillo Golgi (Figure 1.11). The method, often known as Golgi stain, was difficult to perform consistently, but allowed detailed visualization of the shape of nerve cells. A similar method is still sometimes used for this purpose today.

Camillo Golgi also used his method to study the detail of intracellular structures, and in 1898, whilst studying nerve cells stained by the black reaction, Golgi noticed the fine basket-like meshwork surrounding the nucleus and named it the 'apparato reticolare interno' or 'internal reticular apparatus', nowadays known as the Golgi apparatus (Figure 1.12). Despite its discovery, this structure could not be consistently seen in stained preparations of fixed cells and not at all in living cells.

Figure 1.11 Camillo Golgi (1843–1926). Camillo Golgi studied and worked at the famous Italian Medical School of Pavia under the influence of some of the most famous clinicians of the time and was inspired by his tuition in histology and cell biology. Despite moving away from Pavia to a poorly equipped hospital which lacked even basic laboratory facilities, he continued his laborious research into cell staining techniques and developed his most famous scientific achievement, the difficult and unpredictable histological staining method known as the 'black reaction'. He achieved recognition for his pioneering work in establishing the structure of the fine neuronal network in the central nervous system using this metal-impregnation stain and was awarded a prestigious position in Pavia where he held the chair of Histology and General Pathology until his retirement. He established a school of thinking that produced many famous scholars and in 1906 was awarded the Nobel Prize for Physiology or Medicine.

Figure 1.12 The Golgi apparatus, as first seen by Camillo Golgi.

○ Why might many of Golgi's contemporaries have doubted the existence of the structure he described?

● The structure was not always visible, so it is possible that it could have been caused by a change in the normal arrangement of the cell brought about by the methods Golgi used to prepare his specimens.

Changes in tissue structure due to the methods and chemicals used to prepare specimens for microscopy are sometimes seen, and are known as **artefacts**. Another common problem with tissue preparation is shrinkage. Microscopists must take these changes caused by tissue preparation into account when interpreting what they see under the microscope.

It was only the introduction of the electron microscope many years later that resolved this debate and confirmed the existence of the Golgi apparatus. You will learn more about this organelle, which has proved to be a vital component of eukaryote cells and is still the subject of much research, later in this chapter.

The 19th century microscopists produced elegant descriptions and drawings of different cells and tissues. Their work provided valuable information about the shapes and general chemical properties of cells and some organelles, but was restricted by two technical problems. First, the limited **resolution** (the smallest distance by which two objects are separated and still be seen as separate entities) of the light microscope, which did not allow the high magnification needed for detailed analysis of small cell components. Second, the lack of sensitive staining methods to allow the location of specific molecules within tissues and cells. Further developments in the 20th century resolved both these problems, and light microscopy is still one of the most widely used techniques in cell biology. Different types of light microscope are used for different applications.

FLUORESCENCE MICROSCOPY

Fluorescence microscopes are used to visualize cells that contain molecules that emit fluorescent light when illuminated by ultraviolet (UV) light at particular wavelengths. Such molecules are now widely used as markers and tools in cell biology (see Figure 1.6c). They include dyes that can be microinjected into cells and fill their cytosol, and so reveal their shape, as has been used in studies of the shape of neurons, and 'detector' molecules such as antibodies that are tagged by fluorescence markers (see Section 1.2.4, Box 1.2). Most recently, methods that allow the use of fluorescence markers in living cells have been developed. These methods include the use of dyes that are sensitive to ionic changes within cells (see Chapter 6), and most recently, the 'engineering' of cells so that the gene for a specific protein that is normally produced is coupled to an introduced gene that encodes a fluorescent protein, known as **green fluorescent protein (GFP**; a protein naturally produced by the jellyfish, *Aequorea* spp.). In this way, when a living cell expresses the protein of interest, it can be detected by fluorescence microscopy, because GFP is expressed at the same time.

CONFOCAL MICROSCOPY

A major recent development in fluorescence microscopy has been the development of the laser scanning **confocal** microscope. A problem with conventional fluorescent microscopes is that, unless the specimen is very thin, the image obtained from a single part of a specimen is not completely clear because of fluorescence emitted from molecules at several levels in the specimen. In confocal microscopy, electronic technology is used to focus an illuminating beam of ultraviolet light at a restricted point, i.e. at a single plane of focus in a specimen. The image is collected by a detector at the precise point at which it is focused after passing through the specimen. Light focused at different levels is not collected, and does not affect the image, which is therefore very sharp. A laser scans the specimen, and the image is captured electronically. The process is then repeated with the light focused at different levels in the specimen. In this way, a series of images can be collected at different levels in the specimen, and a composite three-dimensional image can be generated. This technique, combined with specific fluorescent labelling methods (Section 1.2.4 and 1.2.5) has proved to be a powerful tool in cell biology and has allowed three-dimensional reconstruction of cell and tissue organization.

1.2.2 ELECTRON MICROSCOPY: OBSERVATION OF THE INTERNAL STRUCTURE OF CELLS

The problem of limited resolution of the traditional microscope was overcome in the 1930s, by the development of electron microscopes, which use beams of electrons instead of light. The resolution of a microscope is dependent upon the wavelength of the light or the beam of electrons that is used. The best resolution possible for a standard microscope using visible light is 0.2 µm. Electron beams have a shorter wavelength than that of visible light, and the wavelength of a beam of electrons decreases as the velocity at which they travel increases. Electron beams accelerated at high velocity through an appropriately prepared tissue section and focused on a fluorescent screen can hence be used to resolve cellular components that are as small as 1 nm and which cannot be seen by light microscopy.

Electron microscopy (EM) has been greatly refined since the first commercial electron microscope became available in 1939. The method has allowed detailed examination of cell *ultrastructure* (the structure of the components of the cells, particularly the organelles, sometimes also called *fine* structure) and resolved issues about the existence of cell organelles such as the Golgi apparatus.

1.2.3 BIOCHEMISTRY: THE CHEMISTRY OF CELLS AND ORGANELLES

While the histologists were studying the organization of tissues, biochemists had been studying their chemical properties. By grinding up tissue specimens in different solutions and subjecting the resulting extracts to a range of chemical procedures, their component molecules could be separated and studied. By the end of the 19th century most of the chemical components of cells had been identified, and the properties of the macromolecules were beginning to be characterized. This work involved many biochemists and took many years.

Although the term, 'protein' was coined (by Jons Berzelius) in 1838 and most amino acids had been identified by the end of the 19th century, it was not until 1953 that the exact amino acid sequence of a protein (insulin) was determined for the first time, by Frederick Sanger.

Nevertheless, even though protein sequences were not known, much was being discovered about protein functions, in particular about enzyme activity, which was first demonstrated at the turn of the 19th century. The key central metabolic pathways (the glycolytic pathway and the TCA, or tricarboxylic acid cycle, which you will learn about in Chapter 4) were unravelled in the 1930s. The methods used to study proteins today are described in Chapter 2.

CELL FRACTIONATION: LINKING CELL STRUCTURE WITH CHEMICAL FUNCTION

Many of the enzymes studied in the first half of the 20th century had been prepared from cell extracts, so their normal location within the cell was not known. However, the vital link between cell structure and biochemistry was made possible by developments in a technique known as **centrifugation**, a process by which particles in a liquid medium are separated by spinning, at high speeds, around a central axis. In the 1940s and 50s advances in the technology of centrifugation allowed samples to be spun at very high speeds indeed, a refinement known as *ultra*centrifugation.

Centrifugation can be used in a number of ways, depending upon the nature of the samples, the liquid medium used, and the speed at which they are spun. For example, cells of different sizes or densities can be separated from a preparation of mixed cells; different cell organelles can be separated from each other and even different sized proteins can be separated using the appropriate types of preparation, solutions and centrifugation speeds. Here we focus on **cell fractionation**; the separation of the different components of cells (Box 1.1).

Ultracentrifugation methods have been of great importance in cell biology, because they enabled the functions of cell organelles to be elucidated. In some cases, the method provided the first evidence for the existence of some organelles, such as lysosomes and peroxisomes (small membrane-bound organelles that contain different types of degradative enzymes).

○ If you were interested in determining whether a specific enzyme is associated with a particular cell organelle in intestinal epithelial cells, what methods could you use?

● Cell fractionation followed by biochemical assay for the enzyme.

○ Would this procedure allow you to determine if (a) *only* the intestinal epithelial cells contained the enzyme, and (b) whether *all* the cells in the intestinal epithelium contained this enzyme?

● No, neither (a) nor (b) could be established with certainty, unless (a) the epithelial cells could be separated from the other cells of the gut, and (b) the contents of individual epithelial cells could be analysed separately.

BOX 1.1   CELL FRACTIONATION

If a preparation of cells is disrupted, for example by detergents or ultrasound, or by homogenization (disruption in apparatus rather like a kitchen blender), and placed in an appropriate physiological solution, many of the organelles such as nuclei, mitochondria and Golgi apparatus (see Figure 1.1) remain intact. The cell membrane and the endoplasmic reticulum (Figure 1.1) are disrupted, but in appropriate solutions their membranes re-seal to form vesicles. Vesicles formed from the endoplasmic reticulum are known as *microsomes*. If conditions are right, the original chemical properties of the organelle are retained during the preparation, even the vesicles formed from the cell membrane and ER retain their properties (see Figure 1.13a).

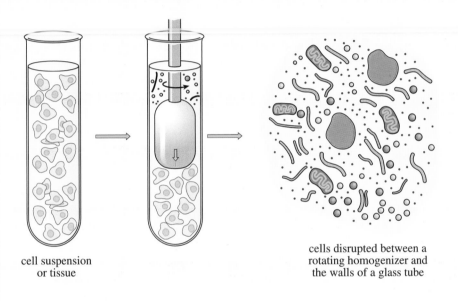

cell suspension
or tissue

cells disrupted between a
rotating homogenizer and
the walls of a glass tube

Figure 1.13a   A cell suspension or pieces of tissue are disrupted by mechanical agitation. Under the right conditions, a homogenate is formed with most membrane-bound organelles remaining intact.

The different components resulting from the disruption of cells are then separated by centrifugation. The samples are placed into special test tubes that are fitted into a rotor that fits into the centrifuge (Figure 1.13b). Separation is on the basis of size (or sometimes density), the largest components moving fastest towards the bottom of the centrifuge tube. Several types of centrifugation can be used.

In *differential sedimentation*, larger components are spun to the bottom of the tube, where they form a 'pellet' (Figure 1.13c). The pellet is separated from the remaining solution (known as the *supernatant*) which contains the smaller components. The pellet can be resuspended and its components studied; the supernatant can be transferred to another centrifuge tube and spun at higher speed to precipitate the smaller components into another pellet. A series of such steps can be performed to separate the different components of a cell homogenate.

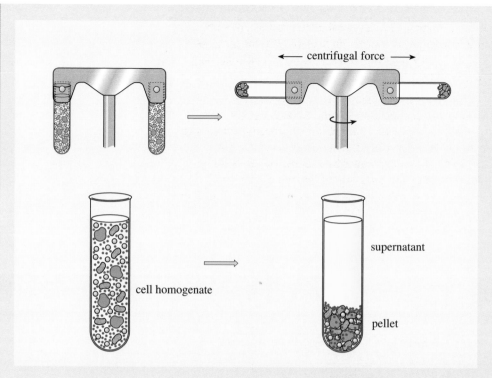

Figure 1.13b Centrifugation: the homogenate constituents separate according to size or density and a pellet of most dense components forms at the bottom of the centrifuge tube.

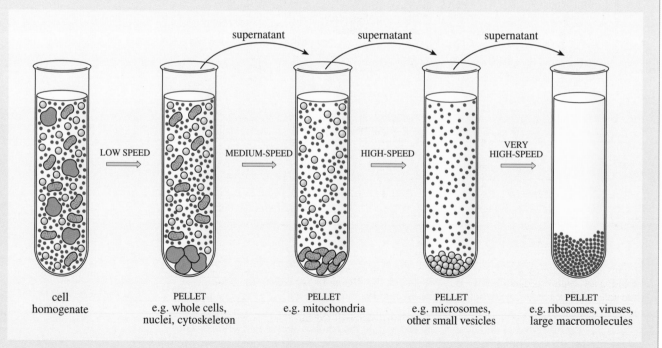

Figure 1.13c Differential sedimentation: low, medium, high and very high speed centrifugation separates out the different components of the original pellet.

What are the speeds used for ultracentrifugation? In a typical ultracentrifuge, rotation at speeds of 30 000 revolutions per minute (rpm) produce a force of 100 000 times that of acceleration due to gravity 'g' (i.e. $100\,000 \times g$ or $100\,000 \times 9.8$ ms^{-2}). Centrifugation speeds are typically expressed as 'g' forces.

A problem with differential sedimentation is that separation is not complete, pellets actually contain something of a mixture of cellular components. A more sensitive and widely used method is *density gradient centrifugation*, which uses a concentrated sucrose solution through which the preparations are centrifuged. Different types of density gradient centrifugation allow separation of particles either by their density or their size. Particles of a particular size or density end up as bands or *fractions* at different parts of the centrifuge tube (Figure 1.13d) and can be collected using a fine pipette, or by piercing the bottom of the tube and collecting the fractions as drops.

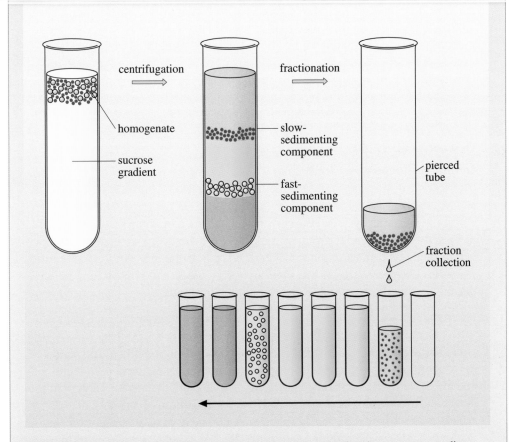

Figure 1.13d Density gradient centrifugation: the homogenate is placed on a sucrose gradient solution and centrifuged to produce bands or fractions of different size or density particles. The separate fractions are then collected in a sequence of tubes.

Once separation is achieved, the biochemical properties of the different fractions can be analysed.

The problem of localization of molecules to particular cells was solved by the introduction of specific labelling techniques that could be applied to the sections prepared for light and electron microscopy.

1.2.4 LOCALIZATION OF SPECIFIC MOLECULES WITHIN CELLS

A number of methods are now available to localize molecules within cells. The first major approach to be used was *enzyme histochemistry*, which as the name implies, involves the localization of enzymes in histological preparations by chemical reaction. The method utilizes enzymatic activity to visualize cells in which a particular enzyme is present, or in some cases, to identify the location of particular enzymes within a cell. Tissue sections are incubated in physiological solutions and at physiological temperature with substrates and/or additional reagents that generate a coloured reaction product after the enzyme has acted. Although this technique is very useful, not all enzymes can be studied by this method, because some may be lost or inactivated by the preparation and processing of the tissue. The methods cannot, of course, be used to study the localization of the many important molecules present in cells that are not enzymes (or proteins). A much more widely applicable and highly sensitive method to localize specific molecules within cells is known as *immunohistochemistry*.

IMMUNOHISTOCHEMISTRY

Immunohistochemistry makes use of the specificity of antibodies. Antibodies, also known as *immunoglobulins*, are large glycoproteins (proteins which have sugars attached) secreted by leukocytes, known as B lymphocytes, of the vertebrate immune system. Antibody molecules have regions that bind with high specificity to a particular group of molecules (known as an antigen, or *epitope*), which might be a short sequence of amino acids on the surface of a bacterium, for example. The specificity of this binding is very great, and plays a fundamental part in the specificity of the adaptive immune response.

An immune response can be generated by injection of an inactivated pathogen that still retains its antigenic properties, or of antigenic molecules. This response is the basis of immunization. A series of such injections results in the rapid cell division of those lymphocytes that produce antibodies that bind to that antigen, and also to an elevated level of antibody molecules in the blood. These antibodies can be purified from blood samples. Thus immunization of animals such as rabbits with antigenic molecules of interest can be used as a means of obtaining antibodies that specifically recognize and bind to those molecules. More recently, the use of cultured cells, to produce antibodies (known as monoclonal antibodies), has become increasingly popular.

The purified antibodies can then be applied to tissue sections. When sections are incubated in a solution containing purified antibodies, the antibodies bind only to those parts of the section in which the molecule is present. If the antibodies are 'tagged' in some way (for example with a fluorescent or coloured marker), so that they can be visualized under the microscope, then those parts of the section that contain the molecule of interest can be identified. The method can also be applied to other types of cell preparation, such as cultured cells, cell suspensions or other tissue preparations (when applied to cell preparations, the methods is frequently known as immuno*cyto*chemistry). The principles of the technique are shown schematically in Box 1.2, Part 1.

Today, simultaneous immunolocalization of more than one molecule, and immunolabelling combined with other cellular labelling methods, provide much information about the nature and distribution of specific molecules present in a single sample of cells or tissue preparation. Immunohistochemistry is now in routine use and forms the basis of essential diagnostic work in hospital histopathology laboratories, as well as being an important research tool. Antibodies are also used to purify and assay molecules, and as tools in functional studies using living cells. Some of the many important uses of antibodies in cell biology are shown in Box 1.2.

Box 1.2   EXAMPLES OF THE USE OF ANTIBODIES IN CELL BIOLOGY

1   IMMUNOLABELLING

The first immunohistochemical procedure was introduced in 1941 by Coons, who used immunoglobulin (antibody) molecules chemically linked to fluorescent markers to localize specific molecules in tissue sections.

Individual immunoglobulin molecules are 'Y'-shaped and have two antigen binding sites. These sites bind to the molecule of interest in the tissue section. The bound antibody is visualized either directly, if it was labelled (with a fluorescent molecule, or *fluorochrome*, for example) as in 'direct' immunolabelling (Figure 1.14a), or if it was unlabelled, indirectly, after addition of a secondary labelled antibody that recognizes part of the sequence of the immunoglobulin molecule itself (Figure 1.14b).

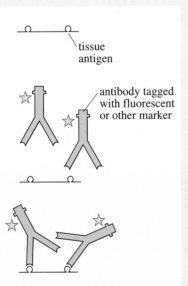

tissue antigen

antibody tagged with fluorescent or other marker

Figure 1.14a   Direct immunolabelling: labelled antibody molecules bind to the antigen in the tissue sample.

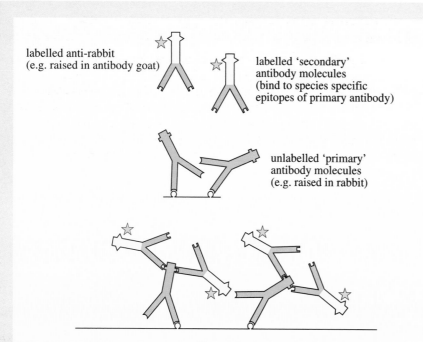

labelled anti-rabbit
(e.g. raised in antibody goat)

labelled 'secondary'
antibody molecules
(bind to species specific
epitopes of primary antibody)

unlabelled 'primary'
antibody molecules
(e.g. raised in rabbit)

Figure 1.14b Indirect immunolabelling: unlabelled 'primary' antibody molecules bind to the antigen. Labelled 'secondary' antibodies recognize and bind to species specific sequences on the primary antibody.

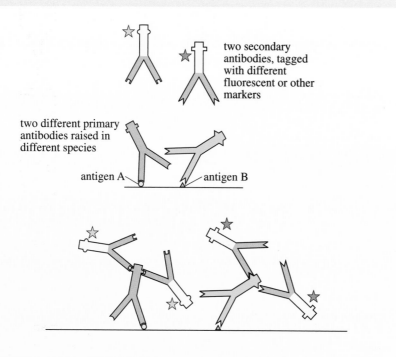

two secondary
antibodies, tagged
with different
fluorescent or other
markers

two different primary
antibodies raised in
different species

antigen A   antigen B

Figure 1.14c Double immunolabelling: two different antigens can be localized in the same specimen using two primary antibodies, raised in different species. Two different secondary antibodies are then applied, each coupled to a different fluorescent or coloured marker.

A range of labelling systems are now available, and two or even three antibodies, visualized by different enzymes giving coloured reaction products or fluorescence of different wavelengths, can be applied to localize different molecules in the same specimen (Figure 1.14c).

2   PURIFICATION OF MOLECULES AND CELLS USING ANTIBODIES

Molecules can be purified by a process known as immunoabsorption. A column (Figure 1.14d) of special small beads is made. Specific antibodies against an antigen of interest are chemically bound to the beads. A solution of molecules including the antigen is then passed down the column. Most of the antigen binds to the antibodies on the column; and almost all of the other molecules pass through. The column can then be washed, and the bound molecules selectively washed off, or *eluted*, by rinsing the column with a solution that breaks the links between antigen and antibody.

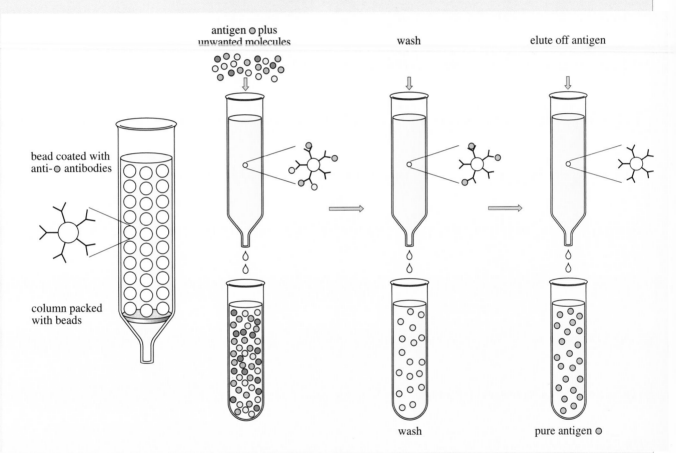

Figure 1.14(d)   Immunoselection. The red circles represent the antigen of interest and the unwanted molecules are represented by other colours.

Cells can be purified by a method known as immunoselection. Antibodies that specifically recognize an epitope on the surface of a subpopulation of cells are used. The antibody is bound either to a plastic plate, or to a column of beads. A mixture of cells is then added to the plate or passed down the column. The cells that express the epitope recognized by the antibody bind to the plate or beads. The others do not bind and are removed by rinsing. The required cells can then be separated from the plate or beads.

3 ASSAY OF MOLECULES USING ANTIBODIES — IMMUNOASSAY

Antibodies are widely used to measure the amount of a particular molecule in tissue samples. The sample, which contains an unknown amount of molecule 'X' is prepared as a solution and mixed with a known amount of a standard solution of the same molecule 'X'. The known standard is either radioactively labelled (in radioimmunoassay) or bound to an enzyme that catalyses a reaction with a coloured reaction product (enzyme-linked immunoabsorbent assay or *ELISA*). A set amount of specific antibody to 'X' is then added, and the known standard competes with 'X' in the sample for binding. The more of 'X' that there is in the sample, the less labelled standard binds to the antibody. After binding, the reaction product is separated from the rest of the solution and the radioactivity or coloured reaction is measured. The amount of competing molecule in the sample can hence be calculated.

4 FUNCTIONAL ASSAYS

Antibodies are frequently used in functional assays performed using cultured cells (see Section 1.2.5). Specific antibodies can be added to cells or tissues, at levels that saturate the antigen (i.e. that bind to all antigen present), and hence block its natural action. An example is in the study of the factors that regulate the growth of neurons. Antibodies to a factor needed for growth of some neurons, (known as nerve growth factor, or NGF) can stop nerve growth in culture and also *in vivo*. Experiments using such molecules have provided important evidence about the role of this factor in the development of parts of the mammalian nervous system.

We will look at two examples of how immunolabelling can provide information about the localization of molecules within tissues and within cells. The first is illustrated in Figure 1.15, which shows double immunolabelling (localization of two different molecules) of hormone-producing cells in the pancreas. The figure shows immunolabelling using two antisera, one that recognizes insulin, the other which recognizes another pancreatic hormone, glucagon. The binding of the two antisera is visualized indirectly, by the subsequent application of secondary antibodies that have been chemically coupled to enzymes that produce different coloured reaction products.

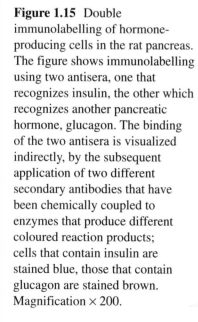

Figure 1.15 Double immunolabelling of hormone-producing cells in the rat pancreas. The figure shows immunolabelling using two antisera, one that recognizes insulin, the other which recognizes another pancreatic hormone, glucagon. The binding of the two antisera is visualized indirectly, by the subsequent application of two different secondary antibodies that have been chemically coupled to enzymes that produce different coloured reaction products; cells that contain insulin are stained blue, those that contain glucagon are stained brown. Magnification × 200.

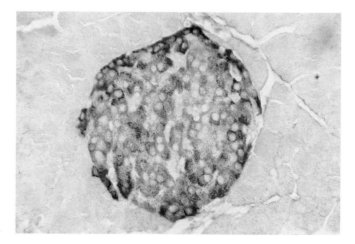

○ Looking at Figure 1.15, what can you deduce about the cells that produce insulin and glucagon in the pancreas?

● The two hormones are produced by different cells.

Immunohistochemical methods are also now available to allow labelling of cellular structures at the electron microscope level, by tagging antibody molecules with electron dense substances, the most effective being small gold particles. Antibodies can be tagged with particles of different sizes, allowing labelling for more than one molecule to be performed. Our second example shows how immunocytochemistry at the EM level can provide information about the localization of molecules in different parts of individual cells. Figure 1.16 shows a bacterium, *Neisseria meningitidis*, labelled with an antiserum that recognizes an oligosaccharide. The binding of the antiserum is visualized using a secondary antiserum coupled to tiny gold particles 15 mm in diameter.

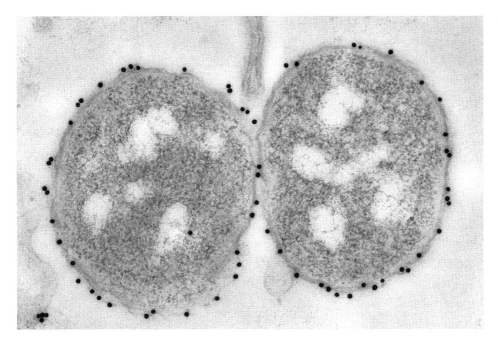

Figure 1.16 Electron micrograph showing two cells of the bacterial species *Neisseria meningitidis* immunolabelled with a primary antiserum that recognizes an oligosaccharide followed by a secondary antiserum that has been coupled to 15 nm gold particles. Magnification × 100,000.

○ Looking at Figure 1.16, in which part of the bacterium is the oligosaccharide located?

● The oligosaccharide is found on the outer surface of the bacterium.

Immunocytochemistry thus allows sensitive and accurate localization of molecules, particularly proteins, within cells.

○ Does the presence of a protein within a particular cell show that it was synthesized in that cell?

● No, the protein may have been synthesized in another cell, secreted by that cell, and taken up into a second cell.

○ What specific molecule must be present in a cell that is synthesizing a particular protein?

● The presence of the specific messenger RNA molecule that encodes that protein indicates that the protein is being synthesized within that cell.

A method that allows localization of specific mRNA molecules in tissue samples has been developed. This method is known as *in situ* hybridization and is described in Chapter 9. One final method that we will describe here, however, allows study of cell *activities*, including cell division and protein synthesis.

AUTORADIOGRAPHY

Autoradiography utilizes radiation to identify molecules within a tissue or cell. Molecules that are used as 'building blocks' in the synthesis of macromolecules are manufactured to include radioactive isotopes of particular atoms. Some commonly used isotopes are ^{14}C, ^{3}H and ^{35}S, which can be used to make, for example, 'labelled' amino acids (e.g. ^{35}S methionine) or nucleic acid precursors (e.g. ^{3}H thymidine, a nucleoside incorporated into DNA). The tissues or cells of interest are then incubated with the molecule containing the isotope, which is taken up into the cell and incorporated into newly synthesized proteins, or nucleic acids. The fate of the labelled molecule is then followed, by subsequent fixing and processing of the tissue for histology (Figure 1.17). The presence of the radioactive isotope is detected by placing a photographic film or emulsion onto the sample; the emitted radiation causes the formation of silver grains in a similar way that light does on photographic film. The process must therefore be carried out in a darkroom; otherwise the results are ruined by unwanted silver grains, as occurs in an overexposed photograph!

An example of how autoradiography can be used is in the study of cell division. Cells that are synthesizing DNA prior to undergoing cell division take up the precursors needed for DNA synthesis and can hence be identified by the incorporation of ^{3}H-labelled thymidine into their nuclei.

Autoradiography can be used in a variety of ways, to study different processes. For example, binding of labelled molecules to cell surface receptors can be distinguished from uptake into cells by use of brief incubation times and cooler temperatures which allow binding to specific cell surface receptor molecules, but slow down uptake. Uptake into cells usually requires longer incubation times and warmer temperatures and is often energy dependent, as you will learn in Chapter 3.

The *amounts* of the labelled molecule bound to or taken up by a tissue can also be measured, or *assayed*, by measuring the amount of isotope per unit weight of tissue using a machine such as a scintillation counter, that measures radioactivity. The *fate* of the labelled molecule after uptake can be followed by biochemical analysis of the molecules that become radioactively labelled. A radiolabelled amino acid, for example, is incorporated into the proteins being synthesized by the tissue at the time of uptake. You will learn how these proteins can be identified in Chapter 2.

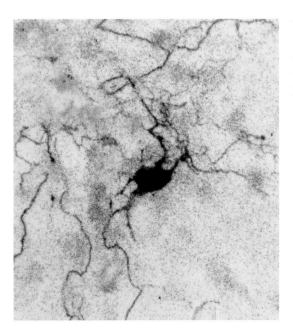

Figure 1.17 Photomicrograph showing autoradiographic labelling of a neuron in cell culture that has taken up a ^{3}H-labelled amino acid precursor. Magnification × 400.

Many of the methods that we have considered so far have been concerned with the study of cells that have, of necessity, been killed during tissue preparation, or cell processes that have been studied in cell homogenates, in the test tube. The ultimate of course, would be to be able to study molecules and processes in living cells. A technique for doing so is cell culture, the final technique that we will describe briefly.

1.2.5 CELL CULTURE: THE STUDY OF LIVING CELLS

If tissues are removed from an organism and provided with all the nutrients that they normally require for their metabolism, an appropriate surface, or *substrate* on which to grow and suitable conditions of temperature and pH, then most cells remain alive, and even grow and in many cases, divide. Cells from all kingdoms have been grown in culture, including bacteria, fungi, protoctists, plants and many animal cells, including all kinds of mammalian cells.

Single-celled organisms such as bacteria can be grown in a liquid medium, but cells that form part of a tissue require some solid support, such as specially coated glass or plastic, or an artificial 'gel'-like medium. The first experiments utilized glass dishes (hence the term, *in vitro*, from the Latin, meaning 'in glass') and small pieces of tissue. The success of the technique was found to depend upon the size of the tissue; since, in the case of mammals, the blood supply is necessarily lost, gases must pass by diffusion to all the cells of the tissue. Cells in the centre of larger chunks are thus vulnerable to lack of oxygen and build up of carbon dioxide. Since these early experiments, however, methods have been refined, and enzymes and gentle mechanical agitation are frequently used to carefully break down the extracellular molecules that hold the cells of a tissue together, so they can be separated and obtained as a suspension. The cells are then 'plated' on to appropriately treated, specially made dishes, provided with synthetic culture 'medium' containing all the necessary nutrients, and incubated in incubators that have the appropriate temperature and gaseous conditions for the cells in question.

The cells grown in such cultures are usually clearly visible under the light microscope, so living cells can be examined. However, since animal cells are translucent, special optics which allow some cell components to be visualized are needed in order to see the living cells clearly, as shown in Figure 1.18. One such method is *phase contrast microscopy*, which uses the difference in the way light passes through different parts of the specimen to increase the contrast of the image, allowing some cell components such as the cell membrane and nucleus to be seen.

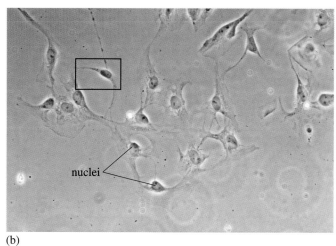

(a) (b)

Figure 1.18 Living cells in culture viewed by (a) standard light microscopy, and (b) phase contrast microscopy. In (a) almost no detail of cell structure is visible, whereas in (b), the cell membrane, nuclei and nucleoli are clearly visible, and some detail of the cytoplasm can be seen. The box indicates the same cell viewed by the two types of microscopy. Magnification × 240.

The ability to grow selected cell types in tissue culture offers many advantages for cell biologists. One advantage is the ability to assess clearly the effects of exogenous agents added to the cultured cells, so minimizing the need to use whole animals. Although the effects seen in culture may be different from those seen *in vivo*, tissue culture offers an extremely useful initial procedure with which to screen the possible harmful effects of new drugs and chemicals. A second advantage is the ability to manipulate precisely the external environment of the cultured cells, which has proved invaluable to biologists who are interested in understanding cellular processes such as cell division, and the factors that control cell proliferation, cell longevity and cell movement, to name but a few. The genes expressed by cultured cells can also be manipulated, by a technique known as *transfection*, which allows the roles played by specific gene products to be studied. You will learn about this method in Chapter 10.

Now we have described some of the main ways in which cells are studied, we will go on to examine cells in more detail, beginning with the prokaryotes.

SUMMARY OF SECTION 1.2

1   Our understanding of the chemical nature and organization of cells, and how individual cells function has come from microscopy, biochemistry, and cell biology techniques such as cell culture.

2 Light microscopy (LM) provides valuable information about the organization of tissues, but initially did not allow precise localization of specific molecules to particular parts of a tissue or cell.

3 The internal organization of cells is studied by electron microscopy (EM), which allows cell organelles to be visualized.

4 Cell fractionation techniques allow cell organelles to be separated by ultracentrifugation. Subsequent biochemical analysis allows functions such as the activity of particular enzymes to be pinpointed to specific cell organelles.

5 Advances in LM and EM methods and the advent of immunohistochemistry (which makes use of the specificity of antibody binding) and autoradiography (which utilizes radioactively labelled precursor molecules), have allowed localization of specific molecules to particular cell types and to cell organelles.

6 Antibodies are used in a variety of techniques, including immunohistochemistry, immunopurification, immunoassay, and others.

7 Cell culture allows living cells to be studied. Individual cells can be observed and the effects of specific molecules on cells and cell processes, such as cell division, can be analysed.

1.3 THE ORGANIZATION OF PROKARYOTE CELLS

Prokaryote cells have a deceptively simple structure, which belies their biochemical complexity and diversity. The Archaea, in particular, have a very simple structure and are rather shapeless, whilst Bacteria have a greater structural diversity, some having structural specializations, and a few (such as the actinomycetes) being multicellular. An electron micrograph of a common bacterium is shown in Figure 1.19.

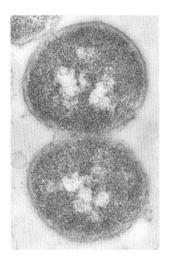
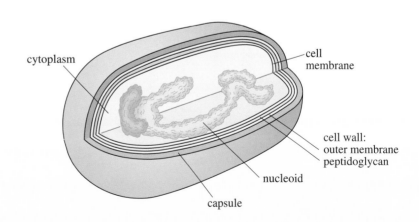

Figure 1.19 (a): Electron micrograph showing two individuals of *Neisseria meningitidis*. DNA is pale (electron lucent) while the rest of the cytosol is dark (electron dense) and granular in appearance because it contains many ribosomes. The cell wall is also visible. Magnification × 60,000. (b) Schematic diagram showing the organization of the cell wall and the capsule that is a feature of some types of bacteria.

We will not describe the structure of prokaryotes in great detail here. It is important to remember, however, that prokaryote and eukaryote cells differ in a number of ways.

○ How do eukaryote and prokaryote cells differ?

● Eukaryotes have a nucleus, cytoskeleton and organelles, prokaryotes do not.

The most distinctive feature of bacteria, when viewed at high or low magnification, is their surface. At high power it can be seen that there are several distinct components to the structure that surrounds the bacterium. Like all other cells, bacterial cells are surrounded by a *cell membrane,* which is the *innermost* of these components. Many bacteria also have an outer *cell wall* that surrounds the cell membrane and provides support and gives the cell its shape. The cell walls of Bacteria, but not of Archaea, are composed of proteoglycan (also known as peptidoglycan), which consists of a protein core to which one or more long polysaccharide chains are attached. Some bacteria have another outer membrane that is frequently surrounded by a polysaccharide capsule.

Some bacterial species have structures extending from the cell membrane; these are of two types, *flagella* (singular, flagellum) and *pili* (singular, pilus). Bacterial flagella differ from those of protoctists and are relatively long, distinctive structures that produce movement. Some types of bacteria have a single flagellum, while others have several and others none at all. You will learn how flagella cause movement in Chapter 7. Pili are much shorter and thinner structures than flagella and are involved in adhesion either of different bacterial individuals during mating, or of bacteria and various substrates, including eukaryote cells during infection.

Although the internal structure of prokaryotes shows little organization, when viewed under the electron microscope, areas of different electron density can be seen. The area in which DNA is located appears pale, and ribosomes, where protein is synthesized, can be seen as small dark particles (Figure 1.19a).

Not all bacteria have such a simple internal structure as the one shown in Figure 1.19. Some bacteria do have internal specializations; for example the photosynthetic bacteria, in which the cell membrane folds into the cytoplasm, sometimes forming stacks of membrane, where photosynthesis occurs. In other prokaryotes, the cell membrane folds inwards in a more irregular arrangement.

SUMMARY OF SECTION 1.3

1   Prokaryotes do not exhibit great structural diversity, although they do have a range of sizes, shapes and some structural specializations.

2   Prokaryotes do not have a nucleus, cytoskeleton or internal membrane-bound organelles.

3   Most bacteria have a wall that lies outside the inner membrane and is composed of proteoglycan; many have an outer membrane too.

4   Two structural specializations associated with the cell membrane of some bacteria are flagella, which are involved in movement, and pili, which are involved in adhesion. Some bacteria have membrane specializations.

1.4 THE ORGANIZATION OF EUKARYOTE CELLS

In this section, we will focus on animal cells but also will consider plant cells, briefly. We will not consider fungi or protoctists in detail here.

We are going to centre our attention on the cell membrane, cytoskeleton and cell organelles, describing their structure and functions. You will find out that cell organelles play essential roles in eukaryote cells, but it is important to remember that the cytoplasm is also the site of very many other essential cellular activities, such as many of the crucial chemical reactions that are fundamental to metabolism.

1.4.1 THE CELL MEMBRANE: THE CELL'S INTERFACE WITH ITS ENVIRONMENT

Like prokaryotes, eukaryote cells are surrounded by a cell membrane, which acts as a barrier and interface with the external environment. The cell membrane is composed predominantly of phospholipids, arranged in a bilayer. Within the bilayer are a variety of proteins and glycoproteins, many of which span the entire width of the membrane (Figure 1.20). These proteins play crucial roles in the interactions of the cell with its environment. Some membrane proteins act as transporters that allow selective movement of nutrients into the cell. Others, often glycoproteins (proteins which have sugars attached), act as *receptors* which respond to specific molecular changes in the environment and transduce information about the environment to the inside of the cell, thus allowing appropriate responses to be initiated. Yet other glycoproteins act as *recognition molecules*, and can promote adhesion between adjacent cells of a tissue.

The cell membrane is also linked to proteins on its cytoplasmic surface, some of which have a structural role, maintaining the shape of the cell.

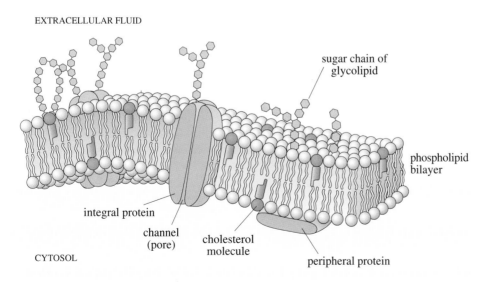

Figure 1.20 Schematic diagram of the animal cell membrane.

Now consider the cell membranes of our representative cells from the intestine. You will recall that epithelial cells and neurons are organized in a highly polarized way that relates to their functions (Figures 1.4 and 1.6). This polarity is not only due to cell shape: different regions of epithelial cells and neurons are also specialized to perform different functions because there are specific proteins embedded in different parts of the membrane. The smooth muscle cells, fibroblasts and leukocytes that are also present in the intestine, however, are not so highly polarized, although their membrane proteins are not necessarily uniformly distributed throughout the cell membrane. We will return to consider how the polarized arrangement of cell membrane proteins and shape occurs, later in this chapter.

Membrane structure is fluid; phospholipid molecules move freely within the two dimensional plane of most parts of the membrane. However, our understanding of the structure and function of the cell membrane is far from complete. For example, recent studies suggest that cell membranes have specialized areas, known as *rafts*, that are involved in specific functions; also, that the mechanisms by which the membrane allows selective molecular movement and responses to occur are now realized to be extremely complex. You will learn more about recent advances in our understanding of the cell membrane in Chapter 3.

1.4.2 THE CYTOSKELETON: SHAPE, SUPPORT, CELL MOVEMENT AND INTRACELLULAR TRANSPORT

The cytosol of eukaryote cells contains a system of specialized proteins that together form what is known as the **cytoskeleton**. Another term often used is 'scaffolding', which is perhaps rather misleading, since the proteins that make up the cytoskeleton are constantly changing and play an essential role in the transport of organelles and some molecules within the cell. Cytoskeletal proteins also have other roles; their actions produce all kinds of cell movements including the movement of motile cells and intracellular movements such as those of chromosomes during mitosis. They are thus essential for plant cells as well as animal cells. In animal cells, cytoskeletal proteins also provide mechanical strength and support, and maintain cell shape. In plant cells, the cell wall fulfils this role.

Cytoskeletal proteins are long, filament-like molecules. There are three types of filaments, formed from different protein subunits; **microfilaments** (also known as *actin filaments*), **microtubules** and **intermediate filaments** (Figure 1.21). All three types of filaments are associated with other proteins in the cell.

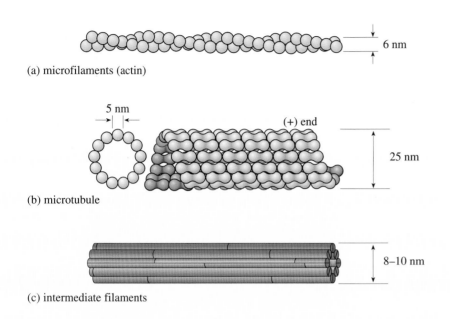

Figure 1.21 Diagrams showing some of the properties of (a) microfilaments; (b) microtubules; and (c) intermediate filaments.

(a) microfilaments (actin)

6 nm

5 nm

(+) end

25 nm

(b) microtubule

8–10 nm

(c) intermediate filaments

MICROFILAMENTS

Microfilaments are present in all eukaryote cells and are the thinnest of the filament types, having a diameter of about 6 nm and a thread-like appearance under EM (Figure 1.21a). They are composed of molecules of the protein **actin**, and so are also sometimes called actin filaments. Most microfilaments do not occur singly but are linked together in networks or bundles.

Networks of microfilaments are particularly prominent around the edges of cells, in a region just below the cell membrane, sometimes called the cell *cortex*. Bundles of microfilaments are found in microvilli of absorptive epithelial cells, and in the leading edge of moving cells where the ability of actin polymers to disassemble and reassemble plays a key role in cell locomotion.

MICROTUBULES

Microtubules are, as their name implies, tubular structures and are polymers composed of subunits of a protein conveniently known as **tubulin**. They are present in all eukaryote cells and play a crucial role in cell organization, the movement of cell organelles, and the reorganization of chromosomes into the daughter cells during mitosis.

Microtubules are effectively hollow tubes consisting of thirteen parallel filaments of polymerized tubulin, and measure about 25 nm in external diameter (Figure 1.21b). They radiate from a structure near the nucleus, known as the **centrosome**. Microtubules are very unstable, and are constantly being disassembled and reassembled; they begin polymerization at the centrosome, and the growing tubules extend in a radial direction, towards the edges of the cell. Some tubules disassemble before they reach the edge of the cell, but others reach the cortex, where, if they bind to a protein known as a capping protein, they stabilize.

○ What might happen to the shape of a cell if the capping proteins become confined to one part of the cell cortex?

● Microtubules would only stabilize to that region of the cell periphery, so the cell would become polarized, i.e. it would acquire an asymmetrical shape.

○ What types of cells are inherently asymmetrical?

● Neurons and epithelial cells are asymmetrical.

This selective arrangement of microtubules, determined by the location of capping proteins, is an important factor in determining cell shape. The arrangement of microtubules also plays an important role in the arrangement of organelles *within* the cell. Microtubules are also components of cilia and flagella, which are specialized structures of some eukaryote cells that produce cellular movement; these are described in more detail in Chapter 7.

INTERMEDIATE FILAMENTS

Intermediate filaments are so called because they are intermediate in diameter between the microfilaments and microtubules; measuring about 10 nm (Figure 1.21c). There are several different types of intermediate filament, but they all have a rope-like structure that confers great strength, their main role being in mechanical support. Different cell types have different types of intermediate filament (Figure 1.22). The arrangement of the different types of cytoskeletal components in mammalian intestinal epithelial cells is shown in Figure 1.23.

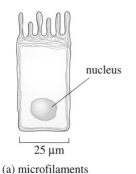

nucleus

25 μm

(a) microfilaments

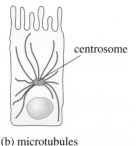

centrosome

(b) microtubules

(c) intermediate filaments

Figure 1.23 The arrangement of cytoskeleton proteins in intestinal epithelial cells: (a) microfilaments form a scaffold around the perimeter of the cell; (b) micro-tubules radiate from the centrosome; (c) intermediate filaments link the cell to adjacent cells and the extracellular matrix at specific sites (desmosome and hemidesmosome junctions, see Figure 1.35) at the surface of the cell.

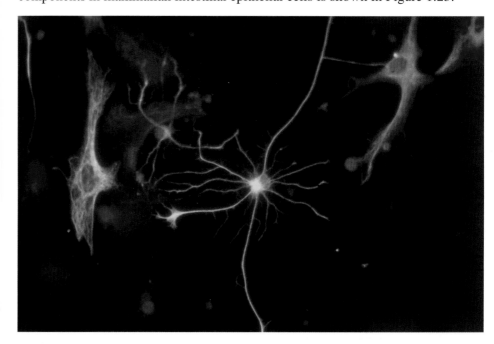

Figure 1.22 Immunofluorescent micrograph showing intermediate filaments in cultured supporting cells (astrocytes) of the brain. Magnification × 375. Cultured cells have been immunolabelled with a primary antiserum that recognizes a type of intermediate filament found only in these cells and a secondary antiserum coupled to a fluorescent marker.

1.4.4 CELL ORGANELLES

In this section we describe cell organelles, focusing on their functions, with the aim of providing an overview of cell activities as groundwork for later chapters in the book. We begin by following the cellular 'pathways' involved in the formation, processing and delivery of proteins to their final destinations in the cell. A number of organelles are involved in this essential cellular activity. As you know, this process actually begins in the nucleus, where the genetic information needed for protein synthesis is stored.

THE NUCLEUS

The nucleus is the largest, and so usually the most distinctive, cell organelle. In a typical animal cell the nucleus is roughly spherical in shape (Figure 1.24). The nucleus is often, but certainly not always, situated near the centre of the cell.

Inside the nucleus, as you know, is the genetic information of the cell, DNA (a small amount of DNA is also present in mitochondria and chloroplasts).

○ A number of major activities take place in the nucleus. Name two of these activities.

● DNA replication and transcription of DNA into RNA.

You will recall that DNA replication is the synthesis of new DNA in preparation for cell division and that transcription is the production of mRNA from the DNA template, the first step in the production of proteins. Another important process that takes place in the nucleus is the assembly of ribosomes, which translate mRNA into protein.

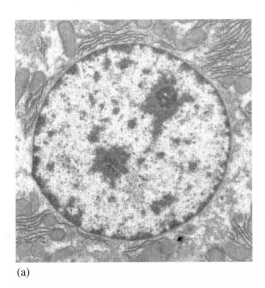

(a)

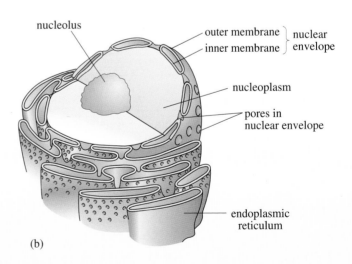

(b)

Figure 1.24 (a) Electron micrograph of the nucleus from a rat liver cell. Heterochromatin (dark areas), and euchromatin (light areas) can be seen. Two nucleoli are also clearly visible. Magnification × 8000. (b) Schematic diagram showing the structure of the nucleus, which is linked to the endoplasmic reticulum.

In order for these three major activities to take place, much co-ordination and many other 'subsidiary' activities are necessary. For example, replication and transcription do not take place at the same time. The enzymes needed to synthesize DNA or transcribe it into RNA must be present at the right places and times, and there must be a means of exporting mRNA out of the nucleus, and protein into it. How does the organization of the nucleus and its component molecules allow all these activities to take place?

First, consider the way in which DNA is arranged in the nucleus. You will recall that in eukaryotes DNA is organized into chromosomes, each of which consists of a single, very long DNA molecule. These molecules are much longer than the diameter of the nucleus, and are packaged by binding to special proteins known as **histones**. The complex of DNA and proteins is known as **chromatin**. The binding of DNA with histones is very ordered and the degree of packing varies, as shown in Figure 1.25 (overleaf). The most tightly packed DNA results in the condensation that occurs during mitosis, when the chromosomes can be seen under the light microscope. Usually, individual chromosomes are not visible by light microscopy.

The packing of DNA differs for DNA that is being transcribed and that which is not. If you look at Figure 1.24a, you see that the chromatin has a granular appearance under EM; some areas of chromatin have a dark, electron-dense appearance, other areas appear pale. The chromatin in the dark areas is known as **heterochromatin** and is more highly condensed than that in the pale areas. In a typical cell that is not about to divide, heterochromatin forms about 10% of the total chromatin, whereas during mitosis, the figure approaches 100%. Most heterochromatin is transcriptionally inactive; that is, it is not used to make RNA. In mammals and some other eukaryotes, much heterochromatin lies around the edge of the nucleus (see Figure 1.24a), and it has been suggested that in these regions the chromosomes might be attached to sites on or near to the inner nuclear membrane, preventing the different chromosomes from becoming entangled.

Another function of heterochromatin is in the regulation of gene expression, where it acts to prevent access to the molecular machinery of transcription. It is known that in female mammals, one X chromosome in each cell is completely condensed into heterochromatin, forming a structure known as a Barr body. This state is permanent and is thought to prevent overproduction of the protein products of the X chromosome (males, of course, only have one copy of the X chromosome). You will learn much more about the control of gene expression in Chapter 9.

The pale areas of chromatin are known as **euchromatin**, and are less densely packed than heterochromatin. Around 10% of euchromatin is even less condensed than the rest; this euchromatin can be actively transcribed.

Another example of the way that the organization of chromosomes within the nucleus relates to function in the **nucleolus**, where ribosomes are assembled. When viewed by electron microscopy, nucleoli appear as rounded patches of an electron-dense material with a granular appearance. The genes needed for the production of ribosomal RNA are located in clusters on several chromosomes and the relevant sections of these chromosomes loop into the nucleolus (Figure 1.26).

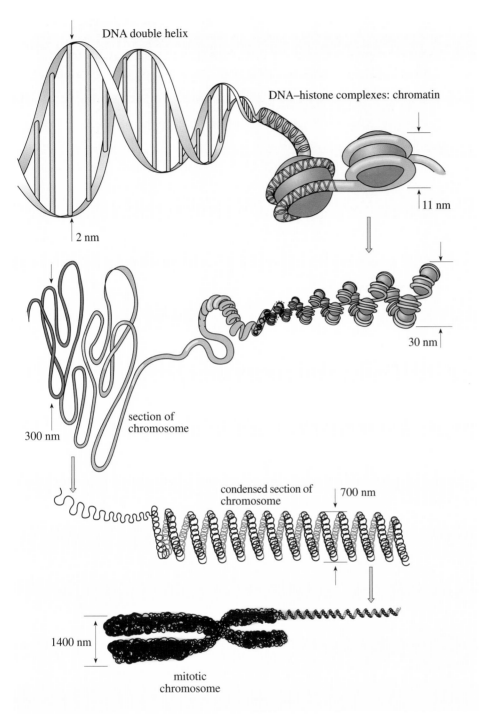

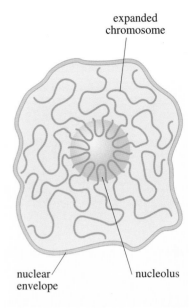

Figure 1.26 Schematic illustration of the nucleolus. The regions of the chromosomes that contain clusters of genes encoding ribosomal RNA loop to the nucleolus.

Figure 1.25 Schematic diagram illustrating the ordered binding of DNA to histone proteins. The double helix is wound around globular histone proteins (shown in purple), forming a 'beads on a string' arrangement, known as nucleosomes, packing the complex down to a strand which has a width of 11 nm. The complex winds further and then loops and condenses. The greatest condensation is seen in mitotic chromosomes.

The ribosomal RNA molecules transcribed from this DNA are packaged together with proteins imported from the cytosol, to form ribosomes. This process is actually quite complex and involves RNA processing and the involvement of many different polypeptides. The assembly of ribosomes thus requires additional molecules that are thought to assist or catalyse the process, including complexes of small RNA molecules and protein, which are known as *small nuclear ribonucleoproteins*, or snRNPs (pronounced snurps!), and play important roles in RNA processing.

The components of the nucleolus give it its granular appearance when viewed by electron microscopy. The size of the nucleolus reflects the activity of the cell.

○ What does the size of the nucleolus indicate about the activity of a cell?

● The presence of a large nucleolus suggests that the cell is synthesizing a large amount of protein, as the nucleolus is the site of ribosome assembly. The presence of a small nucleolus suggests that a cell is not synthesizing much protein.

Now we will turn to two other aspects of nuclear organization: how its structure is maintained, and how the flow of molecular traffic into and out of the nucleus is controlled.

The structure of the nucleus is maintained by intermediate filament proteins known as **lamins**, that polymerize to form a network of filaments that lies just within the nuclear membrane. This network is called the **nuclear lamina** and is linked both to the chromatin and the nuclear membrane.

When viewed at high magnification, it can be seen that the membrane that surrounds the nucleus is actually a double membrane, or **nuclear envelope**, as it is sometimes called. Within the envelope are gaps, or pores (Figure 1.24). These **nuclear pores**, which have a channel size of about 9 nm, allow passage of RNA molecules and ribosomes out of the nucleus and selected small proteins into the nucleus. Small water-soluble molecules diffuse freely through the nuclear pores. Large proteins are too big to move freely through the nuclear pores.

○ What type of proteins would you predict to be transported into the nucleus from the cytoplasm?

● Histones, which are needed for the packing of DNA; the enzymes and other proteins needed for replication and transcription of DNA and the proteins needed for ribosome assembly; also the proteins of snRNPs and the proteins that make up the nuclear lamina.

The nucleus is therefore the site of DNA replication, transcription of DNA into messenger RNA, RNA processing and ribosome synthesis. You have seen that the ribosomes and mRNA molecules leave the nucleus through the nuclear pores. What happens to them after this?

The exported mRNA molecules are translated into protein by the ribosomes, many of which are free in the cytosol. Cytosolic proteins and proteins that are destined for the mitochondria, chloroplasts and peroxisomes are synthesized by free ribosomes. Recent evidence suggests that some mRNA molecules may be directed to specific sites in the cell before they are translated. These mRNAs have nucleotide sequences that act as 'postcodes' and bind proteins, which in turn bind to the cytoskeleton, along which molecules are transported to distant sites in the cell. Many mRNAs, however, are translated by ribosomes that are attached to one of the main cell organelles, the endoplasmic reticulum. These encode proteins that are destined for export from the cell, via the Golgi apparatus, or for lysosomes.

THE ENDOPLASMIC RETICULUM: SYNTHESIS OF LIPIDS, AND INITIAL PROCESSING OF PROTEINS FOR EXPORT

The nuclear membrane is continuous with an extensive membrane system that extends through much of the cytoplasm. This system of membranes is known as the **endoplasmic reticulum (ER)** and is the site of many important activities. The membranes of the ER form tubes and sacs, the interiors of which are separate from the cytosol. Depending on the plane in which a section is cut through the cell, the ER may appear either as spherical or parallel systems of membrane, or any shape in between, as illustrated in Figure 1.27.

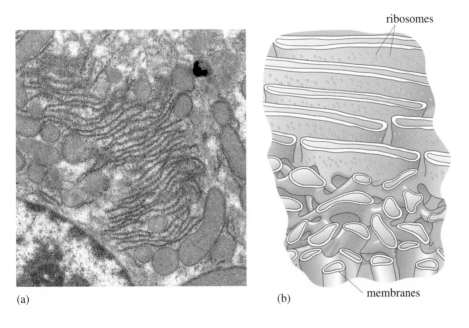

(a)   (b)

ribosomes

membranes

Figure 1.27 (a) Electron micrograph of rough endoplasmic reticulum from a rat liver cell. The granular appearance is due to ribosomes that are attached to the endoplasmic reticulum membrane. Magnification × 11,000. (b) Schematic diagram of the endoplasmic reticulum.

Some parts of the endoplasmic reticulum appear smooth when viewed by EM and are hence named **smooth endoplasmic reticulum (SER)**. Smooth endoplasmic reticulum is involved in the production of phospholipids and steroids and also in the detoxification of substances such as drugs or ingested chemicals. Ingestion of large amounts of a toxic substance, such as accidental ingestion of pesticide, results in an increase in the amount of SER. Normally, however, in most cells, most of the endoplasmic reticulum appears granular, being dotted with ribosomes (Figure 1.27a). Such endoplasmic reticulum is given the name **rough endoplasmic reticulum (RER)**, and is the site where proteins that are destined for export from the cell or for inclusion in many intracellular membranes are synthesized and processed.

THE CORE OF LIFE

What determines whether a particular mRNA molecule is translated by ribosomes that are attached to the RER, or by ribosomes that are free in the cytosol? The answer lies in the *amino acid sequence* of the protein being synthesized. Proteins destined for export from the cell via the cell membrane, or that are to be associated with certain of the internal membrane systems, have specific **signal sequences**, specific short sequences of amino acids. The 'tagging' of polypeptides by signal sequences composed of specific amino acids is an important general mechanism used by cells. Thus signal sequences effectively act as 'address labels', enabling cellular machinery to recognize and hence deliver proteins to specific sites in the cell.

Once the growing polypeptide begins to enter the ER, one of two things may happen: either it continues to enter, until finally the complete protein lies within the ER, or it remains embedded within the ER membrane.

○ Thinking of how polypeptides are 'directed' to the ER, suggest a molecular mechanism which would determine whether a particular protein *remains* in the ER membrane, or enters the ER lumen.

● A protein that is destined to remain in the ER membrane could have a special 'stop' sequence of amino acids, that keeps it in the membrane and thus prevents it from entering the lumen.

That is indeed what happens. In fact there are several different ER signal sequences that permit the threading of the polypeptide chain to begin at different positions along the chain, thus allowing loops of protein to span the ER membrane. This process will be described in much more detail in Chapter 3, but for now, the point to note is that some proteins do remain embedded in the ER membrane. These proteins are either destined to be delivered to other membranes, such as the cell membrane, or remain in the ER, where they play a role in ER function.

In what way are the proteins that are destined for export to other parts of the cell 'processed' in the RER? An important modification that begins in the RER is protein *glycosylation*, that is, the addition of sugar residues. Some such residues can serve as 'address labels', and so be involved in delivery, others have different roles. The initial glycosylation of proteins occurs in the ER, by the action of enzymes that are embedded within the ER membrane, with their catalytic site protruding into the ER lumen. Modified proteins that are destined either to be exported from the cell or to be delivered to some other organelles or to the cell membrane then pass from the ER to the Golgi apparatus, for further processing.

The proteins and glycoproteins leaving the ER are transported to the Golgi apparatus in small lipid-bounded spheres, known as **vesicles** (or transport vesicles). After further processing, sorting and packaging in the Golgi apparatus, the modified proteins are again packaged into vesicles and delivered to other organelles (*except* the mitochondria, chloroplasts and peroxisomes) or to the cell membrane. Vesicles are thus used to transport many different molecules within cells, and there are many different types of vesicle, even in cells that are not specialized for secretion.

How do vesicles move within cells, and what mechanism ensures their correct delivery? Vesicles move short distances within the cytosol by diffusion, but movement to distant sites in a cell is mediated by the action of proteins associated with microtubules. It is not just proteins and glycoproteins that are transported in vesicles. Newly-synthesized lipids are incorporated in the vesicle coat, and so are also delivered to organelles and the cell membrane in these 'mini' organelles.

THE GOLGI APPARATUS

When viewed in the electron microscope the **Golgi apparatus** appears as stacks of smooth, flat membranous sacs, known as *cisternae*, that are slightly curved and surrounded by vesicles of various sizes (Figure 1.28). The Golgi is now known to have different regions, or compartments and currently it is accepted that there are four major compartments, named the *cis*, medial, *trans* and *trans* Golgi network (or TGN), regions (Figure 1.28). The *cis* face lies next to the ER; proteins (in vesicles) enter the Golgi here. They then pass sequentially from the *cis* to the TGN, where they are sorted and packed for 'delivery'. The Golgi often has a relatively inconspicuous appearance compared to the RER and its size varies in different cell types; two reasons why the early histologists could not always detect the Golgi apparatus in some of their preparations.

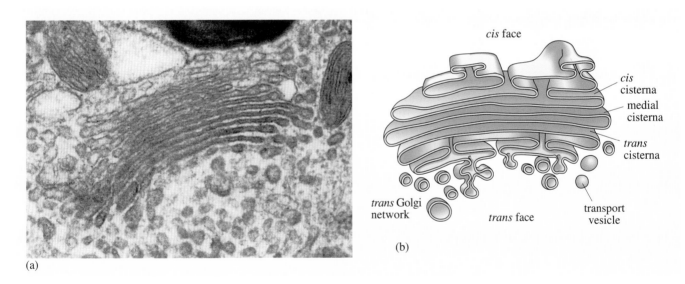

(a)

(b)

Figure 1.28 (a) Electron micrograph of the Golgi apparatus from a rat liver cell. The *cis* and *trans* faces and cisternae can be seen. Magnification × 75,000. (b) Schematic drawing of the Golgi apparatus, showing the *cis*, medial and *trans* cisternae and the trans Golgi network.

○ Why might the size of the Golgi be different in different types of cells?

● Different cells export different amounts of products. Some cells, such as hormone or enzyme secreting cells for example, secrete large quantities and so are specialized for the production and packaging of molecules for export. Other types, such as smooth muscle cells, export very little.

○ Would you expect a cell that does not export any molecules to have a Golgi apparatus?

● Yes, all cells have proteins embedded in their membranes and organelles, and all cells need at least small quantities of lipid to be delivered to organelles and cell membranes. So, all eukaryote cells have a Golgi apparatus.

You already know about the early controversy surrounding the Golgi apparatus. Even now, more than a hundred years later, it is still the subject of intense research and controversy. The reason for the great interest in the Golgi apparatus is its key role in the processing, sorting and packaging of proteins into vesicles. In other words, Golgi function is essential not only for correct modification of proteins, but also for appropriate *delivery* to particular parts of the cell. The Golgi therefore has an essential role in cell function, and also in generating cell diversity.

The complexity of Golgi function is well illustrated by the example of intestinal epithelial cells. As you know, there are several types of such cell; some are specialized for absorption, having membrane proteins called transporters in their apical membrane. It is now known that there are many different types of transporters; you will learn more about how they work in Chapter 3. Other intestinal epithelial cells secrete a proteoglycan called mucus into the lumen of the intestine, where it acts as a lubricant, aiding the passage of material along the gut. Yet other epithelial cells secrete local hormones, from the sides of the cell that contact other cells (the basolateral sides) either into blood vessels or to nearby cells. Each type of cell is polarized; its surface is not uniform, either in shape or function, as shown schematically in Figure 1.29.

The situation is further complicated if you consider the differences in *demand* for different types of exported molecules, and also the *nature* of their release. Some substances, for example, are constantly delivered to the cell membrane, and are released in small quantities all the time. This sort of release is known as *constitutive* release. Other molecules, however, are only released at certain times, in response to some kind of signal. This type of release is known as *regulated* release. An example is the release of gastrointestinal hormones and digestive enzymes, in response to ingestion of food. So within each of these three types of intestinal epithelial cell, a complex sorting and delivery system must take place. All these membrane-associated and secretory molecules are processed and packaged in the Golgi apparatus, as are all the many other such molecules that we have not mentioned. Different packages are produced for molecules that are released constitutively and by regulated processes, and for lysosomal enzymes. How different proteins are sorted, packaged and delivered is an area of cell biology that is currently intensively studied.

So, we have completed our 'journey' through the cell, from DNA in the nucleus to the delivery of protein to target sites in the cell, such as the cell membrane. What about the mechanism by which molecules are exported from cells? The vesicles are released from the cell, by a process known as **exocytosis**.

The converse process, by which substances or pathogens are taken into the cell by engulfment into a vesicular structure surrounded by cell membrane is known as

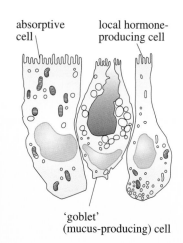

absorptive cell

local hormone-producing cell

'goblet' (mucus-producing) cell

Figure 1.29 Schematic illustration, showing the polarized nature of three types of intestinal epithelial cell. Absorptive cells have a large area of many microvilli, which increases the surface area of the cells available for absorption, they also have an asymmetrical distribution of transporter proteins (not shown, but see Figure 1.4b). The mucus–producing 'goblet' cells have many secretory vesicles that convey the mucus to the large invagination, or 'goblet'. Hormone-producing cells have only a small part of their surface exposed to the lumen of the gut, their primary role is the detection of nutrients in the gut, and the appropriate secretion of hormones into blood vessels on the basal side of the cell. These cells thus have secretory vesicles on the basal side of the cell.

phagocytosis. Organisms such as amoeba feed by phagocytosis, and cells of the immune system, known as *phagocytes*, ingest bacteria in this way. The general term for such ingestion is **endocytosis**. You will learn more about exocytosis and endocytosis, and other ways in which substances cross cell membranes later, in Chapter 3 of this book. What is the fate of the materials that the cell ingests? They are broken down by yet another type of organelle, the lysosomes.

LYSOSOMES AND PEROXISOMES

Lysosomes are small organelles, measuring about 0.5–1 μm across, that contain digestive enzymes. They break down large molecules that have been taken into cells by endocytosis, and also digest 'old' organelles. Lysosomes contain many different kinds of digestive enzymes, and the inside of the lysosome is acidic, having a pH of around 5. The enzymes of the lysosome are thus specialized to perform their function at this pH, and, should they leak out into the cytosol, which has a pH of around 7.2, do not do a great deal of damage. The inside of the lysosome is made acidic by the action of specialized transport proteins that lie in the lysosomal membrane and 'pump' hydrogen ions into its interior. Other lysosomal membrane proteins transport the useful products of digestion out of the lysosome, into the cytosol.

○   What useful materials would be produced by digestion in the lysosome?

●   The products would depend upon the starting material, but could be amino acids, sugars and nucleotides.

Peroxisomes are also small enzyme-containing organelles, measuring between 0.2–1 μm in diameter. They are thought to be present in all eukaryote cells. In mammals they are plentiful in liver cells and adipocytes but are much less abundant in other cells. Peroxisomes contain enzymes that break down fatty acids and amino acids, resulting, among other things, in the production of the toxic substance, hydrogen peroxide. Peroxisomes thus also contain high levels of an enzyme known as *catalase* that breaks down hydrogen peroxide.

Lysosomes and peroxisomes are shown in Figure 1.30.

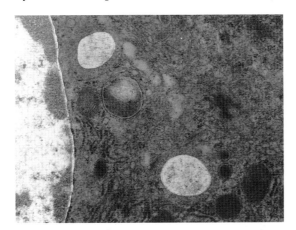 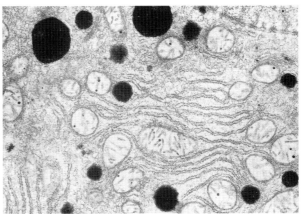

Figure 1.30 Electron micrographs showing (a) lysosomes, and (b) peroxisomes (dark-staining structures) seen in liver cells. Magnification × 18,000.

For many years, peroxisomes were thought to be identical to lysosomes; the difference was discovered as the result of cell fractionation, different fractions being found to be associated with different enzyme activities. It is now known that the two organelles are very different.

Last, but far from least, we move to an organelle that you will already know something about, the mitochondrion, which plays a fundamental role in the generation of ATP in eukaryote cells.

MITOCHONDRIA

Mitochondria have a distinctive appearance when viewed by electron microscopy. They are rounded, sausage-shaped structures, measuring about 0.5–1 μm in diameter and 2 to 8 μm in length, although their size and shape vary and they are often much bigger in plants. Observations of mitochondria in living cells have shown that the shapes of individual mitochondria change, and that their positions in the cell are not fixed. Mitochondria have a *double* membrane; the inner membrane is thrown into folds known as **cristae**, which are what gives the organelle its distinctive appearance. The two membranes effectively create two compartments in the mitochondrion. The intermembrane space lies between the two membranes; the much larger **mitochondrial matrix** lies within the inner membrane, as shown in Figure 1.31.

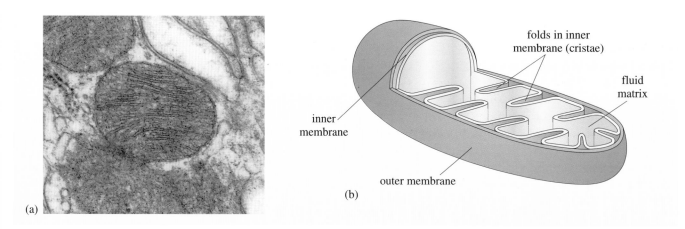

Figure 1.31 (a) Electron micrograph of mitochondria from a rat liver cell. The double membrane and cristae are clearly visible. Magnification × 60,000. (b) Schematic diagram of a mitochondrion.

The mitochondrial matrix contains many enzymes, including those of the TCA cycle. It also contains **mitochondrial DNA**, and the molecules needed to transcribe and translate it into protein. It thus also contains ribosomes, and transfer RNA. The mitochondrial genes encode most of the proteins of the inner mitochondrial membrane, which plays a fundamental role in the generation of ATP (see Chapter 5). Most other mitochondrial proteins, however, are synthesized in the cytosol and imported into the mitochondrion. Mitochondrial genes vary greatly among different kingdoms of eukaryotes.

Apart from the special proteins needed for electron transport and ATP synthesis, the inner mitochondrial membrane also contains proteins that make it selectively permeable to movement of molecules between the matrix and intermembrane space. The inner membrane is impermeable to ions, except via these proteins. In contrast, the outer mitochondrial membrane is permeable to most small molecules, even small proteins, because it contains a protein known as *porin*, which forms channels that allow movement across the membrane. You will learn more about channel proteins in Chapter 3.

Mitochondria therefore produce most ATP in eukaryote cells, and are hence more abundant in cells that have high requirements for energy, such as muscle cells.

1.4.5   PLANT CELLS

All the eukaryote cell components described above are found in plant cells. Plant cells however, have several additional features. One of the most distinctive features of plant cells is actually an extracellular structure, the **cell wall**, which is rigid and surrounds the cell membrane, conferring shape and support. It is composed predominantly of a polysaccharide, cellulose. Small channels in the cell walls allow the passage of water, ions and small molecules from cell to cell.

Plant cells contain two organelles that are not found in animal cells, the chloroplast and the vacuole.

CHLOROPLASTS AND VACUOLES

Chloroplasts are one of a type of organelle found only in plant cells, known as *plastids*. Chloroplasts, like mitochondria, have their own DNA. They are usually larger than mitochondria, and have three membrane systems. In addition to an outer and inner membrane, which encloses a space known as the *stroma*, chloroplasts have a complex internal membrane system known as a **thylakoid**, which encloses a space known as the **thylakoid space**. The thylakoid membranes form a series of linked stacks, known as *grana*, and are the site of the reactions of photosynthesis, which you will learn about in Chapter 5. The organization of a chloroplast is shown in Figure 1.32.

Figure 1.32 (a) Electron micrograph of a chloroplast. Magnification × 11,000; (b) schematic diagram of a chloroplast showing clearly the linked stacks of grana within the stroma.

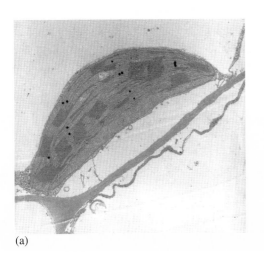

(a)

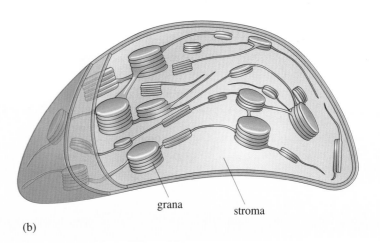

(b)

grana   stroma

The other organelle that is prominent in plant cells is the **vacuole** (Figure 1.1b). Vacuoles can be very large and have a number of roles. In mature cells, the vacuole is typically a membrane-bound space that fills most of the centre of the cell and is basically a storage compartment for water, ions and small organic molecules. The vacuolar membrane has different transporters to those of the plasma membrane and vacuolar pH is lower than that of the cytoplasm.

BIOGENESIS OF ORGANELLES

Before we leave cell organelles, there is a final aspect that we will consider, and that is organelle biogenesis. New organelles form by expansion and division of existing organelles, processes which are independent of nuclear division. The formation of new organelles requires the production of new phospholipids, most of which are assembled in the ER. The phospholipids then pass to the other organelles in two ways. The first is by budding and fusion of vesicles derived from the ER; the Golgi and lysosomes form in this way. The second is by incorporation via special membrane proteins; the mitochondria, chloroplasts and peroxisomes incorporate most new lipid in this way, as they do *not* fuse with vesicles.

SUMMARY OF SECTION 1.4

1   Eukaryote cells contain cytoskeletal proteins and organelles.

2   The cytoskeleton is composed of three types of proteins: microfilaments (also known as actin filaments), microtubules and intermediate filaments. The cytoskeletal proteins provide shape, support, an internal transport system and are responsible for cell movements.

3   DNA, which is packaged by binding to histone proteins to form chromatin, is located in the nucleus, where transcription of DNA into RNA, and the assembly of ribosomes takes place. RNA and ribosomes leave the nucleus, and structural and ribosomal proteins and the enzymes needed for DNA replication and transcription enter it, through pores in the nuclear envelope.

4   Messenger RNA is translated into protein at the ribosomes in the cytoplasm. Cytosolic proteins and many proteins of the mitochondria and chloroplasts are synthesized by ribosomes that are free in the cytoplasm. Proteins destined for export or for other cell organelles are synthesized by ribosomes attached to the rough ER. These proteins are targeted to the ER by specific amino acid signal sequences.

5   The smooth ER is the site of detoxification, phospholipid assembly, and some protein modification.

6   Proteins and lipids pass from the ER to the Golgi apparatus for further processing (e.g. glycosylation), and sorting and packaging into vesicles, which deliver specific proteins to specific parts of the cell, e.g. to different regions of the cell membrane and to lysosomes.

7   Vesicles move short distances within the cell by diffusion, but are transported longer distances along microtubules.

8   Movement of molecules and vesicles to specific sites in the cell is achieved because they have molecular 'address labels' that may be specific signal sequences of nucleotides in the case of mRNAs, or amino acids in the case of proteins.

9   Substances are secreted from cells by exocytosis. One way in which substances are imported into cells is by engulfment into a cell membrane-bound vesicle. This process is known as endocytosis.

10 Ingested materials and old organelles are digested within lysosomes. Some fatty acids are broken down in peroxisomes.

11 Mitochondria are the site of the majority of ATP production. They have a double membrane, the inner membrane of which is folded, and their own DNA.

12 Plant cells have a cell wall and two organelles not found in animal cells, the chloroplast and the vacuole.

13 New organelles form by growth of pre-existing organelles, followed by division. These processes are independent of nuclear division.

1.5 ANOTHER LOOK AT CELL COMMUNITIES

You already know that in multicellular organisms, cells tend to be organized into groups, or tissues. Here we will consider the structural components of animal tissues that hold their constituent cells together. These are *cell junctions*, and an important component of all tissues, that we have as yet only mentioned in passing, the *extracellular matrix*.

1.5.1 EXTRACELLULAR MATRIX

The **extracellular matrix** is material that is produced and secreted by cells and laid down externally. The properties of the extracellular matrix vary enormously, depending upon its chemical composition. The amount and type of extracellular matrix also varies from tissue to tissue, and it is especially abundant and diverse in animals. In many tissues the extracellular matrix acts rather like cement, in others it forms a support or scaffold, while in others, it can be associated with individual cells, as in the different kinds of cell walls of plants and bacteria, for example.

In animal tissues, the major component of the extracellular matrix is a gel-like substance, composed of several different macromolecules, in which proteins are embedded. Three families of macromolecules, together with water, form the 'gel'. They are the *glycosaminoglycans* (GAGs) which are long polysaccharide chains made up from disaccharide subunits containing amino groups, the proteoglycans, which you have already learnt about in Section 1.3, and glycoproteins, which are proteins to which small chains of sugars are attached. The GAGs are negatively charged, and attract positively charged ions, particularly sodium ions. The concentration of ions leads to the movement of water by diffusion into the tissue, giving it its gel-like properties, which resist compression.

Different proteins and other substances in the extracellular matrix provide additional strength or elasticity. The most abundant extracellular protein in animal tissues is *collagen*, of which there are several types. Collagen is a very tough protein that can, in its different forms, provide great strength and/or flexibility. *Elastin*, as its name suggests, is a flexible protein that is found in the extracellular matrix of tissues such as blood vessels. In bone, mineral salts are laid down in connective tissue to provide support. Some examples of extracellular matrix are shown in Figure 1.33.

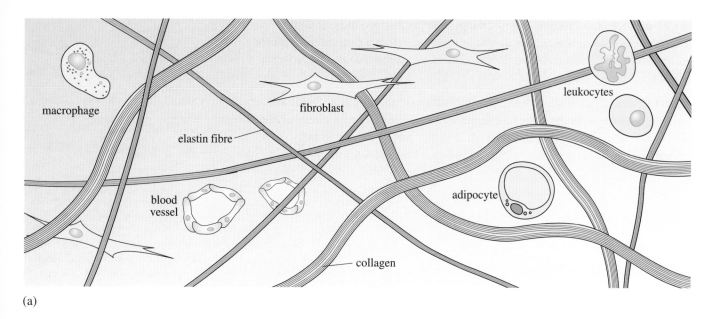

(a)

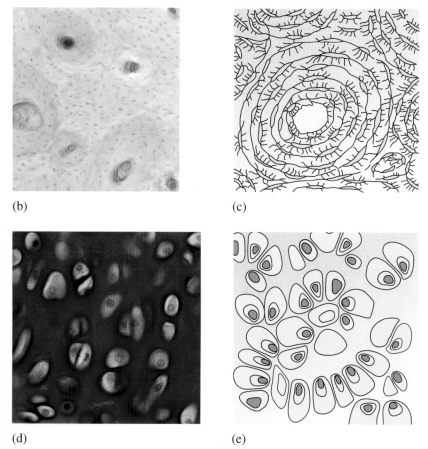

(b)

(c)

(d)

(e)

Figure 1.33 Examples of extracellular matrix. (a) Schematic diagram showing loose connective tissue, containing blood vessels, collagen and elastin fibres, fibroblasts, adipocytes, and different types of leukocytes. (b) Micrograph showing human compact bone. Most of the tissue is composed of extracellular material, mainly collagen and proteoglycans in which calcium, phosphate and other minerals are deposited, and which is secreted by specialized connective tissue cells known as osteoblasts. A network of canals (large 'channels' are dark brown, small channels can just be seen) provides osteoblasts with nutrients, and removal of wastes. Magnification × 75. (c) Schematic diagram illustrating the organization of compact bone. (d) Micrograph showing cartilage, from lung. The extracellular material is stained green. The specialized connective tissue cells that secrete this extracellular material are known as chondrocytes. Magnification × 300. (e) Schematic diagram illustrating cartilage. The pale areas around the nuclei are lipid.

Cells are linked to proteins (e.g. a protein known as fibronectin) of the extracellular matrix via membrane glycoproteins known as *integrins*. On the inside of the cell, integrins are linked to actin filaments of the cytoskeleton, as shown in Figure 1.34.

The amount of extracellular matrix varies from tissue to tissue. Tissues that have a large proportion of extracellular material are often known as *connective tissues*. In connective tissues, the cells that are synthesizing and secreting the extracellular matrix molecules may be completely separate from other cells. In other tissues, cells lie within lesser amounts of extracellular matrix, but may be in contact with each other, as described in the following section.

1.5.2 CELL JUNCTIONS

A variety of types of structural arrangement can occur where two cells come into contact, and these different cell contacts play extremely important functional roles. For example, in some tissues, it is essential that there is very close contact between cells, so that a barrier is set up and pathogenic microbes and even harmful or unwanted molecules cannot readily pass between them.

○ Give an example of circumstances where close contact between adjacent cells is important.

● One example is in the epithelial tissue that lines the gut wall, where it is important that there are not large spaces between the cells, so that harmful microbes in ingested food cannot enter the body. Another example is the skin, which also plays a major protective role.

In other cases, exchange of molecules and/or electrical activity between adjacent cells is important. An example is the smooth muscle of the intestine, which must contract in a coordinated manner for peristalsis to occur. The smooth muscle cells have special contacts known as **gap junctions** that allow transmission of molecules and electrical activity between the smooth muscle cells.

Gap junctions are just one of several different types of specialized cell junction. The tissue type that has most different types of junction is *epithelial tissue*, which is composed of closely packed sheets of cells. The different kinds of cellular junctions have specific functions and are formed by specialized proteins, their arrangement is shown in Figure 1.35.

Tight junctions, as their name suggests, link cells very closely, and prevent movement of membrane proteins. Hence they are important in maintaining the polarity of the epithelial cells of the intestine, for example.

Adherens junctions link the actin skeleton of adjacent cells together, often forming a belt-like arrangement around each cell of an epithelial sheet. The link occurs via transmembrane proteins known as *cadherins*, and intercellular proteins that link cadherins to the cytoskeleton. You may recall that actin is involved in cell movements; adherens junctions play a role in the infolding of sheets of epithelial-type cells that occur during development.

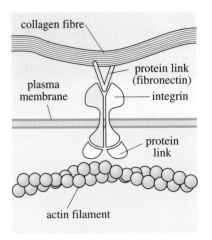

Figure 1.34 Schematic diagram showing how certain cells are linked to the extracellular matrix, via integrin molecules, that span the cell membrane. Outside the cell, integrin links via fibronectin to collagen. Inside the cell another type of protein links integrin to actin filaments.

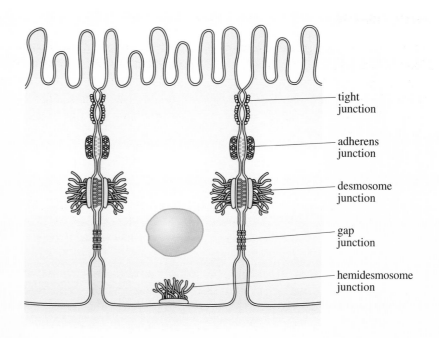

tight junction

adherens junction

desmosome junction

gap junction

hemidesmosome junction

Figure 1.35 Schematic diagram showing cell junctions and their functions in epithelial tissue. Epithelial cells are characterized, in part, by their close packing. They are held together by specialized membrane proteins that form specialized junctions between adjacent cells.

Desmosomes and hemidesmosomes (often known as *anchoring junctions*) link adjacent cells together, or in the case of hemidesmosomes, to the extracellular matrix. Again, these links occur via cadherins. In this case, however, the link is to intermediate filaments of the cytoskeleton. You will learn more about cell junctions in Chapter 3.

Other specialized types of connections also occur between some animal cells, such as the special contacts between neurons and their targets, known as synapses (Chapter 6).

SUMMARY OF SECTION 1.5

1 The cells of animal tissues are held together by the extracellular matrix and by cell junctions.

2 The extracellular matrix in animals is composed of a hydrated mixture of polysaccharides, proteoglycans, and glycoproteins, in which various proteins, especially collagen, are embedded. The nature of the proteins determines the properties of the matrix, which vary from tissue to tissue.

3 Cells can be linked by several types of cell junctions, formed by specialized proteins.

CONCLUSION

In this chapter we have given an overview of the diversity of cells and tissues, and have also described the uniformity of structure that underlies this diversity, at the cellular and subcellular level. Some of the methods by which cells and tissues are studied have been described. We have also, we hope, emphasized the dynamic nature of cells, and set the scene for later chapters that show how cells perform their many varied functions.

FURTHER READING

Alberts, B., Bray, D., Johnson, A., Lewis, J., Raff, M., Roberts, K., and Walter, P. (1998) *Essential Cell Biology*, Garland Publishing, London. [A concise and readable book on Cell and Molecular Biology, presented in a similar style to Alberts *et al.* (1994), of which it is a shorter version.]

Alberts, B., Bray, D., Lewis, J., Raff, M., Roberts, K., and Watson, J. D. (1994) *Molecular Biology of the Cell* (3rd edn), Garland Publishing, London. [A comprehensive and accessible book on Cell and Molecular Biology.]

Lodish, H., Berk, A., Zipursky, S. L., Matsudaira, P., Baltimore, D., and Darnell, J. (2000) *Molecular Cell Biology* (4th edn), W. H.Freeman and Company, NewYork. [A detailed and comprehensive book on Cell and Molecular Biology.]

Trends in Cell Biology, Vol. 8, No.1, January 1998, Golgi centenary issue, Elsevier Science Ltd., UK. [A detailed account of research on the Golgi complex over the past 100 years and several reviews discussing current understanding of different aspects of Golgi biology.]

PROTEINS: STRUCTURE AND CATALYTIC FUNCTION

2.1   INTRODUCTION

The previous chapter considered the cellular level of organization, together with subcellular organelles, and an outline of their various functions. These subcellular structures are composed principally of macromolecules and macromolecular aggregates. It is to this level of organization that we now turn.

In this chapter we focus on proteins, which have a central role in defining the structure and function of living organisms. These biopolymers are of huge significance in both quantitative and qualitative terms: about 60% of the dry mass of a typical eukaryote cell is protein, and cells contain of the order of 10^4 different types of protein. This class of polymer therefore admirably exemplifies the theme of diversity. So what do all these proteins do? We haven't the space to answer this question comprehensively, but we shall provide an overview to enable you to appreciate the various sorts of functions that proteins have, both in individual cells and within whole multicellular organisms.

Proteins have a diverse range of functions. By far the largest group of proteins are the enzymes, which are biological catalysts. Others form structural support for cells, bind to other molecules during transport, or act as storage molecules. Many are 'information' molecules: some carry signals between cells, or form the receptors with which these signals interact. On the surface of cells many proteins behave as 'identity' labels, so distinguishing one cell type from many others. The information coded within DNA cannot be decoded without interaction with a variety of proteins that control the activity of genes. Other proteins have even more specialized functions. Table 2.1 introduces you to the diversity of proteins and their functions. We return to this topic in Section 2.3.

At all levels of biological organization, function is dependent on structure, and this principle is amply illustrated at the molecular level in the case of proteins. We start, therefore, by examining protein structure. You will see what features proteins have in common, and what it is about their structure that permits diversity. Every one of the many thousands of different proteins is unique, but there are many structural similarities within this vast range of diversity. Proteins therefore exemplify another important theme, namely that of uniformity. Most proteins have a common hierarchy of structure. This concept provides the appropriate background for our subsequent study of protein function.

One class of proteins, the enzymes, receives particular attention, and forms the subject of the second half of this chapter. As you will see, this emphasis is justified by the crucial importance of enzymes in cell metabolism, and thus for the functioning of all cells and the organisms of which they are a part. The scene is thereby set for Chapters 4 and 5, in which the control of metabolism and the interconversions of energy in biological systems are dealt with in some detail.

Table 2.1 Examples of different protein functions

Type of protein	Function	Examples
enzymes	biological catalysts	pepsin digests protein in the stomach; DNA polymerase makes DNA
structural proteins	provide mechanical support for cells and tissues	collagen and elastin found in extracellular matrix; tubulin forms microtubules inside cells
transport proteins	carry small molecules or ions	serum albumin carries lipids; haemoglobin carries oxygen
membrane transporters	carry molecules or ions across membranes	glucose transporter enables cells to take up glucose
motor proteins	generate movement in cells	myosin in skeletal muscle cells; dynein enables eukaryotic cilia and flagella to beat
storage proteins	nutrient storage	ovalbumin in egg white; ferritin stores iron in the liver
signalling proteins	carry signals between cells	the hormone insulin controls blood glucose levels; nerve growth factor stimulates some neurons to grow
recognition molecules	attach to cells or form complexes to form identity 'labels'	immunoglobulins become attached to 'foreign' cells for subsequent destruction; numerous cell surface proteins form recognition sites
receptor proteins	detect signals and transmit them intracellularly	rhodopsin detects light in the eye; insulin receptor binds insulin
gene regulatory proteins	bind to DNA to switch genes on/off	*lac* repressor in bacteria 'silences' genes for enzymes that degrade lactose
miscellaneous proteins	various specialized functions	'antifreeze' proteins in polar fish protect blood against freezing

One particular class of enzymes, the kinases, is also introduced here. They are not only important in metabolism, but also play other key roles, for example, in intracellular communication (Chapter 6), and in cell movement (Chapter 7).

However, before proteins can be studied, they need to be obtained in a purified form. Box 2.1 describes some of the techniques used to purify proteins.

BOX 2.1   PROTEIN PURIFICATION AND IDENTIFICATION

Cells contain a large mixture of proteins. For example, a recent estimate suggests that *E. coli* is capable of synthesizing just over 4 000 different proteins. For an investigator interested in studying just one of them, the problem is how to separate the desired protein from all the others. Using the techniques of cell fractionation outlined in Box 1.1, a crude cell homogenate containing a mixture of proteins can be obtained. Here we are concerned with the techniques used to purify and identify proteins from such mixtures. Many techniques are currently available and in use; here we outline just a few.

GEL FILTRATION

Chromatography is commonly used to separate proteins from mixtures. One particular form of chromatography is known as **gel filtration**, which involves the use of a hollow plastic or glass column filled with a polysaccharide gel. The gel contains small porous beads, each consisting of a three-dimensional water-filled network, which acts as a molecular sieve: small molecules enter and linger in the pores, so their passage down the column is retarded; larger molecules, unable to enter the pores, pass more quickly down the column between the beads. When a mixture of different-sized proteins is added to such a column, the molecules are therefore separated on the basis of their size difference (Figure 2.1). The largest molecules are washed through (washing through the column is termed 'elution') quite quickly. Rather smaller molecules can enter some of the larger pores and so take longer to pass through, and molecules below a certain size can enter even the smallest pores so take longer still to pass through. Different gels can be used with different pore sizes, so passage down two or three columns can improve separation. Different-sized proteins are therefore separated on the basis of size, and an elution profile is produced (Figure 2.2).

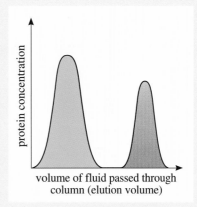

Figure 2.2   An elution profile showing the separation of two different-sized protein molecules.

Figure 2.1   Gel filtration. (a) A solution containing large and small protein molecules is applied to the gel column. (b) During elution, small protein molecules take a longer route passing through the beads than larger proteins, which do not enter the bead pores (see enlargement showing the interaction with the beads). Large proteins are eluted first (c), followed by smaller ones (d).

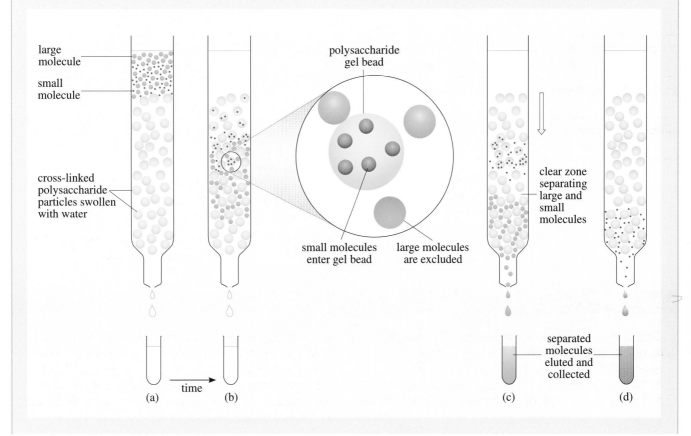

GEL ELECTROPHORESIS

Most proteins have a net positive or negative charge, reflecting the number of charged amino acids they possess. If an electric field is applied to a solution containing proteins, they migrate at a rate determined mainly by the net charge, as well as size and shape. This technique is known as 'electrophoresis', and is the most widely used procedure for separating proteins on the basis of charge. It separates small quantities and is therefore used for analysis; it is not suitable for the production of large quantities of material.

A modified version of this technique, known as **SDS *polyacrylamide gel electro-phoresis*** (abbreviated to **SDS-PAGE**), is used routinely in protein analysis, in which the rate of movement of the proteins depends only on their relative molecular mass (M_r) — that is, size. The protein solution is treated with a detergent called sodium dodecyl sulfate (SDS); the large negatively charged dodecyl sulfate ions bind to proteins. Furthermore, when SDS is bound, all proteins have nearly the same shape. The overall effect is that all proteins treated with SDS become negatively charged and can be separated solely on the basis of their relative molecular mass. The apparatus used for SDS-PAGE is shown in Figure 2.3. Protein samples are placed in small slots ('wells') of a thin slab of polyacrylamide gel. The proteins are pre-treated with SDS and a dye that binds specifically to proteins. When an electric field is applied, the buffer and all the now negatively charged protein molecules penetrate and move down the gel towards the positive electrode. As the gel is a complex three-dimensional network, the migrating protein molecules must squeeze through narrow, tortuous passages. Unlike in gel filtration, smaller molecules pass through more easily, and thus the migration rate *increases* as M_r decreases.

Figure 2.3 Schematic set-up for (vertical) slab gel electrophoresis, here shown capable of running four samples simultaneously. During its preparation the liquid gel has been allowed to harden with an appropriately shaped mould on top to make wells for the samples. Protein samples are pre-treated with SDS and a protein-specific dye. During electrophoresis, an electric field is applied and the negatively charged protein molecules move towards the positive electrode (the anode). After electrophoresis, the stained proteins appear as bands. The region of the gel in which the components of one sample can move is called a lane; thus, this gel has four lanes.

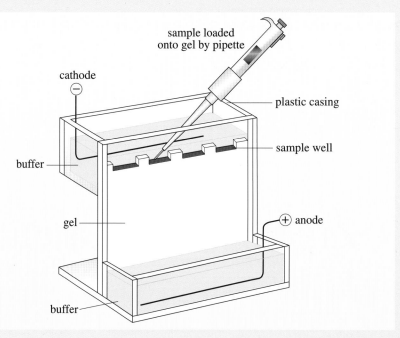

As well as a method for separating proteins in a mixture, gel electrophoresis is often used to check on the purity of preparations. Here, the protein preparation is subjected to SDS-PAGE, and the gel pattern examined. If there are several bands in a single lane, then the preparation still contains a mixture of proteins. A single band could indicate purity.

○ What is the problem with the latter interpretation? Remember that the proteins are treated with SDS to remove the effect of charge.

● Two different proteins of the *same* size would appear as a single band.

SDS-PAGE is a powerful tool in protein analysis because it can be used to separate all types of protein, including those that are insoluble in water. For example, membrane proteins and protein components of the cytoskeleton can be made soluble in water by treatment with SDS. Since the method separates on the basis of size, it also provides information on *subunit* composition of protein complexes (Figure 2.4).

The approximate relative molecular mass may be deduced by comparing the behaviour of the protein of unknown M_r with the behaviour of standard molecules of known M_r. SDS-PAGE is performed by adding a mixture of proteins of known M_r to a lane adjacent to one containing the sample molecule of unknown M_r (as shown in Figure 2.4).

The proteins are then subjected to SDS-PAGE. Unbound dye travels most quickly through the gel, and its position is marked on Figure 2.4 as the 'dye front'; the positions of the various dye–protein complexes are shown as darker bands. The distances travelled by the various proteins are measured relative to the distance of the dye front from the well; the ratios of these distances is called the relative electrophoretic mobility, R_f.

R_f values for the six proteins in lane 1 are plotted against M_r in Figure 2.5. From Figure 2.5 it can be seen that the M_r of protein X = 3×10^4 = 30 000. The value for M_r provided by SDS-PAGE is only approximate; the true value is obtained from analysis of the amino acid sequence.

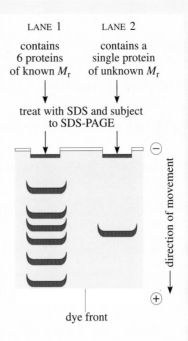

Figure 2.4 Schematic representation of the gel pattern produced in two lanes of a SDS-PAGE experiment. The well for lane 1 contained a mixture of proteins of known M_r. By comparison with these standards, the M_r of the protein in lane 2 can be calculated.

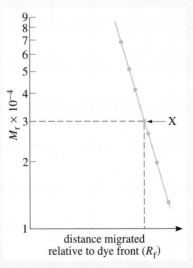

Figure 2.5 Determination of M_r for an unknown protein X by comparing its mobility with that of six standard proteins of known M_r.

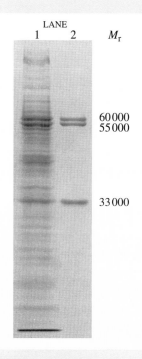

Figure 2.6 Photograph of a real gel showing two stages in the purification of a protein complex. Lane 1 shows a crude extract from the prokaryote *Azotobacter chroococcum*. Lane 2 shows a preparation consisting of three protein bands isolated subsequently from the crude extract.

A photograph of a real gel used to show successive stages in the purification of a protein, and to calculate approximate values of M_r, is shown in Figure 2.6.

TWO-DIMENSIONAL PAGE AND IMMUNOBLOTTING

A problem with SDS-PAGE is that the separation of different proteins it achieves is far from complete. Consider lane 1 in Figure 2.6; the band at $M_r = 33\,000$ could contain different proteins of the same size. Better separation or *resolution* can be obtained using two-dimensional PAGE. It is a two-step process. In the first step the proteins are separated on the basis of differences in their intrinsic charge. Its operation depends on the fact that the net charge on a protein molecule varies with the pH of the solution it is in. The proteins are run in a pH gradient at rates determined by the charge they carry: some move quickly and travel far in the gel, whereas others move slowly and travel only a short distance: this stage is the first dimension of the two-dimensional gel electro-phoresis.

In the second step the gel containing the separated proteins is again subjected to electrophoresis, but in a direction at right-angles to that used in the first step. The proteins are now separated according to their size, as in one-dimensional SDS-PAGE described above, to give a separation as in lane 1 of Figure 2.6. The first gel is cut out and SDS is added; the gel slice is then placed on one edge of an SDS-PAGE slab gel, and again subjected to electrophoresis. Now the separated proteins form discrete spots (Figure 2.7a), and have been separated on the basis of both charge and size. This powerful technique for protein separation can distinguish up to 2000 macromolecules as discrete spots on a single gel. The resolving power is so great that two proteins that differ in only a single charged amino acid can be separated.

A particular protein can be identified in gels in a technique known as 'immunoblotting' (or Western blotting), which is usually done after the separated proteins (Figure 2.7a) have been transferred (blotted) onto nitrocellulose paper. A specific labelled antibody (produced using the techniques described in Box 1.2) can now be used to visualize a particular protein from the large number of those now separated (Figure 2.7b).

SUMMARY OF SECTION 2.1

1   Proteins are very diverse, and a cell may contain several thousand different ones. Proteins have a wide range of functions, including structure, transport, storage, signalling, recognition and gene regulation. A major class of proteins is the enzymes, which are biological catalysts.

2   Gel filtration is a technique used to separate proteins in a mixture on the basis of size differences. The gel acts as a molecular sieve: small molecules enter its pores, so their passage down the column is retarded, whereas larger molecules, unable to enter the pores, pass more quickly down the column between the beads.

3   Proteins can be separated and their M_r measured by SDS-PAGE (SDS-polyacrylamide gel electrophoresis).

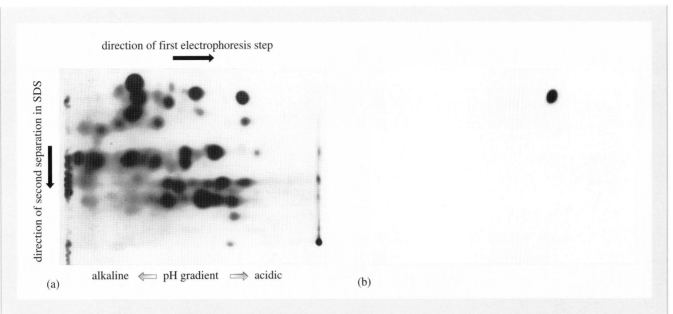

direction of first electrophoresis step

direction of second separation in SDS

alkaline ⇐ pH gradient ⇒ acidic

(a)

(b)

Figure 2.7   (a) Two-dimensional PAGE and (b) immunoblotting.

(a) Proteins are first separated in a one-dimensional gel on the basis of differences in charge in the presence of a pH gradient. A single lane is cut from such a gel, and laid onto another slab gel, and again subjected to electrophoresis, but this time in a direction at right-angles to the first step, and in the presence of SDS, so they are separated on the basis of size differences. Proteins are separated as discrete spots, here identified by a specific protein stain.

(b) A specific immunolabel has been used to identify one particular protein from the mixture, so producing an immunoblot (or Western blot).

2.2   THE STRUCTURE OF PROTEINS

The function of a protein molecule depends on its precise three-dimensional structure, which in turn depends on the sequence of its constituent amino acid monomers. In terms of monomer sequence, proteins are much more varied than the other biopolymers. In proteins there are about 20 structurally different amino acid monomers, each with its particular **R group** or **side-chain**. Given that an average protein chain is several hundred amino acid units in length, there is a huge number of theoretically possible sequences, and therefore of different three-dimensional protein structures. This principle is certainly true for the roughly spherical, **globular proteins** (though as we shall see later, in practice there is rather less diversity in amino acid sequence, and therefore protein structure, than one might expect). In contrast, **fibrous proteins**, which are long and thin, are regular repeats of just a few particular amino acids and so their structure is more uniform. The complexity of protein structure is described in terms of a four-tier hierarchy, from *primary*, through three levels of **higher-order structure** — *secondary*, *tertiary* and *quaternary* — though the latter applies only to proteins that are composed of more than one polypeptide chain. Figure 2.8 summarizes this structural hierarchy.

Table 2.2 Amino acids that occur naturally in proteins, grouped according to type of R group.

Amino acid	Symbol	One letter code	Side-chain (R group)	Amino acid	Symbol	One letter code	Side-chain (R group)
aspartate	Asp	D	COO^- | CH_2 |	alanine	Ala	A	CH_3 |
glutamate	Glu	E	COO^- | $(CH_2)_2$ |	cysteine	Cys	C	SH | CH_2 |
arginine	Arg	R	H_2N—C=$\overset{+}{N}H_2$ | NH | $(CH_2)_3$ |	glycine	Gly	G	H |
				isoleucine	Ile	I	H_3C—CH—CH_2CH_3 |
histidine	His	H	(imidazole ring) CH_2 |	leucine	Leu	L	H_3C—CH—CH_3 | CH_2 |
lysine	Lys	K	$\overset{+}{N}H_3$ | $(CH_2)_4$ |	methionine	Met	M	CH_3 | S | $(CH_2)_2$ |
asparagine	Asn	N	$CONH_2$ | CH_2 |	phenylalanine	Phe	F	(benzene ring) CH_2 |
glutamine	Gln	Q	$CONH_2$ | $(CH_2)_2$ |				
serine	Ser	S	OH | CH_2 |	proline *	Pro	P	(pyrrolidine ring) N—$COOH$ H
threonine	Thr	T	OH | CH—CH_3 |				
tyrosine	Tyr	Y	(phenol ring) OH ... CH_2 |	tryptophan	Trp	W	(indole ring) HN CH_2 |
				valine	Val	V	H_3C—CH—CH_3 |

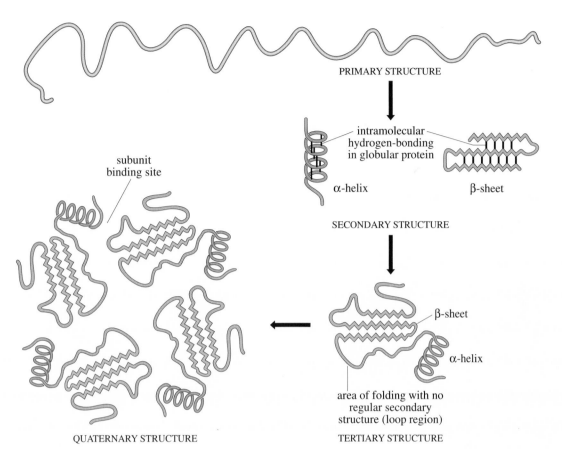

intramolecular
hydrogen-bonding
in globular protein

α-helix   β-sheet

SECONDARY STRUCTURE

β-sheet

α-helix

subunit
binding site

area of folding with no
regular secondary
structure (loop region)

QUATERNARY STRUCTURE   TERTIARY STRUCTURE

2.2.1 PRIMARY STRUCTURE

The **primary structure** of a protein is simply the sequence of amino acid
monomer units, or *residues*, of which it is composed. The essential features of
each amino acid are a carboxyl group ($-COOH$), the carbon atom bonded to it
(known as the α-carbon) to which is also attached a hydrogen atom (H), an amino
group ($-NH_2$), and a side-chain or R group, which differs for each amino acid
(Figure 2.9). The 20 commonly occurring amino acids found in proteins are
shown in Table 2.2.

Figure 2.8   The structural
hierarchy of proteins.

Figure 2.9   The general structure
of an amino acid, and its predomin-
ant (at physiological pH) dipolar
form.

amino
group
α-carbon

side-chain
(R group)   carboxyl
group   dipolar form

Key for Table 2.2: blue, negatively charged side-chains; red, positively charged side-chains; yellow,
uncharged polar side-chains; green, non-polar side-chains.

*Proline has no free $-NH_2$ group. However, it can still form peptide links via its N—H group.

The chemical properties of a protein can be understood by considering the nature of the R groups. Some are negatively charged, some positively charged, others are polar but uncharged, and the remainder are non-polar. Changing the pH of the solution in which a particular protein and hence a particular amino acid occurs, can change the nature of the charge on the R group, which is the reason why pH can affect the activity of enzymes, a subject we return to in Section 2.4.4.

Firstly, consider the amino acid carboxyl group ($-COOH$), which can dissociate (ionize) as follows:

$$-COOH \rightleftharpoons -COO^- + H^+$$

The degree of ionization depends on pH.

In a similar manner, the amino group ($-NH_2$) of amino acids can be charged. In this case a positive charge is acquired by combination with a hydrogen ion; again, the degree of ionization is pH dependent:

$$-NH_2 + H^+ \rightleftharpoons -NH_3^+$$

The same dissociations are also possible in amino acids which contain a carboxyl group or an amino group in their side-chain. A protein is therefore a charged molecule, its overall charge depending on the relative number of different sorts of amino acids it is composed of, and also on the pH of its environment.

The amino group of one amino acid can combine with the carboxyl group ($-COOH$) of another, to form a **peptide bond** (Figure 2.10). The product of this reaction is a dipeptide, which contains a peptide group ($-NH-CO-$). A sequence of amino acids joined together in this way forms a linear **polypeptide** chain. Small chains of amino acids are known as peptides; when the peptide exceeds about 20 amino acids in length, it is known as a protein. However, the distinction between peptide, polypeptide and protein is often arbitrary, and the terms tend to be used interchangeably. A further complication, as we will see shortly, is that a fully functional protein can consist of several *separate* polypeptide chains.

○ Are the two ends of the molecule in Figure 2.10b identical?

● No, the two ends of the tetrapeptide are different.

One end of the peptide has a free $-NH_2$ group, and is known as the **amino terminus**, whereas the other end with a free $-COOH$ group is known as the **carboxyl terminus**. The names of these ends are often abbreviated to N-terminus and C-terminus, respectively. By convention, the sequence of amino acids in a protein is given from the N-terminus to the C-terminus, reading from left to right as in Figure 2.10b.

As you saw from Table 2.2, there are 20 amino acids commonly found in proteins. Typical proteins have relative molecular masses in the range 15 000 to 70 000. The average amino acid has an M_r of 110, so that proteins typically contain 140–640 amino acids. Variations in the number and sequences of the amino acids in these chains give rise to the huge diversity of proteins. The

(a)

(b)

peptide bond

peptide group

dipeptide

$-H_2O$

1   2   3   4

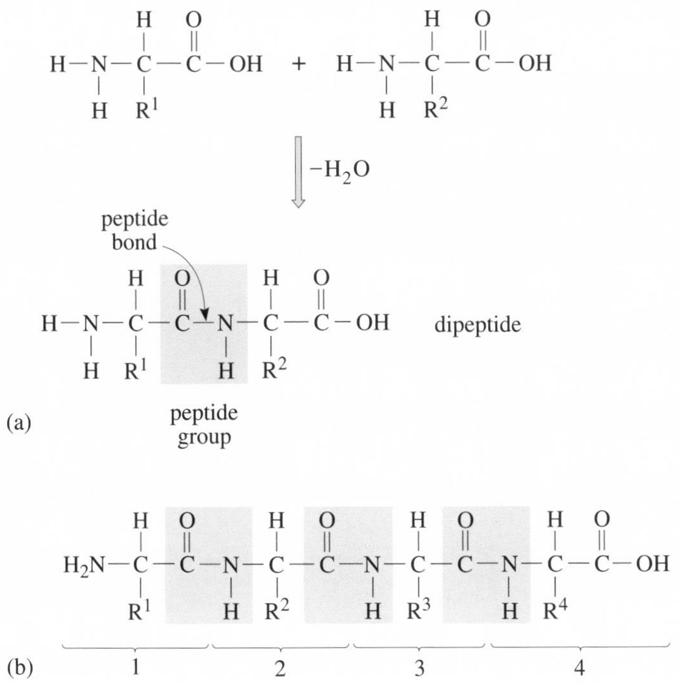

Figure 2.10 Formation of peptide bonds. (a) A dipeptide is formed when two amino acids are joined together by a peptide bond. (b) A tetrapeptide showing the alternation of α-carbon atoms (unshaded) and peptide groups (shaded mauve). The four amino acids are numbered below the chain.

hormone insulin was the first protein for which a complete amino acid sequence was published in 1955 by Fred Sanger (Figure 2.11). This landmark in protein chemistry was the culmination of several years' work. Today the primary structure of many thousands of proteins are known, because the procedure for establishing it is now routine and fully automated: a sample of purified protein is 'fed' to a protein sequencer and the complete primary structure can be produced in a matter of hours for an average-sized polypeptide.

2.2.2 SECONDARY STRUCTURE

The primary structure of a polypeptide chain is not a rigid system. Rotation about each of the α-carbon atoms (Figure 2.9) of the amino acid residues (except proline) is possible, which allows a very flexible structure and folding of the chain in a theoretically huge variety of ways.

The folding of the linear polypeptide chain into its precise higher-order structure is largely determined by its amino acid sequence. In general terms, the chain folds into the most energetically favourable shape, or **conformation**; in this conformation, the hydrophobic ('water-hating') amino acid side-chains are clustered together in the interior of the molecule, away from the aqueous environment, and the majority of the hydrophilic ('water-loving') side-chains are on the surface of the molecule where they interact with the surrounding water molecules. However, this description is rather too simplistic; the protein is not an amorphous blob with a hydrophobic core surrounded by a hydrophilic shell. Rather, there are regions of so-called **secondary structure**, in which the polypeptide chain is folded into regular, stable patterns. The two most common folding patterns are the α-**helix** and the β-**sheet** (Figure 2.12), proposed by Linus Pauling in 1951 (Figure 2.13).

Figure 2.11 Fred Sanger published the first amino acid sequence of a protein, bovine insulin, in 1955, for which he was awarded the Nobel Prize for Chemistry in 1958. His later work on DNA sequencing gained him his second Nobel Prize in 1980. His close interaction with molecular biologists culminated in the establishment of a new Laboratory of Molecular Biology on the outskirts of Cambridge. He is commemorated in the name of the Sanger Centre, Cambridge, a major research laboratory for genome mapping and sequencing, including that of humans.

Figure 2.12 Two common folding patterns found in proteins. (a) and (b) show, respectively, structural and schematic representations of the α-helix, in which the N—H group of every peptide bond is hydrogen-bonded to the C=O of a neighbouring peptide bond located four peptide bonds away in the same chain. (c) and (d) show the β-sheet; in this example, adjacent parts of a polypeptide chain run in opposite (antiparallel) directions; they can also run parallel. The different sections of polypeptide chain in a β-sheet are held together by hydrogen bonds between the C=O and N—H groups of peptide bonds in the adjacent sections. (a) and (c) show all the atoms in the polypeptide backbones, but the R groups are denoted simply by R. In contrast, (b) and (d) show the α-helix and β-sheet as ribbons. Here we adopt the convention of showing α-helices in blue and β-sheets in red.

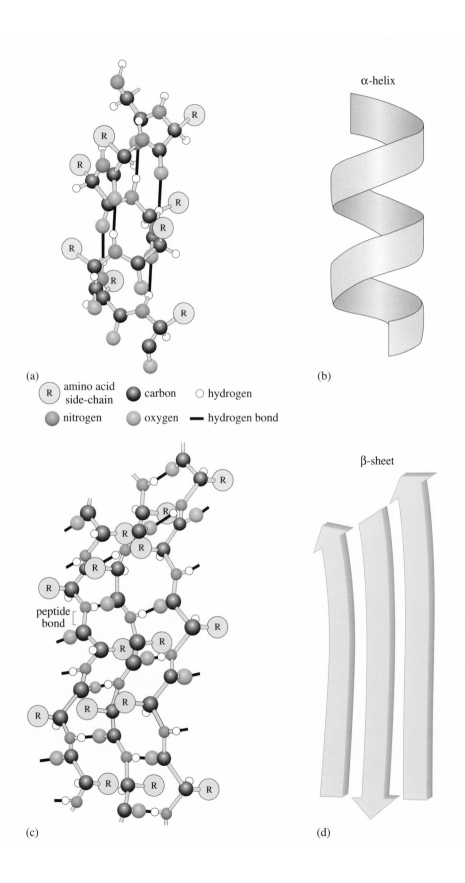

(a)

R amino acid side-chain	● carbon	○ hydrogen
● nitrogen	● oxygen	▬ hydrogen bond

(b)

α-helix

peptide bond

(c)

(d)

β-sheet

Figure 2.13 Linus Pauling's (1901–94) book, *The Nature of the Chemical Bond*, was published in 1939. It revolutionized the study of chemistry according to physical principles, and demonstrated the importance of thinking in three dimensions. He recognized the central role of hydrogen-bonding and other weak interactions in determining and maintaining the structure of macro-molecules. Later (1951) he proposed structures for the α-helix and β-sheet of proteins. He was awarded the 1954 Nobel Prize for Chemistry in recognition of these contributions. As a consequence of the Second World War he became convinced that radiation was harmful to living organisms, especially their genes, an outrageous concept at that time. He campaigned against the military use of radioactive materials, which won him the 1962 Nobel Prize for Peace, and hence became a member of a very select band to be awarded more than one Nobel Prize.

Both these structural patterns arise as a result of hydrogen bond formation between the peptide bond C=O and N—H groups (Figure 2.14). In the case of the α-helix, there is hydrogen-bonding in the direction of the helix axis between the C=O of one peptide bond and the N—H of the peptide bond four amino acid units along the chain. This structure places the polar, hydrogen-bonded C=O plus N—H pairs within the hydrophobic interior of the helix. Thus, a section of α-helix made up of amino acids with non-polar side-chains presents a hydrophobic surface. The β-sheet structures are produced by hydrogen-bonding perpendicular to adjacent chains, via their opposed peptide C=O and N—H groups. Pairs of polypeptide chains that form a β-sheet can either run in the same direction (i.e. both N-terminal to C-terminal) or in opposite directions (one N to C, the other C to N). These two alternative β-sheet arrangements, which are both stable, are described as *parallel* and *antiparallel*, respectively.

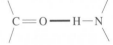

Figure 2.14 Hydrogen bond formation found in protein secondary structure between the N—H group of one amino acid and the C=O group of another.

In fibrous proteins, nearly all the polypeptide chain is folded into a uniform secondary structure. Spiders' webs are composed of silk, which is predominantly a fibrous protein (Pond, 2001). The silk protein *fibroin* is all in β-sheet form, which is why silk is so strong: the large number of hydrogen bonds are very difficult to separate by mechanical forces. In contrast, the *intermediate filaments* that contribute to the cell's internal skeleton, or *cytoskeleton*, which you met in the last chapter, are (for most of their length) pairs of α-helices coiled around each other and held together by non-covalent interactions. The extracellular fibrous protein *collagen*, a major component of skin, tendons and connective tissue in vertebrates, has a rather different structure. It is made up of three intertwined polypeptide chains, each with the repeating amino acid sequence: glycine–X–proline (X can be any amino acid). The three chains are held together by inter-chain hydrogen bonds.

Globular protein molecules, on the other hand, do not have a regular secondary structure throughout. Between the various sections of α-helix and β-sheet are *loop regions*, which have an irregular yet precise shape (Figure 2.8), giving the molecule its unique conformation. These sequences are exposed on the surface of the protein molecule, where they often contribute directly to its specific function.

2.2.3 TERTIARY STRUCTURE

The **tertiary structure** of a globular protein is the three-dimensional arrangement of the entire polypeptide chain — α-helix, β-sheet and all the intervening loop regions (Figure 2.8).

A level in the structural hierarchy *between* secondary and tertiary can also be identified: the **domain**. A domain is an independently folded, globular unit, comprising regions of secondary structure and the loop regions between them. Many proteins are made up of several domains, each with a distinct function. An example of a protein consisting of two domains is shown in Figure 2.15. Here the domains are separated by a hinge region, which provides flexibility: the two domains can move relative to one another as the molecule performs its biological activity. Although different proteins with the same type of function differ in their primary structure, they are generally found to have one or more domains in common; for example, all immunoglobulins or antibody molecules (Gillman and Davey, 2001) have several domains, many of which are in common and are shared by other non-immunoglobulin molecules.

Figure 2.15 The structure of a protein composed of two domains. Here there are two distinct globular regions separated by a hinge region. This particular example is the glycolytic enzyme phosphoglycerate kinase, whose primary sequence contains 416 amino acids.

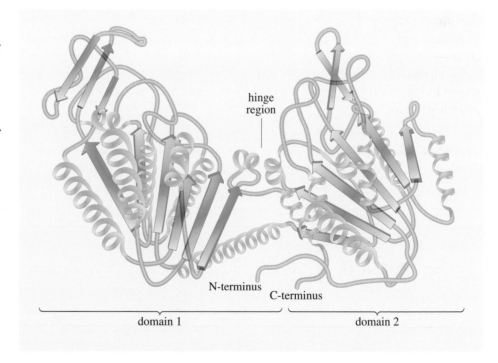

hinge region

N-terminus
C-terminus

domain 1   domain 2

Moving on from domains, we come to tertiary structure proper, the three-dimensional shape of proteins. Most proteins have compact tertiary structure, roughly spherical in shape, and are described as *globular proteins*; most enzymes, for instance, are of this shape. In contrast, long and thin proteins, such as fibroin and collagen, are *fibrous proteins*; they typically have a structural role.

The tertiary structure results from the folding of the primary sequence, so we go from a long, thin and 'floppy' shape to one that is shorter, and more compact. Covalent bonds maintain the amino acid sequence or primary structure, whereas weak interactions maintain the tertiary structure. These latter interactions are formed between the R groups (Table 2.2). The most important interactions that maintain tertiary structure are:

- ionic bonds between oppositely charged groups on amino acids, such as positively charged lysine and negatively charged glutamate:

$$-NH_3^+\cdots\,^-OOC-$$

- hydrogen bonds between a hydroxyl group ($-OH$), e.g. in tyrosine, and a carboxylate group of aspartate or glutamate:

$$-OH\,\rule[0.5ex]{2em}{0.8pt}\,O\!=\!\overset{\displaystyle O^-}{\underset{|}{C}}-$$

- hydrophobic interactions between the hydrocarbon R groups of phenylalanine, leucine, isoleucine and valine.

The sum of all these R group or side-chain interactions results in a stable and biologically active tertiary structure for each protein.

Another aspect of structure which can be conveniently dealt with here is the **disulfide bridge** (disulfide bond), which is a covalent bond. It occurs when two cysteine residues in adjacent polypeptide chains (or different regions of the same chain — i.e. not side by side), with their reactive $-SH$ groups, are oxidized (that is, lose hydrogen) to form a cystine residue. The formation of a disulfide bridge is shown in Figure 2.16. We shall return to these bonds and their importance in protein structure when we consider how proteins fold in Section 2.2.5.

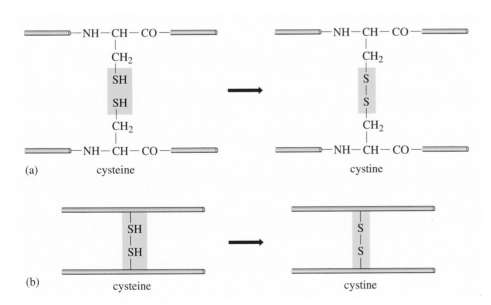

(a) cysteine   cystine

(b) cysteine   cystine

Figure 2.16 (a) Disulfide bridge formation between two cysteine residues to give a 'cystine group', which links two adjacent lengths of polypeptide chain. (b) Simplified representation of disulfide bridge formation. A convention adopted here is that disulfide bridges are shown in yellow.

Figure 2.17 Tertiary structure of a small globular protein stabilized by several types of weak side-chain interactions and disulfide bridges. (Note that the interactions are not shown to scale with the 'backbone' of the polypeptide chain. In reality, the 'backbone' is much larger than the individual side-chain features shown.)

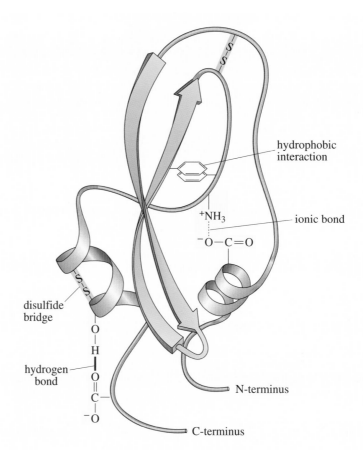

Figure 2.17 shows a few representative side-chain interactions in a small protein. Of the three types of interaction listed above, hydrophobic interactions are especially important. They tend to cluster together in the interior of proteins away from the external aqueous environment. This feature of tertiary structure is particularly important in membrane-bound proteins, as you will see in the next chapter.

○ Using Figure 2.17 to review some detail of protein structure, summarize the features of primary, secondary and tertiary structure exhibited by this protein.

● The protein has a single polypeptide chain, with N- and C-termini. There are two disulfide bridges. There are two short lengths of α-helix and two lengths of β-sheet, which are antiparallel. They are joined together by loop regions of irregular structure.

○ What effect does the secondary structure have on the tertiary structure of this protein?

● Secondary structure provides a certain degree of rigidity to regions of the molecule, but note that they are interspersed by irregularly folded regions providing some flexibility.

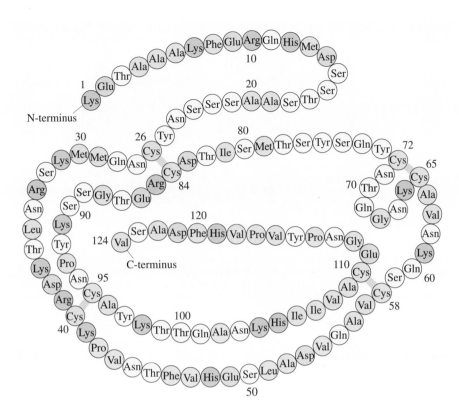

Figure 2.18 The primary structure of RNAase, held together by four disulfide bridges.

We shall now bring the generalized features of protein structure to life using a real example, for which we have chosen bovine pancreatic ribonuclease, abbreviated as RNAase, illustrated in Figures 2.18–2.20. (This enzyme degrades RNA to its constituent nucleotides.)

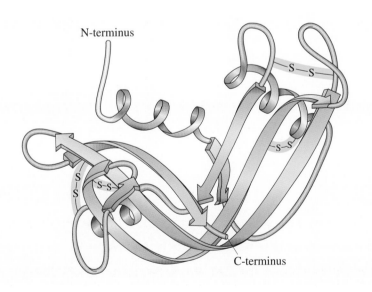

Figure 2.19 The tertiary structure of RNAase shown as a 'ribbon' drawing. β-sheets are shown in red and α-helices in blue.

In summary, the primary structure (Figure 2.18) of RNAase is a single chain with eight cysteine residues. It has some clearly defined secondary structure within a highly folded tertiary structure (Figure 2.19), and contains four disulfide bridges.

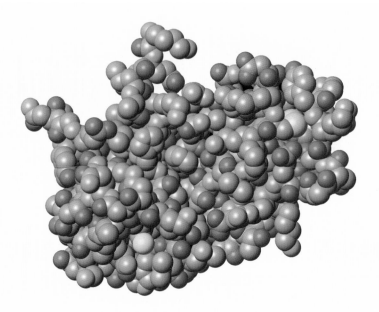

Figure 2.20 The tertiary structure of RNAase shown as a space-filling representation; that is, the volume of space occupied by each atom is indicated by a sphere. Water molecules and hydrogen atoms are not shown.

○ The final representation of RNAase is shown in Figure 2.20. What overall impression do you gain from this illustration of the tertiary structure, compared with the primary structure (Figure 2.18)?

● The tertiary structure is relatively compact; that is, it is a globular protein.

The tertiary structure of a protein is the one that is significant for its biological activity. How, though, do proteins work? This topic is complex, because different proteins work in different ways, but we shall describe the functions and modes of action of some major groups of proteins. The first group of proteins to be considered from a structure–function perspective are the enzymes in Section 2.4. Here, though, we shall merely make the general statement that all proteins (except structural ones) function by interacting with specific **ligands**, a general term for other molecules or ions. These ligands bind to proteins at specific **binding sites.** Different proteins bind to a vast range of ligands, ranging from small ions, through small molecules or other proteins, to the largest molecules of all, DNA. The important functional point is that this binding is highly specific, such that a given protein may bind to just one or two ligands. We shall return to the relationship between protein structure and function in Section 2.2.5, but first we shall complete our description of protein structural hierarchy.

However, before we consider the final layer of hierarchy in protein structure, it is important to appreciate how the tertiary structure of proteins is determined. The principal technique is X-ray crystallography, explained briefly in Box 2.2.

BOX 2.2 X-RAY CRYSTALLOGRAPHY

X-ray crystallography has been a powerful tool in studying the three-dimensional structures of proteins. The basis of the technique is that interatomic distances in proteins are of the same order of magnitude as the wavelength of X-rays (c. 10^{-10} m), which allows the protein to function as a diffraction grating when irradiated with X-rays, leading to the precise detection of the three-dimensional positions of the atoms in a protein. Analysis of these data enables the shape of the protein to be determined. A basic requirement of the technique is a preparation in which molecules are regularly arranged, usually in a crystal. Protein crystals are generally obtained by adding the sample to a concentrated salt solution. This stage has often been the stumbling block in X-ray crystallographic studies, since a number of proteins refuse to crystallize!

The principal components used in X-ray crystallography are shown in Figure 2.21a, namely a source of X-rays and the protein crystal; the detector, a computer, is not shown. A narrow beam of X-rays is fired at the crystal. Part of the beam goes straight through the crystal; the rest is diffracted (scattered) in various directions. The degree of scattering of the X-rays is determined by the number of electrons in an atom: a sulfur atom, for example, scatters six times as strongly as a carbon atom. This differential scattering is important in detecting the different atoms in the final X-ray diffraction patterns obtained. Diffraction of the X-ray beams is detected by a computer as a large series of spots. The position and intensity of each spot in the X-ray diffraction pattern contains information about the position of the atoms in the protein crystal that gave rise to it (Figure 2.21a). A computer is then used to construct three-dimensional electron-density maps from the spot intensities. In conjunction with the primary sequence of the protein, these maps can be used to produce a molecular model. As interpretation is often difficult, the simplified version in Figure 2.21b shows the essential features of the molecule.

Interpretation of the electron-density maps requires complex mathematics. All you need to appreciate is that application of the technique of X-ray crystallography has enabled precise three-dimensional structures to be worked out for over three thousand different proteins. The protein shown in Figure 2.21 is ribulose bisphosphate carboxylase (RUBISCO), an enzyme that plays a central role in CO_2 fixation during photosynthesis.

Figure 2.21 The technique of X-ray crystallography. (a) The principal components of X-ray crystallography apparatus: a source of X-rays and a protein crystal produce an X-ray diffraction pattern of the enzyme ribulose bisphosphate carboxylase. (b) Image of the same protein showing the major structural features.

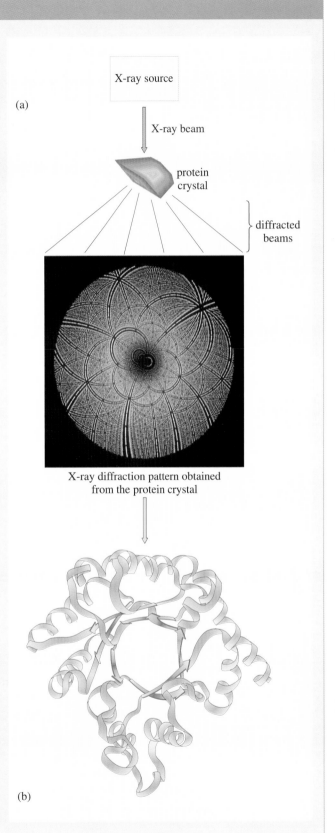

(a)

X-ray source

X-ray beam

protein crystal

diffracted beams

X-ray diffraction pattern obtained from the protein crystal

(b)

2.2.4 QUATERNARY STRUCTURE

For globular proteins that are made up of more than one polypeptide chain, there is a further tier in the structural hierarchy called the **quaternary structure**. Here, the constituent polypeptide chains, each folded into its tertiary structure, are held together by weak, non-covalent interactions. In this context, the polypeptide chains are called **subunits**, and their association as a quaternary structure, is called a *multisubunit complex*. Formation of four different types of quaternary structure is shown in Figure 2.22. In each case, the free subunit has a binding site for at least one other subunit; here, the ligand that binds to the polypeptide chain is in fact another polypeptide chain (subunit). The simplest case (Figure 2.22a) is when just two subunits interact to form a dimer. More complex quaternary structures are the tetramer (Figure 2.22b), the helix (Figure 2.22c) and the ring (Figure 2.22d). These four are merely examples; a whole range of other inter-actions is possible. For simplicity, in each of the four examples just considered, identical subunits are shown interacting. However, such protein complexes are often made up of more than one type of non-identical subunit, each type having a different function. We shall meet an example of a protein complex when con-sidering how enzyme function is controlled in Section 2.4.7. A simpler example (Figure 2.23) shows the quaternary structure of haemoglobin, the oxygen-carrying protein found in almost all vertebrate and several invertebrate phyla.

○ How many subunits make up a biologically active molecule of haemoglobin, and what other features of haemoglobin structure are shown in Figure 2.23?

● The quaternary structure of haemoglobin consists of four subunits. Each subunit is a single polypeptide chain with a haem group (which is the oxygen binding site). Notice too that the subunits of haemoglobin are non-identical: there are two α and two β subunits.

Protein molecules also exist as part of water-insoluble cellular structures in association with non-protein molecules, such as nucleic acids or lipids. For example, ribosomes are aggregates of specific proteins and RNA molecules; eukaryotic chromosomes are DNA–protein complexes; viruses are composed of a nucleic acid core of either RNA or DNA surrounded by a protein coat; membranes are lipids arranged as a bilayer with protein molecules interspersed between them. Again it is mainly weak, non-covalent interactions (in this case hydrophobic interactions) that hold the proteins and lipids together.

2.2.5 FROM AMINO ACID SEQUENCE TO FOLDED PROTEIN

It used to be assumed that once a sequence of amino acids had been assembled into a polypeptide chain at the ribosome then the chain would spontaneously fold into its biologically active form (known as the 'native conformation') as a result of the interactions between the constituent amino acid residues. There is experi-mental evidence that amino acid sequence can be sufficient to determine higher-order structure as shown, for example, by C. B. Anfinsen's landmark experiment on the reversible denaturation of RNAase (Box 2.3).

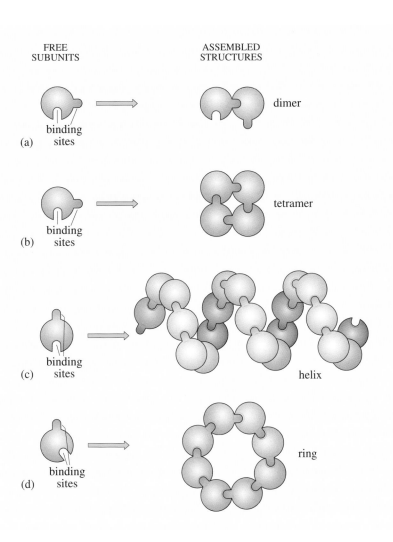

FREE
SUBUNITS

ASSEMBLED
STRUCTURES

(a) binding
sites

dimer

(b) binding
sites

tetramer

(c) binding
sites

helix

(d) binding
sites

ring

Figure 2.22   Four examples of protein quaternary structure. In each case, the subunits are identical.

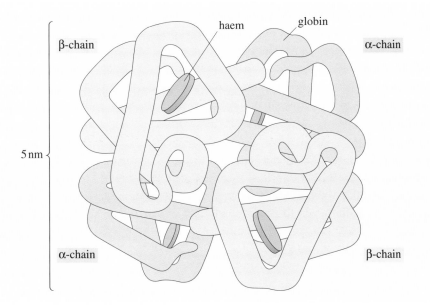

β-chain

haem

globin

α-chain

5 nm

α-chain

β-chain

Figure 2.23 The quaternary structure of haemoglobin. The haem groups are non-protein planar structures with an iron atom at the centre where oxygen is bound; they are shown in red. The four polypeptide chains are shown in blue or green. Note the scale of the haemoglobin molecule.

HS—CH₂—CH₂—OH

β-mercaptoethanol
(2-thioethanol)

We deliberately chose RNAase as our example of protein tertiary structure, because this enzyme was used in a classic study of protein folding by Christian Anfinsen in the early 1960s. His research demonstrated an important concept, namely the relationship between a protein's primary structure, its three-dimensional shape and its biological activity.

RNAase has eight cysteine residues, which form four specific disulfide bridges in the intact, biologically active molecule (Figure 2.19). Anfinsen treated this protein with two reagents: β-mercaptoethanol (also known as 2-thioethanol), a reducing agent, which breaks —S—S— bonds to produce two —SH groups, and urea, which disrupts hydrogen bonds.

○ What effect would these reagents have on the structure of RNAase?

● The tertiary structure of the protein should be disrupted with this treatment. The disulfide bridges and hydrogen bonds which maintain the tertiary structure would be broken.

The result of the experiment was indeed loss of three-dimensional tertiary structure, and a 'random coil' was produced — that is, a molecule with no defined structure (Figure 2.24). The protein is said to be 'denatured' by this treatment. As well as the tertiary structure being destroyed, enzymatic activity was lost too.

When β-mercaptoethanol and urea were separated from the larger RNAase protein molecules in the presence of oxygen, the disulfide bridges reformed, the tertiary structure was regained and 95% of the biological activity was recovered. This process is termed **reversible denaturation**, for the obvious reason that the original structure and activity can be regained in a suitable chemical environment. From a statistical point of view, this reversibility is quite remarkable: the eight cysteine residues can combine to give four disulfide bridges in 105 different pairings, 104 of which display no biological activity. The fact that the reverse process leads to 95% recovery of activity suggests that most molecules revert to the original tertiary structure with the cysteine residues combined in the same way as at the start of the experiment.

Figure 2.24 Reversible denaturation of RNAase.

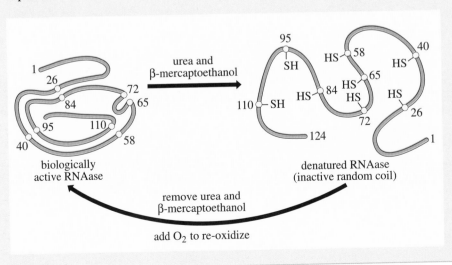

Anfinsen's experiment was the first demonstration of one of the basic tenets of molecular biology, namely that the primary structure of a protein or polypeptide determines its higher-order structure and hence biological activity. In this case, a given sequence of amino acids always refolds to give a particular tertiary structure, so that folding of the chain depends solely on the primary structure.

Other small, single-domain proteins refold in this way *in vitro*, but no artificial means has yet been found to make most larger ones, made up of several domains (the majority of proteins), do so. In fact, it is not fully understood how a newly synthesised polypeptide chain becomes folded into its correct conformation *in vivo*. It appears that parts of the molecule fold spontaneously into the correct secondary structure, and that this process starts during synthesis at the ribosome. Thus, in the newly synthesised protein, most of the regions of secondary structure are complete and in the right orientation to one another, but the molecule has a much more open and flexible conformation than the biologically active form. A further process must take place to ensure that this *molten globule* shape develops into the correct tertiary structure. Further folding and condensation from the molten globule state is a relatively slow process, and sometimes results in incorrectly folded intermediate forms, which are then unable to achieve the correct conformation spontaneously. A proportion of such aberrant intermediates can be 'reloosened' by so-called **chaperone** proteins, and are then able to attain the biologically active conformation. Chaperones exert their effect by binding to the misfolded regions, thereby altering their structure and allowing the protein to have another go at folding correctly. Chaperones also have a role in preventing premature folding, as you will see in Chapter 3. Just how chaperone-assisted folding happens is not understood, but it is known to be an ATP-requiring process. Figure 2.25 summarizes a possible mechanism.

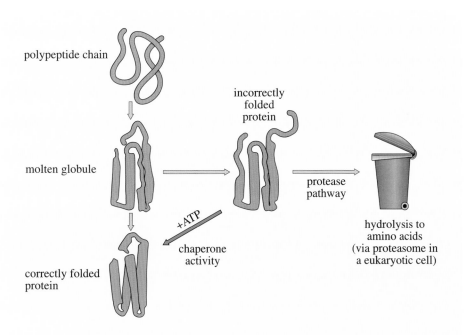

Figure 2.25 Possible mechanism of chaperone-assisted protein folding. A newly synthesised protein rapidly attains a molten globule state. Subsequent folding occurs more slowly and requires interaction with a chaperone to produce a correctly folded protein. Some molecules may still fail to fold correctly, and are recognized as defective and degraded by proteolytic enzymes of the protease pathway.

Proteins that fail to fold correctly are broken down to their constituent amino acids in a process known as **proteolysis**, by a family of proteolytic enzymes, the **proteases**, which catalyse cleavage of peptide bonds. In eukaryotic cells, most proteins are broken down in the cytosol by large complexes of proteolytic enzymes called **proteasomes**. But how does the proteasome select which proteins are to be degraded? Proteins are prepared for degradation by the covalent attachment to a protein known as ubiquitin, a process catalysed by specialized enzymes. Ubiquitin-labelled, misfolded, damaged or short-lived proteins, are recognized by this ubiquitin-dependent proteolytic system. The enzymes that attach ubiquitin to these proteins presumably recognize misfolded or damaged parts, for example sequences that might normally be buried and hence inaccessible in the core of a correctly folded three-dimensional structure.

Proteins that carry out their role in the cytosol are fully functional as soon as the polypeptide product released from the free ribosomes has become correctly folded. Other proteins of a eukaryotic cell are synthesized on ribosomes attached to the cytosolic surface of the endoplasmic reticulum (ER), and those that are intended for export out of the cells or for incorporation into membranes, pass into the lumen of the ER, where they undergo **post-translational modification.**

One type of post-translational process is glycosylation, the addition of short sugar chains to specific sites on the folded protein (to amino acids with $-NH_2$ or $-OH$ groups for the sugar to react with), to form a **glycoprotein**. Some glycoproteins are incorporated into the cell membrane (see Chapter 3) and have important roles in intercellular interactions; others are secreted and function outside the cell.

Even after such intracellular modifications, some secreted proteins are inactive, but may be converted to active proteins by extracellular activation. Such proteins are called **zymogens**. The conversion of a zymogen to the corresponding active protein involves the hydrolysis of specific peptide bonds (proteolysis). Examples include the digestive enzymes, pepsin and trypsin, whose secretion as zymogens ensures that the cells secreting them are not damaged (by digestion) in the process. Other examples are the blood clotting enzymes, which need to be available in the bloodstream in an inactive state until required. However, the classic example of a protein synthesized initially as an inactive zymogen is the hormone insulin, which is initially produced as proinsulin, and folds in a manner similar to that of RNAase to produce a tertiary structure stabilized by disulfide bridges (Figure 2.26a and b). Proteolysis then removes a section of the polypeptide chain known as the *connecting peptide*, which leaves two polypeptide chains joined by two disulfide bridges (Figure 2.26c). However, unlike the case of RNAase, when insulin is treated with β-mercaptoethanol the tertiary structure is broken up irreversibly: the correct bridges do not reform and insulin does not regain its correct, biologically active structure on removal of the β-mercaptoethanol (Figure 2.26d).

○ Proinsulin exhibits reversible denaturation on treatment with β-mercapto-ethanol and its subsequent removal. Why doesn't insulin behave in the same way, which would allow its tertiary structure to be restored and its biological activity to be recovered?

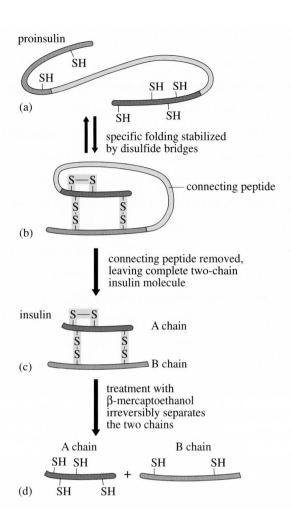

Figure 2.26 The polypeptide hormone insulin cannot spontaneously regain its tertiary structure if its disulfide bridges are disrupted. (a) Insulin is synthesized as a larger polypeptide (proinsulin). (b) Proinsulin folds to form a tertiary structure that is stabilized by disulfide bridges. (c) Proinsulin is cleaved by proteolysis, which removes a connecting peptide to form the biologically active molecule, insulin. (d) Treatment of insulin with β-mercaptoethanol to break the disulfide bridges irreversibly separates insulin into two biologically inactive polypeptides.

- The connecting peptide in proinsulin joins the A and B chains together, and enables the denatured polypeptide to refold and the correct disulfide bridges to form. Once the connecting peptide has been removed, the A and B chains of insulin are unable to remake the correct disulfide bridges.

SUMMARY OF SECTION 2.2

1 Proteins have a four-tier hierarchy of structure: primary, secondary, tertiary and quaternary. All except primary constitute higher-order structure.

2 Primary structure is the sequence of amino acids, which are joined via peptide bonds to form a linear polypeptide chain, which has an N-terminus and a C-terminus.

3 Secondary structure consists of two types of regular folding patterns, α-helix and β-sheet, which are stabilized by hydrogen bonds.

4 Tertiary structure is the three-dimensional arrangement of the entire polypeptide chain. Domains are independently folded globular units with intervening irregular loops. Globular proteins are roughly spherical in shape,

whereas fibrous proteins are long and thin. Tertiary structure is maintained by weak interactions between amino acid R groups. Disulfide bridges can form between two non-adjacent cysteine residues. Ligands attach at specific binding sites. Tertiary structure can usually be determined by X-ray crystallography.

5   A protein consisting of more than a single polypeptide chain is described as having quaternary structure, in which each polypeptide chain is called a subunit. Weak interactions maintain these structures. Subunits can be either identical or non-identical.

6   Proteins consisting of a single polypeptide chain, such as RNAase, can be reversibly denatured by treatment with appropriate reagents, indicating that the primary structure determines the tertiary structure. Proteins with separate polypeptide chains linked by disulfide bridges, or multisubunit proteins, often do not reform after denaturation, and can lose all of their biological activity with such treatment. Correct folding of some proteins is mediated by chaperone proteins. Misfolded proteins in a eukaryote are degraded to their constituent amino acids in proteasomes.

7   Some proteins that are exported from cells undergo post-translational modification, which can involve the addition of short sugar chains to form glycoproteins, or the removal by proteolysis of sections of polypeptide chain from precursor zymogens.

2.3   PROTEIN DIVERSITY

We have now finished our description of the general principles of protein structure. You should now appreciate that proteins come in a wide variety of shapes and sizes. This short section aims to expand a little of this diversity theme. A small selection of proteins is illustrated in Figure 2.27, which provides merely a taster of protein diversity. Just how many different natural proteins are there? This question is at present impossible to answer, but current work on genomes (see Chapter 8) is beginning to shed some light on this intriguing issue. A typical prokaryotic cell such as *E. coli* is believed to be capable of synthesizing about 4 000 different proteins. In contrast, the equivalent figure for a human cell is estimated to be around 10^4. Recall too that different proteins can be produced in different cells of a multicellular, eukaryotic organism. The yeast *Saccharomyces cerevisiae* is also eukaryotic, and a recent estimate suggests that each of its cells can produce around 6 000 proteins. This figure has been obtained, not by purifying these proteins from cell extracts, but by extrapolation from the DNA sequence of its genome. In 1996 the genome of this organism was completely sequenced. This information enabled scientists to estimate that there are 6 000 protein-coding genes, and hence the organism has the potential to synthesize this number of different proteins. The sizes of these putative proteins have also been estimated from the sequence data. The numbers of putative proteins of different sizes are shown in Figure 2.28.

○   Identify two general points about the size distribution of proteins in *S. cerevisiae* from Figure 2.28.

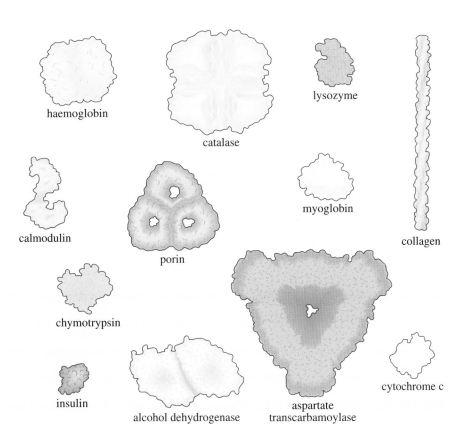

Figure 2.27 Protein diversity. The general shapes of a small selection of proteins, with sizes shown relative to one another.

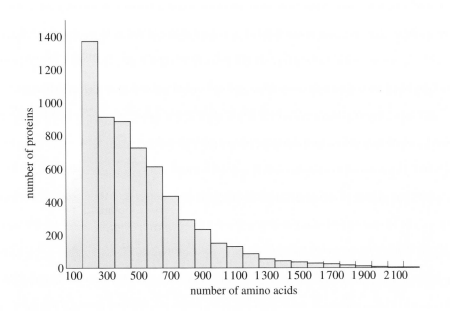

Figure 2.28 Protein diversity in the yeast *Saccharomyces cerevisiae*. The plot shows the distribution of numbers of proteins in terms of the number of amino acids, i.e. sizes of proteins. From left to right along the horizontal axis, the size of proteins is increasing. These data are not based on size estimates of purified proteins, but are derived from estimates of protein sizes encoded by the genes of this eukaryotic organism, predicted from its DNA sequence. The genome was completely sequenced in 1996, so enabling predictions to be made of how many proteins of given amino acid lengths could be synthesized in this organism. For technical reasons, the number of small proteins, especially those with 100 amino acids or less, cannot be determined accurately from the DNA sequence alone.

1   A large number of proteins in this organism are relatively small, with < 200 amino acids in their primary structure.

2   Only a small number of proteins are very large, with > 1 200 amino acids in their primary structures.

If a single unicellular organism such as a yeast is capable of synthesizing about 6 000 different proteins, the answer to our question about the number of naturally occurring proteins might be quite phenomenal. Indeed we may never have an exact answer.

So far, much of this chapter has dealt with protein structure, and we have only touched on functional aspects, and the relationship between structure and function. Table 2.1 introduced the wide range of functions that are performed by proteins, both inside and outside living cells. Much of the rest of this book will introduce you to different proteins and their functions. The second half of this chapter deals with a huge group of proteins, the enzymes, and their activities will be described in outline. First, though, we present a short aside on the theme 'uniformity within diversity'. Proteins may be diverse and different, but often, when different proteins are compared, great similarities are found between them; that is, proteins exist in families.

2.3.1 PROTEIN FAMILIES

A protein family consists of a group of proteins, which have similar amino acid sequences and tertiary structures; hence they are closely related. An example of a group of proteins that are closely related both in their function and in their structure, is a family of enzymes, the proteases, all members of which catalyse the breakdown of proteins. In this particular group of proteases, there is always a serine at the active site (where the reaction is catalysed), and for this reason they are called *serine proteases*. Members of the serine protease family are all secreted as zymogens (Section 2.2.5), and include several protein-digesting enzymes in the gut, such as trypsin and chymotrypsin, and some of the enzymes involved in the process of blood-clotting and the destruction of invading organisms following antibody binding (the so-called *complement* system). When the amino acid sequences of two of these proteins, chymotrypsin and elastase, are compared, they are found to be identical at about 40% of the positions (Figure 2.29). The similarity of their tertiary structures, as revealed by X-ray crystallography (Box 2.2), is even more striking: most of the detailed twists and turns in their polypeptide chains are identical (Figure 2.30).

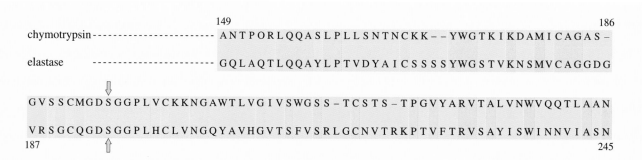

Figure 2.29 Comparison of the amino acid sequences of two members of the serine protease family of enzymes. The C-terminal portions of the two proteins are shown (amino acids 149–245). Identical amino acids are connected by blue bars, and the serine residues in the active sites at position 195 are indicated by arrows. (The single letter codes for the amino acids are explained in Table 2.2.)

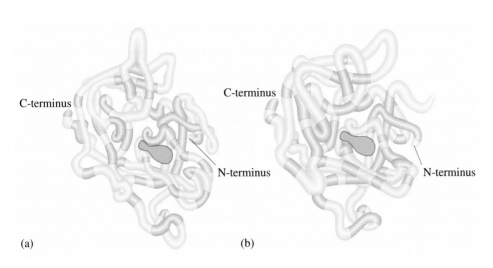

C-terminus

C-terminus

C-terminus

N-terminus

N-terminus

(a)

(b)

Figure 2.30 The three-dimensional structures of two serine proteases: (a) elastase; (b) chymotrypsin. The amino acids shown in blue are the same in both proteins. (The active site, which is shown in red, contains an activated serine residue. Chymotrypsin contains more than two chain termini because it is formed by proteolysis of chymotrypsinogen, the inactive precursor zymogen.)

The story of the serine proteases could be repeated for hundreds of other protein families. However, in many cases the primary structures have diverged much further than for the serine proteases, so that one cannot be sure of a family relationship between two proteins without determining their three-dimensional structures.

In contrast, the existence of structurally similar domains in different proteins makes it possible to infer three-dimensional structure from amino acid sequence data. (The former is a lot more difficult to determine than the latter.) Thus, if a newly discovered protein is found to contain an amino acid sequence very similar to that of a protein domain for which the three-dimensional structure is already known, then it is likely to have a domain with a very similar three-dimensional structure, and hence function. Tertiary structures have been determined for only a small fraction of the proteins for which the amino acid sequence is known. The amino acid sequences of more than 200 000 proteins are known, and about a third are related to at least one of the 5 000 or so known three-dimensional structures. Within these structures, several hundred *protein fold families* have been identified, and it is estimated altogether that there are about 1 000 such families. If a protein of unknown three-dimensional structure has at least 40% of its amino acids in common with a protein of known structure, then the structure of the former can be modelled by a computer. Structures calculated in this way can be quite accurate. As function depends on three-dimensional structure, such predictions of protein conformation are a powerful tool in the interpretation of genome sequencing data — that is, the kind of information shown in Figure 2.28.

SUMMARY OF SECTION 2.3

1   A given cell produces a wide diversity of different proteins, ranging from a few thousand synthesized by a prokaryote to an estimated 10^4 produced by a human cell. In multicellular eukaryotes, different proteins can be produced in different cell types.

2   Proteins often form families, comprising groups closely related both in structure and function — for example, the serine proteases.

2.4 PROTEINS AS CATALYSTS: ENZYMES

Of all the different kinds of proteins in living organisms, the vast majority are enzymes. A given cell may be capable of synthesizing several thousand enzymes, each one catalysing a different reaction. The range of enzymes is truly immense, but their activities display many common features that are examined in this section.

We begin by explaining how enzymes are named and provide a simple classification based on their activity, but like most other classification systems, it is difficult to assign all enzymes to well-defined categories.

As is generally true of all proteins, enzymes are only active when bound to appropriate ligands. The principal ligands are the substrates on which enzymes act, but additional ligands can also influence the interaction between an enzyme and its substrate. We shall examine these interactions in some detail. Physical and chemical factors in the environment of an enzyme can also affect its activity. How do enzymes catalyse (that is, speed up) reactions? This question is very difficult to answer, and at present this can only be done in general terms. However, we do attempt an answer.

Finally, it is important to appreciate that enzymes are subject to control, which is the final topic of this chapter. In a given cell, some enzymes may be very active, whereas others are completely inactivated, depending on the needs of the cell at that particular time. However, the full significance of enzymes in living processes will only become apparent with some understanding of metabolism — the chemical reactions that go on inside living organisms — which is the subject of Chapters 4 and 5.

As a footnote, before we consider enzymes in detail, it is worth mentioning that not all enzymes are proteins; a few are made of RNA and hence are called *ribozymes*. Some specialized RNA molecules can catalyse a change in other RNA molecules, cutting the nucleotide sequence at specific points, and other types of RNA molecule spontaneously cut out a portion of their own nucleotide sequence and rejoin the cut ends. These catalytic ribozymes are not considered further in this chapter, but you should be aware of their existence.

2.4.1 ENZYME NAMES

First, though, there is the question of names. Enzyme names usually, but not always, end in -ase. Exceptions to this general rule include the digestive enzymes that you have met already, for example, pepsin, chymotrypsin and trypsin. Others include thrombin (involved in blood clotting) and lysozyme. There are thousands of different enzymes, so, as with the living organisms that produce these molecules, enzymes too have been classified. Table 2.3 shows some of the major groups of enzymes and the reactions they catalyse. You should note, though, that the distinctions between these categories are not that clear cut. For example, the hydrolases form a very broad group that includes nucleases, proteases, phosphatases, etc. The boundary between synthases and polymerases is also blurred.

Table 2.3   Classification of enzymes

Class of enzyme	Type of reaction catalysed
hydrolases	hydrolysis (splitting of bonds by addition of the components of water molecules)
nucleases	break down nucleic acids by hydrolysing bonds between nucleotides
proteases	break down proteins by hydrolysing peptide bonds
synthases	synthesize molecules by condensing two smaller molecules together
polymerases	catalyse polymerization reactions such as the synthesis of DNA and RNA
kinases	catalyse the addition of phosphate groups to a molecule (protein kinases are an important group of kinases)
phosphatases	catalyse the hydrolytic removal of a phosphate group from a molecule (protein phosphatases are an important group of phosphatases)
oxidoreductases	catalyse oxidation and reduction reactions (removal or addition of hydrogen atoms); enzymes of this type are often called oxidases, reductases or dehydrogenases
transferases	transfer small groups, e.g. amino groups, from one molecule to another

The names we have used so far can be considered to be trivial names, but each enzyme also has a systematic name, which indicates precisely the reaction it catalyses. For example, an enzyme you will meet in Chapter 4 is formally known as 'L-lactate:NAD$^+$ oxidoreductase', as stipulated by the internationally recognized Enzyme Commission (EC). Each enzyme has been given an EC number, which for our example is 'EC 1.1.1.27'. So, with an EC number and systematic name, each enzyme can be identified unambiguously. Trivial names, though, are frequently used, which for this example is 'lactate dehydrogenase', which is usually abbreviated to the shorthand 'LDH' — much easier to remember!

The name of an enzyme often provides information on its substrate, product or the type of reaction it catalyses. Obvious examples include 'DNA polymerase' and 'glycogen synthase', whereas the name 'lactate dehydrogenase' indicates that this enzyme removes hydrogen from lactate, its substrate. Some enzyme names are a single word; fumarase, for example, converts fumarate to malate.

2.4.2 THE KEY CHARACTERISTICS OF ENZYMES

We have already met the general principle of protein function: activity requires a specific ligand (molecule or ion) to bind at a binding site. In the case of enzyme function, the binding of a specific molecule leads to the chemical transformation of that molecule. To express this important contrast, the terms **substrate** and **active site**, rather than ligand and binding site, are used in describing the behaviour of members of this particular group of proteins. So, in order for catalysis to occur, an enzyme binds a substrate at its active site, so forming the **enzyme–substrate complex** or **ES complex** for short. Catalysis then proceeds, and product or products are released from the complex. This fundamental concept of enzyme activity is illustrated in Figure 2.31.

Figure 2.31 Schematic representation of the relationship between an enzyme, its substrate, and the reaction catalysed by the enzyme.

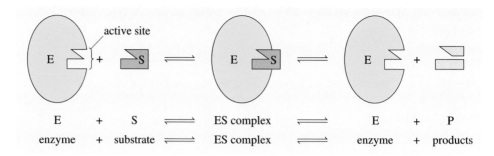

$$E \; + \; S \; \rightleftharpoons \; ES \; complex \; \rightleftharpoons \; E \; + \; P$$

enzyme + substrate ⇌ ES complex ⇌ enzyme + products

Figure 2.31 illustrates in diagrammatic form some other key characteristics of enzymes. Firstly, the catalytic reactions are generally reversible. Enzymes can bind their substrate to form an ES complex, which then immediately dissociates without leading to product formation; successful catalysis implies breakdown of the ES complex into enzyme and product(s). In theory, this step is also reversible, but often products do not bind readily to the enzyme, so in practice this stage of the reaction may not go in reverse.

○ What general principle of all catalytic reactions is illustrated diagrammatically in Figure 2.31?

● The catalyst is the same at the end of the reaction as at the start. After products have been released from the enzyme, the catalytic cycle can begin again.

Another key feature shown in Figure 2.31 is the active site. Here we shall consider briefly the relationship between the enzyme's active site and its substrate; we shall return to this key topic in Section 2.4.6, where the question, 'How do enzymes work?' will be investigated in more detail. For now, the important concept is that the shape of the substrate is complementary to that of the active site. Earlier we used a more appropriate term to describe the three-dimensional shape of a protein or part of it — *conformation*, which means more than just shape. The precise orientation of all parts of the molecule has implications for the arrangement of the charges at the active site. So, both the three-dimensional shape *and* the charge distribution of the substrate and active site are complementary; this relationship is summarized as the **lock and key mechanism**.

○ Which is the lock and which is the key — active site or substrate?

● The active site is the lock into which the substrate — the key — fits.

Another important feature of enzymes is their **substrate specificity**, which can be extremely precise. For example, hexokinase, which catalyses the first reaction of glucose breakdown (glycolysis) in muscle and other tissues (discussed in Chapter 4), uses only glucose as its substrate. However, the digestive protease trypsin is less substrate-specific. It hydrolyses any peptide bond between a basic amino acid (i.e. either lysine or arginine) and the next amino acid on the C-terminal side. In this case, there is no reason for the enzyme to be very specific for a single kind of substrate, because its function is digestion of dietary protein, which may comprise a very heterogeneous collection of molecules.

Enzymes are also quite specific with respect to the reaction or type of reaction they catalyse. A particular molecule (intermediate) may be the substrate of more than one enzyme, but each of these enzymes catalyses the production of a different product(s). For example, as shown in Figure 2.32, pyruvate is the substrate of several enzymes, including lactate dehydrogenase and pyruvate dehydrogenase complex. The former enzyme produces lactate, and the latter produces acetyl CoA and carbon dioxide.

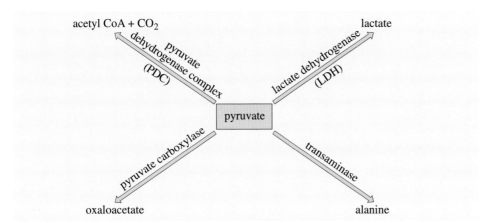

Figure 2.32 Four alternative enzyme-catalysed reactions in which pyruvate is a substrate.

The degree to which a particular enzyme speeds up a reaction is referred to as its **catalytic power**. All chemical reactions, whether enzyme-catalysed or not, go via a high-energy, unstable intervening stage; in other words, there is an energy barrier to be overcome. The height of the energy barrier determines the rate of the reaction. Typically, enzymes can accelerate reactions to between 10^9 and 10^{14} times the rate of the uncatalysed reaction. They do so by providing an alternative reaction pathway in which the energy barrier is lower than for the uncatalysed reaction (Figure 2.33). Thus, enzymes allow reactions to occur at moderate temperatures and generally near-neutral conditions, that would otherwise hardly occur at all or would require high temperatures and pressures and/or extreme pH, conditions which are far from physiological (for the vast majority of organisms). There are, however, some prokaryotes that thrive under extreme conditions, but they too depend on (unusually stable) enzymes for their metabolic reactions.

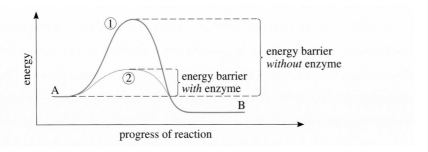

Figure 2.33 The energy changes in the conversion of A to B: curve 1, without enzyme; curve 2, for the enzyme-catalysed reaction. The peak of each curve denotes the energy of the unstable intervening stage (transition state).

A major characteristic of many enzymes, which generally depends on their interactions with specific molecules *other than* their substrate, is controllability — in other words, the topic of **enzyme regulation**. How this control is achieved is discussed in Section 2.4.7. Here we shall briefly consider why enzyme regulation is important. A quick review of Figure 2.32 supplies some of the answers.

○ Consider two identical populations of a prokaryotic organism. Both populations have plenty of pyruvate. Firstly, population A is grown in the complete absence of alanine. What needs to happen to the activity of the transaminase?

● Population A needs to synthesize alanine, so the activity of the transaminase needs to be stimulated so that some pyruvate is converted to alanine.

○ Why would cells of population A need to synthesize alanine?

● Alanine is an amino acid, without which protein synthesis might be disrupted.

○ In contrast, population B is grown in the presence of a high concentration of oxaloacetate. What needs to happen to the activity of pyruvate carboxylase?

● Population B has an excess of oxaloacetate, so the activity of the enzyme pyruvate carboxylase should be suppressed.

It would be wasteful of energy for population B to synthesize oxaloacetate when it is already available in excess. To conserve energy and resources, this population could reduce the activity of pyruvate carboxylase, which actually is what happens. The responsiveness of enzymes to their molecular environment is crucial to the regulation and integration of metabolic pathways within the cell, a topic developed further in Chapter 4.

Most enzymes function inside cells, but we have already met several examples of extracellular enzymes (e.g. digestive enzymes). The majority of intracellular enzymes are present in solution in the cytosol (e.g. those of the glycolytic pathway) or inside subcellular organelles (e.g. the TCA cycle enzymes), and others are membrane-bound. Some exist as single molecules, but others are made up of several subunits held together by non-covalent interactions. For example, triose phosphate isomerase is a two-subunit enzyme (and has two active sites), and phosphofructokinase has four identical subunits (see Chapter 4).

A few enzymes occur in giant complexes consisting of many molecules of several different but functionally related enzymes. One example is the pyruvate dehydrogenase complex (PDC), which catalyses the link reaction in the mitochondria. PDC comprises three enzymes acting in sequence. There are tens of molecules of each of these three enzymes in a multienzyme complex (60 of one, 20–30 of the other two), giving a relative molecular mass (M_r) of about 9×10^6. This structural integration of the three kinds of enzyme allows the product of one reaction to move directly to the next enzyme in the sequence without diffusing into the surrounding medium.

Structural integration of groups of enzymes is at its most sophisticated in the membrane-bound systems, such as the mitochondrial and photosynthetic electron transport chains (Chapter 5). In these systems, enzymes, other proteins and various non-protein molecules involved in energy transduction to ATP are arranged in a precise sequence and orientation with respect to each other (and to the membrane).

2.4.3 RATES OF ENZYME-CATALYSED REACTIONS

Using appropriate protein purification techniques (Box 2.1), individual enzymes can be extracted from living or freshly dead cells and tissues, and their properties studied *in vitro* (in a test-tube). It must be borne in mind, however, that enzyme activity *in vitro* may not always be an accurate reflection of *in vivo* activity. To measure the rate of enzyme reactions, **enzyme assays** are used (Box 2.4).

BOX 2.4   ENZYME ASSAYS

To measure the amount of enzyme present in a preparation, an enzyme assay is performed; assay here means 'measurement'. What is usually assayed is the activity of the enzyme — in other words, the rate of the reaction catalysed by the enzyme preparation.

○ Consider Figure 2.31. What could be measured to assess the activity of a given enzyme?

● As the enzyme reaction proceeds, substrate is converted to product, so substrate is consumed and product appears. Activity could therefore be assessed by measuring the rate of removal of substrate or the rate of formation of product.

This relationship is indeed the basis of an enzyme assay. Quite often it is most convenient to measure the appearance of product as the enzyme reaction proceeds. Products that have particular chemical properties are most readily measured. For example, a coloured product can be quickly measured in a colorimeter, and a gas measured in a gas analyser. In some enzyme catalysed reactions, protons are either consumed or produced, so here changes in pH can be measured. Yet other enzymes interconvert oxidized and reduced forms of coenzymes, which can be distinguished using appropriate techniques.

○ Look again at Figure 2.32. What could be used as the basis for an assay of the enzyme PDC?

● Pyruvate is the substrate; acetyl CoA and CO_2 are products. PDC could therefore be assayed by measuring concentrations of any of these. The rate of appearance of CO_2 is probably the most convenient basis for an assay in this case.

However a given enzyme is assayed, its activity is usually expressed as specific activity, which by convention is expressed relative to the amount of protein (in mg, which can be measured chemically) contained in the preparation. Specific activity of an enzyme preparation is therefore defined as:

specific activity = micromoles of substrate converted per minute per mg protein (i.e. $\mu mol\,min^{-1}\,mg^{-1}$).

Note that the expression 'micromoles of substrate converted' has a predictable relationship to 'micromoles of product formed'.

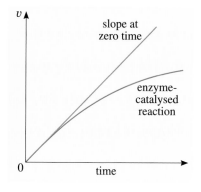

Figure 2.34 Time course of an enzyme-catalysed reaction.

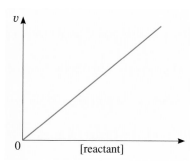

Figure 2.35 Relationship of initial reaction rate against initial reactant concentration for an uncatalysed reaction involving one reactant.

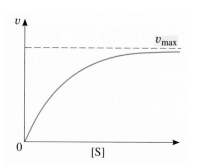

Figure 2.36 Plot of initial reaction rate v against initial substrate concentration [S] for an enzyme-catalysed reaction.

Using an assay, we can study many different features of a given enzyme. In particular, an important factor that affects the rate of an enzyme-catalysed reaction is substrate concentration (written as [substrate] or [S] from here on).

The study of the rates of enzyme-catalysed biochemical reactions, or **enzyme kinetics**, is of particular interest. Suppose an enzyme is added to a solution of its substrate, with the pH and temperature at or near optimum values (see Section 2.4.4). The reaction goes fast to start with but slows down over time (Figure 2.34). (The decline in reaction rate can be due to several factors — for example the reduction in substrate concentration, or the accumulation of a product that inhibits the enzyme.) For this reason, rates of enzyme-catalysed reactions (symbol v) are always measured right at the beginning of the reaction (just past time zero); in other words, the initial rate is measured.

For an uncatalysed reaction (i.e. without an enzyme) involving a single reactant, the plot of initial reaction rate against initial reactant concentration [S] is a straight line (Figure 2.35); hence the initial rate varies directly with the initial substrate concentration. In contrast, for an enzyme-catalysed reaction the relationship between v and [S] is a curve that levels off at very high values of [S] (this shape of graph is known as a rectangular hyperbola). In other words, there is a limit to the reaction rate that can be attained; this **maximum rate** is referred to as v_{max} — spoken as 'vee max' (Figure 2.36). This relationship between v and [S] can be explained as follows. At low values of [S] — that is, when there are many more enzyme molecules than substrate molecules — the reaction rate increases as [S] increases, hence the steep part of the curve close to the origin. As [S] increases further, an increasing proportion of the enzyme molecules have a substrate molecule bound to them, and the overall reaction rate becomes more dependent on the rate at which the product is formed, liberating the enzyme again; hence the slope of the curve decreases. When all the enzyme molecules are involved in the reaction — that is, when the enzyme is *saturated* — the reaction rate cannot increase any further (without changing the conditions), so the curve becomes a horizontal line.

INTRODUCING K_M

A mathematical equation, called the Michaelis–Menten equation, can be derived, which describes the hyperbolic plot of v against [S]. In other words, if v values are calculated from this equation for a range of values of [S], and plotted, then the resulting graph is the same as that obtained experimentally. The derivation of the Michaelis–Menten equation is based on the assumption represented in Figure 2.31, namely that the enzyme (E) binds reversibly to the substrate to form an enzyme–substrate complex (ES), which subsequently breaks down into enzyme and product(s) (P):

$$E + S \rightleftharpoons ES \longrightarrow E + P \tag{2.1}$$

X-ray crystallography and other studies of enzymes have provided *direct* evidence for an ES complex formation, as described in Section 2.4.6 below.

In addition to the variables v and [S], the Michaelis–Menten equation includes two terms that are constant for a particular enzyme (under a particular set of conditions). We have just met one of them: v_{max}. The other is the **Michaelis constant** or K_M. To understand K_M we need to look at the Michaelis–Menten equation:

$$v = \frac{v_{max}[S]}{K_M + [S]} \qquad (2.2)$$

K_M can be obtained from the plot of v against [S] as shown in Figure 2.37.

○   What is the problem of trying to calculate K_M from Figure 2.37?

●   We do not know for certain that v_{max} has been reached.

K_M is a very useful parameter in enzyme kinetics. It is defined as the substrate concentration that gives half the maximum reaction rate, so that K_M is the value of [S] at $\frac{1}{2}v_{max}$. For some enzyme-catalysed reactions (those in which the conversion of ES to E + P is much slower than its dissociation back into E + S), K_M is a measure of how tightly the substrate is bound to the enzyme; that is, it represents the **affinity** of the enzyme for the substrate. The lower the value of K_M, the greater the enzyme affinity and vice versa.

The numerical value of K_M depends on the reaction conditions. Thus, quantitative analysis of changes in its apparent value caused by pH, temperature, inhibitors, etc., provides valuable insights into enzyme mechanisms. Comparison of K_M values provides a means of comparing the properties of enzymes prepared from different sources. Notice the large range of K_M values for the enzymes listed in Table 2.4.

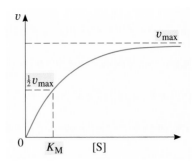

Figure 2.37 Plot of initial reaction rate v against initial substrate concentration [S] for an enzyme-catalysed reaction. K_M is the value of [S] at which the reaction rate is equal to half v_{max}.

Table 2.4 K_M values for selected enzymes (do not worry about the names; they are just used as examples)

Enzyme	Substrate	K_M/µmol l⁻¹
catalase	hydrogen peroxide	1 100 000
carbonic anhydrase	carbon dioxide	12 000
β-galactosidase	lactose	4 000
pyruvate carboxylase	pyruvate	400
LDH	pyruvate	59
fumarase	fumarate	5

○   Which enzyme in Table 2.4 has the lowest affinity for its substrate and why?

●   Catalase has the highest K_M value, and hence the lowest affinity, of the selection of the enzymes shown.

The value of K_M can often be related to the physiological concentrations of substrates: low values reflect low substrate concentrations *in vivo*, and vice versa.

MEASURING v_{MAX} AND K_M FROM HOFSTEE–EADIE PLOTS

Look back at Figure 2.37, the plot of v against [S] for an enzyme-catalysed reaction, the graphical representation of the Michaelis–Menten equation (Equation 2.2). The dashed line, which the curve approaches, but does not actually reach, intercepts the v axis at v_{max}. However, this value is only approximate because of the uncertainty in the maximum height of the curve. It never flattens out completely. Therefore the value of K_M obtained from the graph at $\frac{1}{2} v_{max}$, must also be approximate. This limitation of the v against [S] plot is overcome by rearranging the Michaelis–Menten equation into a form that gives a *linear* relationship between a term involving v and a term in [S]; that is, the plot of the rearranged data is a straight line. Measurements can thus be made accurately of the slope of the line and the values at which it meets or cuts each of the axes. We shall illustrate this concept with just one type of linear kinetic plot, the Hofstee–Eadie plot.

If we multiply both sides of the Michaelis–Menten equation by K_M + [S], we get:

$$v(K_M + [S]) = v_{max}[S] \tag{2.3}$$

that is,

$$vK_M + v[S] = v_{max}[S]$$

Rearranging, we get

$$v[S] = v_{max}[S] - vK_M$$

Dividing by [S] gives

$$v = v_{max} - \frac{vK_M}{[S]} \tag{2.4}$$

Equation 2.4 is the Hofstee–Eadie equation. It is of the form $y = mx + c$ (the equation for a straight line), so the plot of v against $v/[S]$ is a straight line with a slope of $-K_M$; that is, the distance moved down the vertical axis is K_M times the distance moved along the horizontal axis (Figure 2.38). The minus sign just tells us that the line has a negative slope. Thus, K_M is easily and accurately obtained from a Hofstee–Eadie plot. In addition, v_{max} is simply the intercept on the v axis. This conclusion is obvious, and can also be deduced from Equation 2.4, for at this point $v/[S] = 0$, so $K_M v/[S] = 0$; hence $v = v_{max}$. (By similar reasoning, you may like to satisfy yourself that the intercept on the horizontal axis is v_{max}/K_M.)

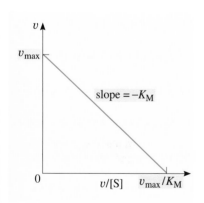

Figure 2.38 Hofstee–Eadie plot of v against $v/[S]$. Using the Hofstee–Eadie equation (Equation 2.4), K_M and v_{max} can be obtained from this plot as shown.

To show you how the Hofstee–Eadie plot (Figure 2.38) works in practice, we shall use some data to produce such a plot, and obtain the key parameters, K_M and v_{max} from it. Table 2.5 has data for a hypothetical enzyme glunase, which converts its hypothetical substrate glunose to unidentified products.

Table 2.5   Data for the hypothetical enzyme glunase.

[glunose]/ μmol l^{-1}	v/μmol min^{-1}
1.0	9.0
1.5	12.5
2.0	16.7
2.7	20.0
5.0	28.6
7.7	37.0
10.0	38.5

These data are plotted in Figure 2.39 with [glunose] along the horizontal axis and rate of hydrolysis v along the vertical axis.

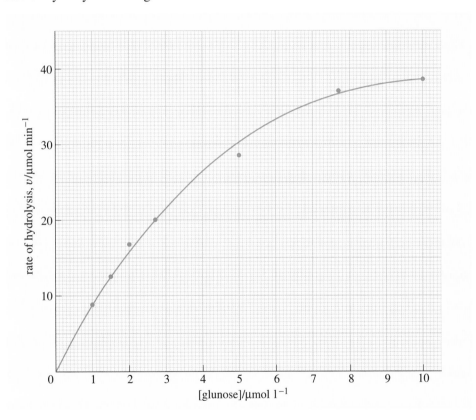

Figure 2.39   Plot of the data in Table 2.5.

○   Could we calculate v_{max} from Figure 2.39?

●   We can only estimate v_{max} from Figure 2.39 because we cannot be sure that the final v_{max} has been reached.

In order to obtain a linear Hofstee–Eadie plot we need to do some simple transformations of the data in Table 2.5. We need to add a third column, in which v is divided by [glunose] to give v/[glunose], as shown in Table 2.6.

Table 2.6   Data for the enzyme glunase.

[glunose]/ μmol l^{-1}	v/μmol min^{-1}	v/[glunose]
1.0	9.0	9.00
1.5	12.5	8.33
2.0	16.7	8.35
2.7	20.0	7.41
5.0	28.6	5.72
7.7	37.0	4.81
10.0	38.5	3.85

The values for v are plotted on the vertical axis against values for v/[S] along the horizontal axis in Figure 2.40. The seven data points fall more or less on a straight line, and the best-fit line has been drawn between them. The line has then been extrapolated to give the broken line intercepts at both the v and v/[glunose] axes. From these two intercept points, the values of K_M and v_{max} can be obtained.

Figure 2.40   Plot of the data in Table 2.6.

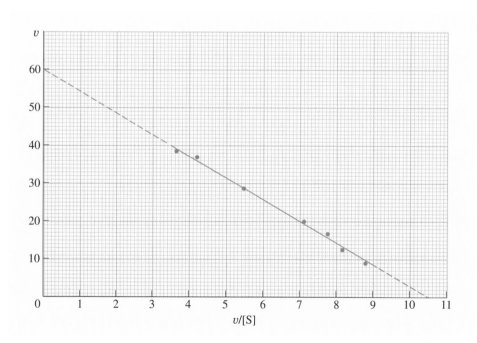

○ What is the value of v_{max} for the enzyme glunase under these conditions?

● Referring to Figure 2.38, v_{max} is the value of the intercept of the line with the v axis; therefore $v_{max} = $ 60.0 μmol min^{-1}. *Notice that the unit of v_{max} is the same as for v.*

○ What is the value of K_M for the enzyme glunase under these conditions?

● K_M can be calculated from the intercept of the line with the v/[glunose] axis $= v_{max}/K_M$. In Figure 2.40 this intercept = 10.5. Therefore, $v_{max}/K_M = $ 10.5.

Above we calculated that $v_{max} = 60.0\,\mu mol\,min^{-1}$.

As $60.0/K_M = 10.5$,

$$K_M = \frac{60.0}{10.5} = 5.7\,\mu mol\,l^{-1}$$

So $K_M = 5.7\,\mu mol\,l^{-1}$. *Notice that the unit of K_M is the same as that of [glunose], namely* $\mu mol\,l^{-1}$.

○ Look back at Table 2.4. What can you conclude from the value of K_M for the enzyme glunase under these conditions?

● Glunase has a low K_M, similar to that of fumarase, which indicates that glunase has a high affinity for its substrate glunose.

From Figure 2.38 you can see that K_M can also be calculated from the slope of the line, but it is easier to work from the intercept on the $v/[S]$ axis, as in our example above.

2.4.4 FACTORS AFFECTING ENZYME ACTIVITY

Many factors affect the rate of enzyme-catalysed reactions. We have already considered one of the most important of these, namely substrate concentration. Three others are now considered: temperature, pH and cofactors.

EFFECTS OF TEMPERATURE

Most enzymes function best within a very narrow range of temperature, with activity falling away dramatically either side of the optimum value (Figure 2.41). To explain the relationships between enzyme activity and temperature, we need to consider the higher-order structure of proteins. As temperature increases, the reaction rate increases as more molecules of substrate overcome the energy barrier. (With many enzymes, a 10 °C rise in temperature increases the reaction rate by a factor of 2.) However, above a certain temperature the active, or *native*, conformation of the enzyme protein is no longer stable. The various non-covalent interactions that hold the enzyme in its native conformation are disrupted, result-ing in a huge and usually irreversible drop in activity. In this state, the enzyme is said to be *denatured*. For example, when you cook an egg, the protein albumin becomes denatured: it turns white and solidifies. Heating albumin results in irreversible loss of protein higher-order structure, which is different from the reversible denaturation of RNAase we studied earlier.

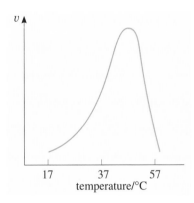

Figure 2.41 Effect of temperature on enzyme activity. The general shape of this curve is characteristic of most enzymes, although peak activity may be very different.

○ What is the optimum temperature of the enzyme activity shown in Figure 2.41?

● The enzyme plot shows that its temperature optimum is about 47 °C.

Many mammalian enzymes have temperature optima at 37 °C. In contrast, some prokaryotes have enzymes with optima much lower or higher than those of animal enzymes. For instance, some of their enzymes can function optimally at 4 °C, and hence could be highly active in your fridge! Others have temperature optima at 80 °C or even higher, and could function in your hot water tank.

EFFECTS OF pH

The effects of pH on enzyme activity are more subtle. You know already that the side-chains on amino acid residues can be charged. pH changes either side of the optimum value alter the degree of ionization (dissociation) of ionizable amino acid side-chains on the surface of the molecule (and also of those in the substrate). For example, if a particular aspartate side-chain is mostly ionized at the pH optimum, it is changed into the uncharged form as pH decreases (i.e. as hydrogen ion concentration increases) from the optimum value:

$$-COO^- + H^+ \rightleftharpoons -COOH$$

A change in the pH of the surrounding solution influences all the ionizable groups on the surface of the enzyme, both those that make up the active site and those elsewhere in the molecule that are essential for maintaining the structure of the active site; the combined effect reduces enzyme activity.

Figure 2.42 shows the effects of pH on the activity of three mammalian digestive enzymes.

○ From Figure 2.42, estimate the pH optima for the three enzymes.

● Estimates for pH optima are: pepsin, pH 2.0; salivary amylase, pH 7.0; chymotrypsin, pH 8.0.

○ How is the pH optimum of pepsin adapted to the environment in which it functions?

● The pH inside the vertebrate stomach where pepsin is secreted is extremely acidic.

As a general principle, pH optima for enzymes are related to the environment in which they function. You will meet further examples later.

COFACTORS

Many enzymes require appropriate concentrations of specific **cofactors** for their activity. Such cofactors may be metal ions (e.g. Mg^{2+} and K^+), or coenzymes, which are organic molecules such as NAD, ATP and ADP. The coenzymes are a diverse group of organic molecules required for the function of many enzymes (Section 4.2.2). Most coenzymes, like substrates, bind reversibly at a specific place in the active site of the enzyme, and are actively involved in catalysis by accepting or donating specific chemical groups. Coenzymes cannot be made from simple starting materials in the bodies of mammals (and probably most other animals). Instead, they are derived from vitamins present in the diet. Only very small amounts are needed, for coenzymes are regenerated either in the reaction in

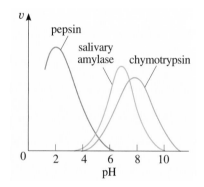

Figure 2.42 Effect of pH on enzyme activity for three mammalian digestive enzymes: pepsin, salivary amylase, and chymotrypsin.

which they take part or in a subsequent reaction with a different enzyme and substrate.

2.4.5 ENZYME INHIBITION

The final factor to be considered affecting enzyme activity is **enzyme inhibition**. The reasons for studying this phenomenon are many:

- enzyme inhibition is an important control mechanism in metabolic reactions: enzyme regulation will be considered in Section 2.4.7;

- many drugs act by inhibiting enzymes;

- the action of many toxins can be explained by enzyme inhibition.

There are many different kinds of enzyme inhibitors which act via different mechanisms. Below is a simple classification of the principal groups:

1 irreversible inhibitors
2 reversible inhibitors

    2a competitive inhibitors

    2b non-competitive inhibitors

1 IRREVERSIBLE INHIBITORS

Irreversible inhibitors are usually substances that are not of biological origin, and act by binding covalently to enzymes, which effectively poisons them. The strong bonds formed between enzymes and inhibitors mean that inhibition cannot be reversed simply by removing the inhibitor from the enzyme solution. To give just one example, the toxicity of heavy metal ions (e.g. mercury, Hg^{2+}) is largely due to their irreversible effects on enzyme activity.

2 REVERSIBLE INHIBITORS

For reversible inhibitors, the inhibition can be relieved by removal of the inhibitor from the enzyme solution. This is because they do not act by forming covalent bonds with the enzyme, but are bound by weak reversible interactions. There are several different groups of reversible inhibitors; here we consider just two, namely competitive and non-competitive inhibitors, which differ according to their effects on K_M and v_{max}.

2a Competitive inhibitors

The action of **competitive inhibitors** is illustrated in Figure 2.43. These inhibitors seem to bind reversibly to groups at the active site, and thus tend to impede the formation of the ES complex. Often the inhibitor resembles the substrate — that is, they have similar conformations and charge distribution — and the occupation of the active site by an inhibitor molecule prevents a substrate molecule from binding at the *same* active site. The enzyme can bind to the substrate to form an ES complex, or to the inhibitor to form an EI complex, but cannot bind to both simultaneously. A competitive inhibitor lowers the rate of reaction by reducing the proportion of enzyme bound to substrate. However, given a fixed concentration of inhibitor, at high substrate concentrations the effect of the inhibitor can be swamped and v_{max} approached — at least in theory.

Figure 2.43 Schematic mechanism for competitive inhibition at the active site of an enzyme. (a) The enzyme E binds substrate S in the absence of the inhibitor to form an ES complex. (b) In the presence of the inhibitor I, an EI complex is formed instead. Note that S and I both bind to the same active site on E.

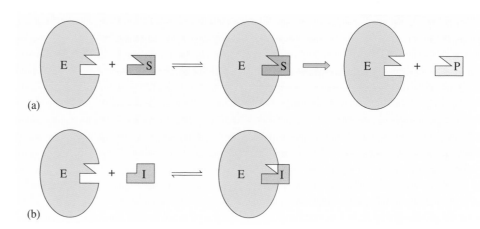

(a)

(b)

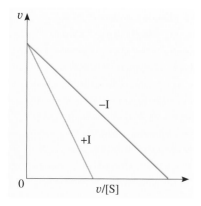

Figure 2.44 The effect of a competitive inhibitor on the Hofstee–Eadie plot for an enzyme.

Figure 2.44 shows the effects of a competitive inhibitor on the Hofstee–Eadie plot for an enzyme.

○ What effect has the competitive inhibitor had on the parameters v_{max} and K_M for this enzyme?

● The intercept on the v axis has not changed, so v_{max} is unaffected. In contrast, the slope of the line has changed in the presence of the inhibitor, so K_M has changed.

○ How has K_M changed?

● The slope of the line has increased (it is steeper), so K_M too has increased (equation 2.4).

○ What is the relationship between this increase in K_M and the affinity of the enzyme for its substrate?

● Increase of the K_M value means that the affinity has decreased.

2b Non-competitive inhibitors

The action of **non-competitive inhibitors** is illustrated in Figure 2.45. These inhibitors are not necessarily structurally related to substrates, and hence do not appear to prevent the formation of the ES complex. They bind to a separate site on the enzyme from the active site where the substrate binds. In contrast to competitive inhibitors, there is no substrate concentration that can totally swamp their effect, and v_{max} can never be approached. In this case, binding of inhibitor at its binding site does not bring about a conformational change at the active site: binding of substrate is unimpeded, but subsequent formation of products does not occur. The ESI complex so formed is catalytically inactive, so overall the rate of catalysis is reduced. Figure 2.46 shows the effects of a non-competitive inhibitor on the Hofstee–Eadie plot for an enzyme.

○ What effect has the non-competitive inhibitor had on the parameters v_{max} and K_M for this enzyme?

● The intercept on the v axis has changed: v_{max} is lower. In contrast, the slope of the line has not changed (the two lines are parallel) in the presence of the inhibitor, so K_M is unaffected.

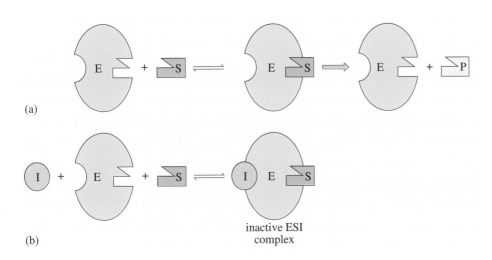

(a)

(b)

inactive ESI
complex

Figure 2.45 Schematic mechanism for non-competitive inhibition. (a) The enzyme E binds substrate S in the absence of the inhibitor to form an ES complex. (b) In the presence of the inhibitor I, an inactive ESI complex is formed instead. Note that S and I bind to different sites on E.

There is yet another type of enzyme inhibition of a reversible kind, called *allosteric inhibition*, which is of great importance when we consider how enzymes work in metabolism, their role in regulation and control. This topic will be covered in Section 2.4.7.

2.4.6 HOW DO ENZYMES WORK?

We now turn to a complex issue of how enzymes work. Earlier we mentioned that the catalytic power of enzymes can increase the rate of reaction by 10^9–10^{14} times. How is such a large increase possible? In a nutshell, the answer to this question is not known. It seems that enzymes bring about catalysis in different ways, such that there is no single answer to this intriguing question. Many of the mechanisms that account for catalytic power are complex and involve difficult chemistry, well outside the scope of this course. Here we shall consider just one or two aspects of the problem, principally related to the relationship between the enzyme active site and binding of substrate.

As described earlier, enzymes reduce the energy barrier of a reaction by forming an enzyme–substrate complex in which the substrate is bound at the active site of the enzyme. Active sites are generally clefts or depressions in the surface of the molecule, so one would expect them to be easily identified. However, it is rarely so simple: the surface of an enzyme molecule is far from smooth, and it is often not possible to identify one particular cleft or depression as the active site without having more information.

To obtain detailed information about the binding of a substrate at the active site of an enzyme requires X-ray crystallography of the ES complex (the technique of X-ray crystallography was introduced in Box 2.2). However, ES complexes are not stable; they break down to give free enzyme and product(s). Nevertheless, there are ways round this problem. Reasonably stable ES complexes can be obtained using a compound that is a relatively poor substrate for the enzyme. For example, yeast hexokinase works well with one substrate, glucose, and much less so with another, such as fructose. Alternatively, a molecule that fits into the active site but does not undergo a reaction can be used. A competitive inhibitor (I) is such a molecule. X-ray crystallography of an appropriate EI complex can yield

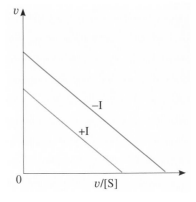

Figure 2.46 The effect of a non-competitive inhibitor on the Hofstee–Eadie plot for an enzyme.

much information about the corresponding ES complex. Lysozyme (an antibacterial enzyme present in tears and other body secretions) was the first enzyme whose three-dimensional structure and active site location were successfully studied by X-ray crystallography of the molecule with bound competitive inhibitor. This pioneering work was led by David Phillips (Figure 2.47).

Figure 2.47 David Phillips (1924 –99) led the pioneering work on lysozyme. This enzyme holds a unique position in molecular biology in that it was the first enzyme for which both a detailed molecular structure and a catalytic mechanism were determined. The structural work started by a group led by Phillips in 1961 and was completed in 1965: the polypeptide chain of 129 amino acids has two α-helices and a β-sheet, the latter being a structure predicted by Linus Pauling (Figure 2.14) but never before observed in three dimensions. The catalytic mechanism was published two years later. This work resulted in Phillips' appointment as the first Professor of Molecular Biophysics at Oxford University.

Comparing the structure of a crystallized enzyme alone with that of its ES complex, it has been shown that in many cases there is a significant change in the shape of the active site on binding substrate. In other words, there is an **induced fit** of enzyme to its substrate. This phenomenon suggests that the shape of the substrate and active site are not precisely complementary, but on binding the substrate induces a change in conformation at the active site such that the two then become complementary. A useful analogy here is a hand and glove: the glove initially loosely fits the hand, but as the glove is pulled on to the hand, the two shapes come to match one another more precisely. Such findings led to a revision of the lock and key mechanism of enzyme–substrate binding, in which the active site was assumed to be a rigid structure exactly complementary in shape to the substrate.

A technique that has proved useful in studying the relationship between active site and substrate binding is protein engineering (Box 2.5).

BOX 2.5   PROTEIN ENGINEERING

How a specific amino acid substitution in a protein molecule affects function can be investigated using the technique of protein engineering (developed in 1982 by M. J. Zoller and M. Smith), which involves changing the base sequence of the gene coding for the protein of interest — hence the alternative name for this technique, *site-directed mutagenesis*. The gene is isolated, a specific base (or bases) is altered chemically so producing a different codon. The modified gene is then inserted into a microbial cell, which is allowed to divide to produce millions of identical cells, each containing the new gene which is directing the synthesis of the altered protein. The protein can then be isolated from the batch, or clone, of microbial cells. You will learn more later about the technique of gene cloning. Protein engineering can be used to investigate the effect of specific amino acid substitutions in any protein whose gene can be isolated, cloned and expressed.

Protein engineering has great potential for the study of enzyme function. One particular example illustrates its value. Carboxypeptidase A is a protease that removes particular amino acids from the C-terminus of its protein substrate. X-ray crystallography (Box 2.2) with and without bound substrate has shown that a big change in the structure of the active site occurs as the enzyme folds around the substrate (Figure 2.48). In particular, the tyrosine in the active site (Tyr 248) moves about one-quarter of the diameter of the whole molecule. These data, taken with other evidence, suggest that the —OH group of Tyr 248 is involved in catalysis. However, an 'engineered' carboxypeptidase A, with phenylalanine (Figure 2.49a) substituted for tyrosine (Figure 2.49b) at position 248, has almost the same catalytic activity as the natural enzyme, indicating that Tyr 248 is *not* essential for enzyme activity. The K_M of the engineered enzyme, however, is larger.

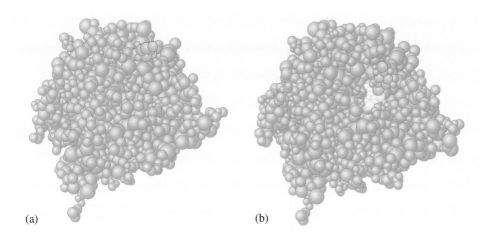

(a) (b)

Figure 2.48 Structure of carboxypeptidase A without (a) and with (b) bound substrate analogue (the dipeptide glycyltyrosine, shown in yellow). Note how the large change in the position of the tyrosine (red), together with smaller changes in other residues, folds the enzyme around the substrate.

○ What does this difference imply for the catalytic properties of the enzyme?

● K_M values indicate relative affinities of enzymes for their substrates (Section 2.4.5). The higher K_M of the engineered enzyme suggests a weaker binding to the substrate, which implies that Tyr 248 is involved in substrate binding in the natural enzyme.

Thus, protein engineering can provide detailed information about how enzymes work.

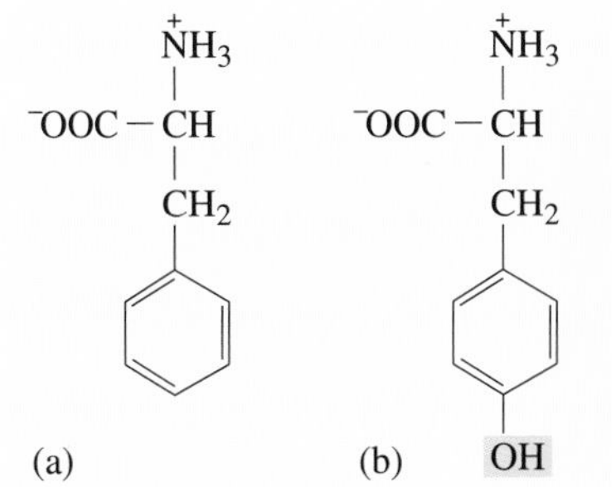

2.4.7 HOW ARE ENZYMES REGULATED?

The reasons why enzyme regulation is important were outlined in Section 2.4.2. Here we consider the mechanisms whereby this regulation is achieved.

There are two main ways in which an enzyme can be controlled — by altering the amount of enzyme present or by modifying the activity of existing enzyme.

The quantity of a particular enzyme made in a cell depends on both the rate of transcription of the corresponding gene and the rate of translation of the mRNA product. (You will learn more about the control of transcription and translation in Chapter 9.) The amount of a particular enzyme present is also influenced by its rate of degradation, and different enzymes are degraded at different rates.

Figure 2.49 Structural formulae of (a) phenylalanine and (b) tyrosine. They differ only by the OH group (red) of tyrosine.

In mammalian liver, for example, enzymes that are subject to regulation are degraded more rapidly than those whose activity is not regulated, thereby ensuring a relatively rapid response to the switching off (and on again) of genes coding for regulatory enzymes.

The mechanisms for controlling intracellular enzyme levels, however, are very much slower-acting than those that operate to regulate the activity of enzyme molecules already present. Before we discuss these intracellular mechanisms, which are readily reversible, mention must be made of an extracellular, irreversible process of enzyme modification, which you met in Section 2.2.5.

○ What is this process?

● The activation of zymogens (e.g. digestive proteases and blood clotting enzymes) by partial proteolysis.

The synthesis of enzymes such as zymogens ensures that the active forms are secreted only when and where they are required. The presence of active digestive enzymes in gut cells or blood clotting enzymes within blood vessels would clearly be very undesirable.

Zymogen activation occurs by cleavage at a specific site in the molecule in an enzyme-catalysed reaction. Often this site is within a loop connecting two non-adjacent domains of the molecule; cleavage loosens the structure, facilitating the formation of the active site of the enzyme.

We now return to the regulation of intracellular enzyme activity. Two main types of process can operate, both of which alter the three-dimensional structure of an enzyme — that is, its conformation — changing the shape and substrate binding properties of the active site, and so modifying the enzyme's activity. This transformation is achieved either by the non-covalent reversible binding of an *effector* (*activator* or *inhibitor*) molecule, in *allosteric regulation*, or by altering the chemical structure of the enzyme, a process called *reversible covalent modification*. Some enzymes are subject to control by both processes, whereas for others just one operates.

ALLOSTERIC REGULATION

Allosteric regulation allows enzymes to make an appropriate response to changes in intracellular conditions, and is a feature of both eukaryotes and prokaryotes; however, by no means all enzymes are subject to allosteric regulation. In **allosteric regulation** an effector (activator or inhibitor) molecule binds to the enzyme at a site other than the active site, called the *allosteric site* (from the Greek: *allos*, meaning 'other' and *steros*, meaning 'shape'), which brings about a modification in the conformation of the active site. (We have already met a number of proteins whose function depends on a substance binding to one part of the molecule and thereby altering the conformation of another part.) The response of allosteric enzymes to effectors is yet another example of this effect. The shape change caused by effector binding modifies the activity of the enzyme, which is of crucial importance for the regulation of enzyme activity, so we shall study it in some detail here.

Allosteric regulation allows an enzyme to respond to an effector immediately. Conversely, removal of the effector immediately restores the enzyme to its former activity. Some enzymes at the beginning of a metabolic pathway are inhibited by products of later enzyme-catalysed reactions in that pathway (Figure 2.50). This *feedback inhibition* of *regulatory enzymes* prevents over-production of the products of a pathway.

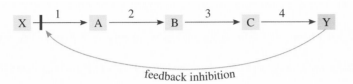

Figure 2.50   Feedback inhibition of a metabolic pathway. The pathway starts at X and produces Y via intermediates A, B and C. There are four enzymes in this pathway, 1–4. End product Y inhibits the activity of enzyme 1 at the start of the pathway.

In the hypothetical example shown in Figure 2.50, end product Y is an **allosteric inhibitor** of enzyme 1. You will meet examples of such feedback inhibition in Chapter 4, which explains the pathways involved in energy metabolism.

An **allosteric activator** can also be an effector. Here the activity of an enzyme is stimulated, rather than inhibited. Allosteric activators are often substrates of earlier steps in a pathway; in such cases, enzyme activation ensures a rapid utilization of starting substance when it is present in large amounts.

One feature of allosteric enzyme behaviour that distinguishes them from enzymes that do not respond to allosteric effectors is their kinetics. For allosteric enzymes, plots of initial reaction rate v against initial substrate concentration [S] (with or without effector present) are not hyperbolic but *sigmoidal* — that is, a flattened 'S' shape (Figure 2.51). At low [S], v is very low and increases only slowly as [S] increases, compared with an enzyme showing Michaelis–Menten kinetics (hyperbolic plot). However, as [S] increases further, v starts to increase very rapidly. Eventually, a value of [S] is reached beyond which the rate of increase in v starts to decline; that is, the curve begins to flatten out. Such kinetics would be expected if each molecule of allosteric enzyme had several identical, active sites, and binding of a substrate molecule to one of them made it easier for substrate to bind at the other sites. This interaction is brought about by conformational changes, relayed across the protein from one active site to another. In other words, substrate binding to the active sites is *cooperative*; the mechanism is known as **cooperativity**.

What is the advantage of cooperativity in substrate binding? Sigmoidal kinetics mean that an allosteric enzyme is extremely responsive to changes in substrate concentration over a particular small range. This sensitivity of regulatory enzymes to substrate concentration allows the fine control of cell metabolism.

○   For a particular allosteric enzyme to carry out its regulatory role, what must be the range of effector concentrations over which it is most sensitive?

●   It must be the range of concentrations that occurs in the cells where the enzyme operates.

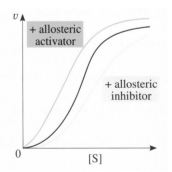

Figure 2.51   Sigmoidal plot of initial rate v against initial substrate concentration [S] for an allosteric enzyme (black). The effects of the presence of an allosteric activator and an allosteric inhibitor are also shown.

The general mechanism of cooperativity between active sites is similar to the mechanism by which binding of an effector at an allosteric site affects catalytic activity at the active site. This resemblance is not surprising, since in both cases a change at one site on the molecule exerts an effect at another site. For an explanation of the mechanism, we need to consider the three-dimensional structure of allosteric enzymes.

To illustrate our discussion, we shall focus on one particular allosteric enzyme that has been extensively studied. An *E. coli* enzyme called aspartate trans-carbamoylase (ATCase for short) catalyses the first step in the biosynthesis of the nucleic acid precursor cytosine triphosphate (CTP) from the amino acid aspartate (Figure 2.52). This enzyme is inhibited by CTP, the end product of the pathway. (It is also activated by ATP.)

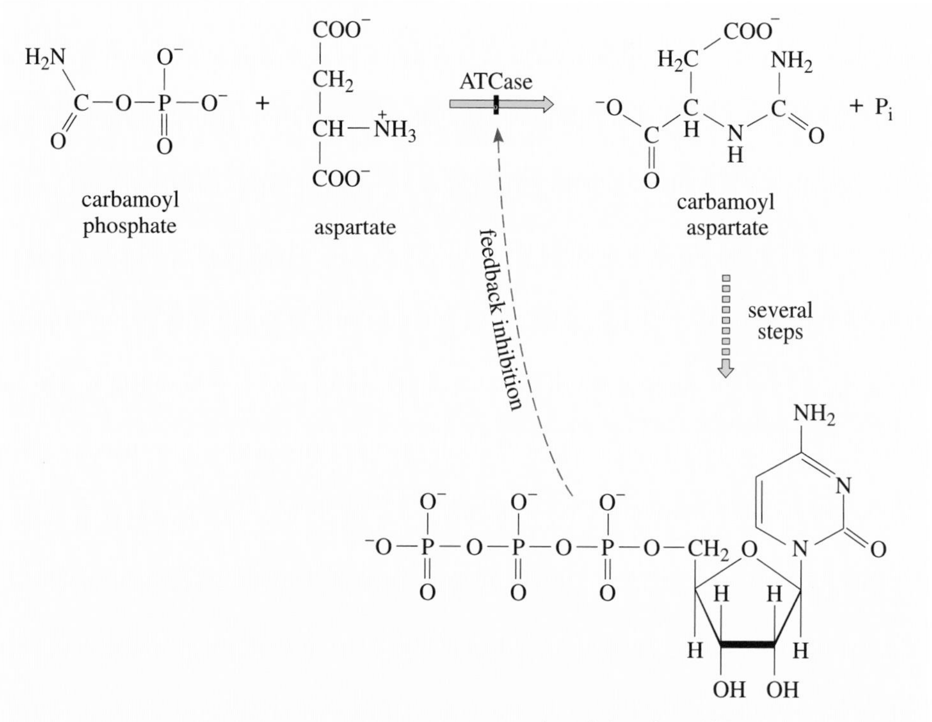

Figure 2.52 The reaction catalysed by ATCase. This enzyme is at the start of a metabolic pathway that leads to the production of CTP, which itself inhibits ATCase. (The inhibition is denoted by a bar across the arrow to carbamoyl aspartate.)

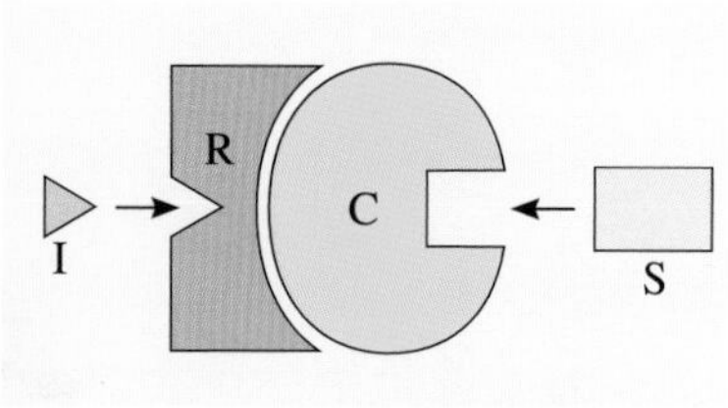

cytosine triphosphate (CTP)

Figure 2.53 Simplified sketch showing the two types of subunit in ATCase. Substrates bind to the active site on the catalytic subunit (C), whereas the allosteric inhibitor (I) binds to a separate allosteric site on the regulatory subunit (R).

Treatment of ATCase with a chemical that causes the subunits of multisubunit proteins to dissociate has two effects: (1) the v against [aspartate] plot becomes hyperbolic (that is, there is no longer any cooperativity between active sites); (2) enzyme activity is no longer affected by CTP. The conclusion is that both cooperativity and allosteric effects can occur only in the intact quaternary structure.

Analysis of ATCase has shown that each molecule is made up of two types of subunit: catalytic subunits, which have the active sites; and regulatory subunits, carrying the allosteric sites. Their structures are shown greatly simplified in Figure 2.53 and in more detail in Figure 2.54.

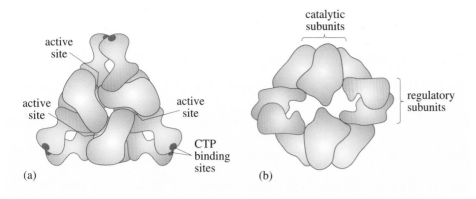

Figure 2.54 The arrangement of the catalytic (blue) and regulatory (brown) subunits in ATCase: (a) looking down on the molecule; (b) side-on view.

The detailed structure of ATCase has been revealed by X-ray crystallography (Box 2.2). There are six catalytic subunits and six regulatory subunits per molecule, arranged as shown in Figure 2.54. Two observations are noteworthy: (1) adjacent subunits contribute to each active site (that is, an active site cannot be assigned to an individual subunit); (2) the distance between catalytic sites and the distance between a catalytic site and an allosteric site are in the nanometre range, at least an order of magnitude greater than bond lengths between the constituent atoms in the molecule. So cooperativity and allosteric effects are long-range interactions.

The key characteristics of an allosteric enzyme can now be listed as follows:

- Allosteric enzymes are generally larger, multisubunit proteins (therefore more complex than 'simple enzymes') and often consist of two different types of subunit: catalytic and regulatory.

- Substrates bind cooperatively to active sites on catalytic subunits.

- Allosteric enzymes do not follow Michaelis–Menten kinetics. A plot of v against [S] produces a sigmoidal or S-shaped curve.

- Effectors for allosteric enzymes are either activators or inhibitors that bind to sites on regulatory subunits. Their binding can also produce S-shaped curves.

- Feedback inhibition can occur: an allosteric enzyme may be specifically inhibited by the end product of a metabolic pathway.

REVERSIBLE COVALENT MODIFICATION

In allosteric regulation we have seen that proteins can be controlled by the non-covalent binding of a small molecule. A second method of enzyme regulation that is commonly used by eukaryotic cells is termed **reversible covalent modification**. This process entails the reversible addition of a small chemical group (e.g. phosphate, acetyl) to the side-chain of a particular amino acid residue in the enzyme. The most common modification is **protein phosphorylation**.

○ Recall from Table 2.3 the classes of enzymes that might be involved in this process.

● Kinases and phosphatases.

Phosphorylation of the —OH group in the side-chains of serine and threonine is catalysed by a protein kinase. The reverse reaction, dephosphorylation, removes

Figure 2.55 Highly schematic picture of protein phosphorylation. (a) The general reaction entails transfer of a phosphate group from ATP to an amino acid side-chain of a target protein by a protein kinase. Removal of the phosphate group is catalysed by a second enzyme, a protein phosphatase. In this example, the phosphate is added to a serine side-chain. The phosphorylation of a protein by a protein kinase can either increase (b) or decrease (c) the protein's activity, depending on the site of phosphorylation and the structure of the protein.

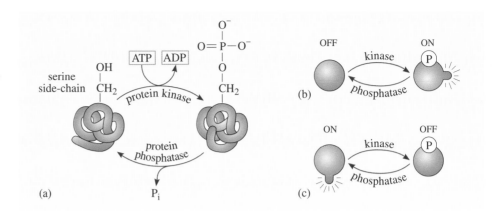

the phosphate group, and is catalysed by a protein phosphatase (Figure 2.55).

Phosphorylation involves the addition of negative charges, which alters the balance of non-covalent interactions that determine the higher-order structure of the protein (secondary, tertiary, and in some cases quaternary). The resulting conformational change may cause activation or inactivation of the protein's function (e.g. enzyme activity), or association or dissociation of subunits.

Eukaryotic cells have hundreds of enzymes that are regulated by reversible phosphorylation/dephosphorylation, and many are components of sequences of protein phosphorylation reactions.

Phosphorylation is just one example of reversible covalent modification. In plants, amino acid side-chain reactions are also important in the control of enzyme activity. A commonly used reversible covalent modification involves the disulfide bridges that link pairs of cysteine residues (Section 2.2.5). The cystine–cysteine reduction process (i.e. breaking of a disulfide bridge) activates certain enzymes in the chloroplasts that are involved in carbohydrate synthesis.

Although covalent modification of enzymes is a very much quicker type of response than changing the amount of enzyme present, it is far from instan-taneous. All such modifications require the activity of another enzyme, which must itself be regulated, and the regulator of that enzyme is subject to regulation too, and so a control system involving a *cascade* results (Figure 2.56). Also, the reversal of a covalent modification requires enzyme activity, for example a specific phosphatase to remove the phosphate from a phosphorylated enzyme.

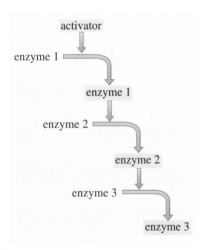

Figure 2.56 A hypothetical control system involving a 'cascade'. Active forms of enzymes are shown highlighted in green, inactive forms in black. Blue arrows denote the process of activation; orange arrows indicate reactions, but are curved here to simulate a water cascade. Enzyme 1 is activated by a (non-enzyme) activator. Enzyme 1 in turn activates enzyme 2, and so on down the cascade.

Reversible covalent modification, notably protein phosphorylation, plays a major role in cell functioning. Metabolic pathway enzymes are activated or deactivated via this process (Chapter 4). Many cells of multicellular organisms, and colonies of unicellular prokaryotes, communicate with one another via signal molecules that transfer information. Processing of this information and responses to it generally involve cycles of phosphorylation/dephosphorylation (Chapter 6). Cell movement, again a feature of many prokaryotic and eukaryotic cells, is equally dependent on protein phosphorylation (Chapter 7).

SUMMARY OF SECTION 2.4

1   The vast majority of proteins in living organisms are enzymes, biological catalysts. Enzyme names usually but not always end in -ase.

2   The substrate binds at the active site of an enzyme, forming the enzyme–substrate complex. Catalysis occurs and products are released. Conformations of the active site and substrate are complementary; hence their interaction is described as a 'lock and key' mechanism.

3   Enzymes usually exhibit substrate specificity, and bind only a single or limited range of substrates.

4   Catalytic power describes the degree to which enzymes speed up the rates of reaction, which can be up to 10^{14} times the rate of the uncatalysed reaction.

5   The study of the rates of enzyme-catalysed reactions is known as enzyme kinetics. Two key parameters are usually calculated for a given enzyme: v_{max} (maximum rate of reaction) and K_M (the Michaelis constant), which are most conveniently calculated from a Hofstee–Eadie plot of v against $v/[S]$. v_{max} is then the intercept on the vertical axis. K_M can be calculated from either the intercept on the horizontal axis (v_{max}/K_M), or from the slope ($-K_M$). K_M can be a measure of the affinity of an enzyme for its substrate: the lower the value of K_M, the greater the affinity, and vice versa.

6   Enzyme activity is affected by various factors, including temperature, pH and cofactors.

7   Enzymes can be inhibited by a range of substances. Irreversible inhibitors are usually poisons. Reversible inhibitors are either competitive or non-competitive. Competitive inhibitors bind at the active site and increase the value of K_M; non-competitive ones bind at sites other than active sites and lower the value of v_{max}.

8   For some enzymes, X-ray crystallography reveals a significant conformational change as the substrate binds to the active site; this is explained as an induced fit.

9   Enzymes are subject to regulation by two principal mechanisms: allosteric regulation or reversible covalent modification.

10 Allosteric enzymes generally consist of two different types of subunit: catalytic and regulatory. Substrates bind cooperatively to active sites on catalytic subunits. Allosteric enzymes do not follow Michaelis–Menten kinetics. A plot of v against [S] produces a sigmoidal or S-shape curve. Effectors for allosteric enzymes are either activators or inhibitors, which bind to sites on regulatory subunits.

11 Reversible covalent modification involves the addition of a small chemical group. The most common example is protein phosphorylation, which involves addition of a phosphate group, catalysed by enzymes known as kinases.

REFERENCES

Gillman, M., and Davey, B. (2001) Defence. In *Generating Diversity*, M. Gillman (ed.), The Open University, Milton Keynes, pp. 151–200.

Pond, C. (2001) Dealing with food. In *Generating Diversity*, M. Gillman (ed.), The Open University, Milton Keynes, pp. 37–88.

FURTHER READING

Alberts, B., Bray, D., Lewis, J., Raff, M., Roberts, K., and Watson, J. D. (1994) *Molecular Biology of the Cell* (3rd edn), Garland Publishing, London. [Includes a good chapter on protein structure and much more molecular biology relevant to later chapters of this book.]

Alberts, B., Bray, D., Johnson, A., Lewis, J., Raff, M., Roberts, K., and Walter, P. (1998), *Essential Cell Biology,* Garland Publishing, London. [A concise guide to cell and molecular biology, which is a shorter version of Alberts *et al.* (1994).]

Wilson, J., and Hunt, T. (1994) *Molecular Biology of the Cell. The Problems Book* (rev. edn), Garland Publishing, London. [A book of problems based on Alberts *et al.* (1994).]

Zubay, G. L. (1998) *Biochemistry* (4th edn), Wm. C. Brown Publishers, Dubuque, USA. [More biochemical than Alberts *et al.* (1994 and 1998), and includes several chapters on protein structure and function, enzyme kinetics and catalysis.]

MEMBRANES AND TRANSPORT

3.1 INTRODUCTION

One of the key messages of the previous chapter, in fact most of this book, is that the functioning of all cells depends on the activities of their constituent proteins, that is, the expression products of their genes. In this chapter, however, you will see that membranes are as fundamental to cell function as genes and proteins. The function of many proteins depends on their being part of the structure of a membrane. In particular, membranes enable enzymes and chains of enzymes to work in sequence and in the required chemical environment; they support the large protein molecules that selectively transport materials into, out of and within cells, transduce energy, and allow cells to communicate with each other and recognize their neighbours; and in animal cells, membranes act with the cytoskeleton to help maintain and adjust cell shape.

One of the main distinctions between eukaryotic and prokaryotic cells is the relative complexity of their membranes. The exchange of materials and signals between cells, under the control of the bounding cell membrane is what enabled eukaryotes to become multicellular, evolving into animals, plants and fungi. Unlike prokarotes, eukaryotic cells have intracellular membranes, which separate the cell contents into different regions, that is, the various membrane-bound compartments (organelles, Chapter 1) and the cytosol. As shown in Tables 3.1 and 3.2 (overleaf), much of the cell volume may be sequestered within these intracellular compartments, which require a correspondingly large amount of membrane to make them. Structural compartmentation within cells allows compartmentation of cellular functions — for example, by restricting a particular enzyme to a particular membrane-bound compartment and maintaining the appropriate concentrations of ions and small molecules that create the chemical environment required for it to function correctly. Intracellular compartments are dynamic, interrelated structures essential for the modification and targeting of many of the cell's newly synthesized proteins to their correct destination.

In the first part of this chapter we focus mainly on the outer membrane of cells, which is commonly referred to simply as the **cell membrane**, although you will also find it called the **plasma membrane** in animals and the **plasmalemma** in plants. Later we discuss intracellular membranes, those of the ER, Golgi and membrane-bound organelles, and their structural and functional relationship to the cell membrane and to each other.

Before describing the diverse roles of membranes outlined above, we need to say a little about membrane structure, first a general overview and then, in Section 3.3, a more detailed look at their molecular composition.

Table 3.1   Relative volumes of the main intracellular compartments of a mammalian liver cell, one of the most thoroughly studied of all cells. (*Note*: the relative volumes in other kinds of animal cells may be very different.) (Adapted from Alberts *et al.*, 1994)

Compartment/organelle	Relative volume (approx. % total)
cytosol	54
mitochondria	22
rough ER	9
smooth ER and Golgi	6
nucleus	6
peroxisomes	1
lysosomes	1
endosomes	1

Table 3.2   Relative areas of different types of membrane in a mammalian liver cell. (Adapted from Alberts *et al.*, 1994)

Membrane type	Relative area (approx. % total)
cell membrane	2
mitochondria	
outer	7
inner	32
rough ER	35
smooth ER and Golgi	23
nuclear envelope*	0.2
peroxisomes	0.4
lysosomes	0.4
endosomes	0.4

*This value is for the inner membrane of nuclear envelope only; the outer membrane is continuous with the rough ER so forms part of that membrane fraction.

3.2   OVERVIEW OF MEMBRANE STRUCTURE

The cell membrane is visible in electron micrographs after heavy metal staining as a three-layered dark-light-dark sandwich-like structure of total thickness around 10 nm. The technique of freeze-fracture (Box 3.1) splits the cell membrane into two layers, and the newly exposed interior surfaces appear bumpy when viewed under the transmission EM.

BOX 3.1   FREEZE-FRACTURE ELECTRON MICROSCOPY OF MEMBRANES

Freeze-fracture electron microscopy enables the interior of biological membranes to be visualized. Cells are frozen at the temperature of liquid nitrogen (−196 °C) in the presence of a cryoprotectant (antifreeze). This substance prevents ice crystals from forming, which would distort the membrane structure. The frozen block is then fractured with a sharp knife. The fracture line usually passes through the plane of the cell membrane, exposing the interior (see Figure 3.1a). The newly exposed surfaces are then subjected to *shadowing*: a heavy-metal (e.g. platinum) vapour is sprayed at an oblique angle onto the fracture surfaces, thereby depositing a metal coating that is thicker in some places than others, so producing a shadow effect, which makes the image look three-dimensional (Figure 3.1b). The result is a metal *replica* of the fracture surface. The replica is then strengthened by deposition of a film of carbon over the metal (Figure 3.1c). Finally, the specimen is dissolved away (Figure 3.1d). When the replica is viewed under the electron microscope, its bumpy surface is revealed (Figure 3.1e, f).

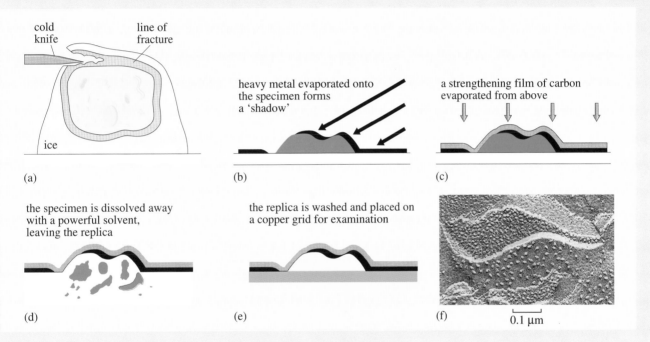

(a)   (b)   (c)

(d)   (e)   (f)   0.1 µm

Figure 3.1 Stages in preparing freeze-fractured membranes for electron microscopy. (a) Fracturing of the frozen specimen. (b) Heavy-metal shadowing of the fracture surface. (c) Deposition of a strengthening film of carbon. (d) Dissolving and washing away the organic material. (e) Placing the replica on a grid for examination under the transmission EM. (f) Freeze-fracture EM of the internal membranes of a chloroplast.

EM and X-ray diffraction studies, in conjunction with analysis of chemical composition, have revealed that eukaryotic membranes are macromolecular aggregates of (mainly) phospholipid molecules, arranged as a bilayer, with protein molecules (the 'bumps' seen in transmission EM photos such as Figure 3.1f) interspersed within the bilayer. The bilayer structure is a consequence of the dual (**amphipathic**) properties of the constituent lipids: a polar, i.e. hydrophilic ('water-loving') part, the **head group**, and a long non-polar, i.e. hydrophobic ('water-hating') section, the **hydrophobic tail**.

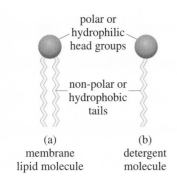

Figure 3.2 Diagrams of (a) an amphipathic membrane lipid molecule; (b) a detergent molecule.

Figure 3.3 Two types of structure formed by the aggregation of synthetic amphipathic lipids in water. (a) Cross-section through a liposome, a sphere bounded by a lipid bilayer. Biological membranes have this bilayer structure, but with protein molecules interspersed between the lipid molecules. (b) Cross-section through a micelle, a very much smaller spherical structure in which the *single* hydrophobic tails of the lipid molecules aggregate in the centre. (In the gut, micelles formed as the result of fat digestion are composed mainly of partially hydrolysed fats and detergent-like bile salts.)

Membrane lipid molecules each have two hydrophobic tails (Figure 3.2a). Detergent molecules, which are also amphipathic lipids, have a single tail (Figure 3.2b).

When mixed with water, amphipathic lipid molecules spontaneously form structures in which the hydrophilic head groups have maximum contact with the water, and the hydrophobic tails are separated from the aqueous medium. Both the 'hiding' (from water) and clustering together of the hydrophobic regions contribute to the stability of amphipathic lipid aggregates. The same principle applies to the higher-order structure of proteins discussed in the previous chapter, but membrane lipids are so good at self-assembly that they don't require the assistance of chaperones, and reassemble spontaneously after all but the most drastic disruption.

The two-tailed amphipathic lipids (i.e. those characteristic of biological membranes, Figure 3.2a) form **liposomes** in water — spherical bilayer structures, with the hydrophobic tails pointing inwards and the polar head groups in contact with each other and the water (Figure 3.3a). The EM appearance of sectioned liposomes (after heavy-metal staining, Chapter 1) is a dark-light-dark sandwich structure, like that of similarly prepared biological membranes.

A stable structure for an aggregate of *single*-tailed amphipathic lipid molecules, e.g. detergent molecules, in water is a spherical **micelle**, a monolayer of molecules with the hydrophobic-inside, hydrophilic-outside orientation, but without an aqueous core (Figure 3.3b). Unlike a liposome, a micelle has a fixed radius defined by the properties of its lipids. If it were any bigger, water molecules could creep into the gaps between the lipid molecules and disrupt the structure. Two-tailed amphipathic lipids have much more difficulty being packed into a micelle than into the bilayered liposome structure. In contrast, amphipathic lipids with one tail readily form micelles but cannot form bilayers. In fact, they destabilize lipid bilayers. For this reason, detergents are routinely used by cell biologists to disrupt cellular membranes and release the cells' contents for study. Interestingly, the activity of the drug polymyxin, which is used against fungal infections of the skin, is due to its detergent action on the fungal cell membranes. (It is safe to use because unless the skin is broken, the living cells of the host's skin do not come in contact with the drug so their membranes remain intact.)

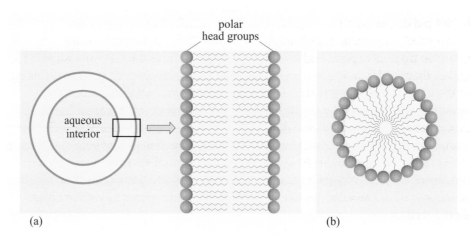

Of course, cellular membranes are much more sophisticated structures than uniform bilayers of two-tailed amphipathic lipid molecules. Not only is there a considerable diversity of membrane lipids but there are also many different proteins present, some of which extend from one side to the other, while others have a more peripheral and/or transient association with the membrane.

3.2.1 MEMBRANE STABILITY

Although the interactions between the molecules that make up membranes are almost exclusively non-covalent, there are so many of these interactions that membranes are remarkably stable structures in their normal, aqueous environment. The tendency of membrane lipids to remain associated in the typical bilayer array is so strong that fragments of membrane remain after excess heat, mechanical disruption or chemical attack has rendered them useless to the cells that made them. The fragments close up into liposomes, as in Figure 3.3a. The greasy appearance of lakes and reservoirs after hot, sunny spells is due to the membranes and resealed membrane fragments of millions of tiny algae, both living and dead. Cell fractionation studies depend on the robustness of membranes: you will recall from Box 1.1 in Chapter 1 that homogenization of cells leaves membrane-bound organelles intact; the cell membrane and the ER are fragmented but, given the appropriate conditions, the resealed fragments retain the functional characteristics of the original membrane.

The maintenance of membrane integrity is critically dependent upon temperature. In many animal and plant cells, death from cold is due mainly to irreversible disordering of the membranes. Almost all structural proteins and the majority of enzymes are perfectly preserved at temperatures far below zero. But most cells and whole organisms are killed by freezing unless immersed in or perfused with cryoprotectant, which does not freeze (Box 3.1). Their membranes lose their selective permeability (to be described later) to different kinds of small molecules and ions, so no longer maintain the right intracellular concentrations of these substances. Another type of cold-induced change in membrane structure is the disruption of sequences of membrane-bound enzymes, so that they are no longer in the correct alignment in which they can work together to form a metabolic pathway.

The main determinant of the temperature range over which a membrane is stable is its lipid composition — in particular, the proportion of saturated and unsaturated fatty acids and cholesterol (see later). For example, bananas are native to tropical regions and their cell membranes have a lipid composition that makes them stable at warm temperatures. Ripening involves enzymatic softening of the carbohydrates in the fruit pulp, and also enzyme-catalysed oxidation reactions which cause the familiar blackening of 'over-ripe' bananas. These processes are greatly accelerated if the bananas are cooled to below 10 °C. You learned in the last chapter that enzyme-catalysed reactions are generally slower at lower temperatures. So this hastening of ripening is unlikely to depend on the properties of the ripening enzymes. Instead, it arises from the temperature sensitivity of the membranes that normally keep these enzymes separate from their substrates.

○ What are the membrane-bound intracellular compartments in which enzymes destined for secretion are synthesized and processed?

● Endoplasmic reticulum and Golgi (Chapter 1).

Cooling bananas causes their membrane lipids to 'freeze', i.e. lose their fluidity, so that the membranes become leaky and enzymes and substrates diffuse across and mix together, allowing the ripening processes to start prematurely. Returning the bananas to room temperature may partially restore membrane function, but the escaped enzymes can't be recaptured. In fact, they then work faster at the higher temperature.

○ Can you suggest why apples, which are native to temperate climates, do not respond to refrigeration in the same way as bananas?

● At the fridge temperature, their cell membranes retain their normal structure and their capacity to segregate cell components.

A similar effect on apples, however, can be achieved at much lower temperatures, i.e. by freezing and subsequent thawing.

Damage to the cell membrane is often even more rapidly lethal to cells than poisoning protein synthesis or altering genes. One of the earliest antibiotic drugs to be developed, gramicidin, kills bacteria by making holes in their membranes: the cell contents leak out, substances normally excluded or pumped out by the membranes diffuse in, and the bacteria soon die.

○ Why is gramicidin no longer used as an oral antibiotic?

● Because it also destroys the host's cell membranes, which are chemically quite similar to those of bacteria, so is too toxic for internal use.

3.2.2 MEMBRANE FLUIDITY

Membranes are fluid structures, as evidenced by the fact that they can easily be punctured with a needle but rapidly reseal. The disruptive effect of cooling on membrane function demonstrates the importance of maintaining fluidity. Both the lipid molecules and the proteins move about freely in the plane of the membrane. Fluidity occurs because there are only weak, non-covalent interactions between these membrane components. (Neither type of component molecule can flip spontaneously from one side to the other, however, for such translocation would require too much energy.) The **fluid-mosaic model** of membrane structure (Figure 3.4), first introduced by Singer and Nicholson in 1972, visualizes the membrane as a *fluid* structure with a *mosaic* of proteins floating in it.

One type of experiment that demonstrated the lateral mobility of membrane proteins was carried out in 1970 by Michael Edidin and colleagues in the USA. It involves the fusion of two different types of cells, each of which has had its (cell-specific) membrane proteins labelled using antibodies with different fluorescent markers, one green and one red. Cells from different species do not normally fuse, but can be made to do so *in vitro* with a virus known as Sendai virus. The hybrid cell which is formed has uniform distribution of both green and red fluorescence (see Figure 3.5).

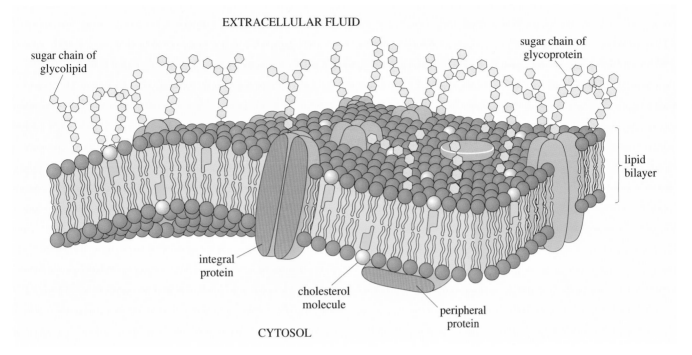

EXTRACELLULAR FLUID

sugar chain of
glycolipid

sugar chain of
glycoprotein

lipid
bilayer

integral
protein

cholesterol
molecule

peripheral
protein

CYTOSOL

Figure 3.4 The fluid-mosaic model of membrane structure. Here the cell membrane is depicted. Intracellular membranes are similar, but the long, branched chains of sugars attached to proteins or lipids shown here are characteristic of the outer face of the cell membrane.

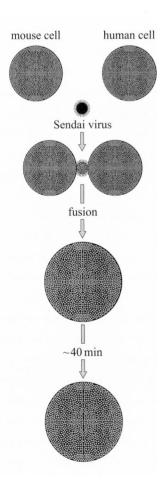

mouse cell

human cell

Sendai virus

fusion

~40 min

Figure 3.5 Membrane fusion, illustrating the fluid nature of membranes. A cultured mouse cell and a cultured human cell are made to fuse together by treatment with Sendai virus. This virus itself has an outer membrane that merges with the membrane of both cells, causing them to fuse. Each of the cells has some of its membrane proteins labelled with different fluorescent markers, green or red. About 40 minutes after the cells have fused, the distribution of both green and red fluorescence has become uniform, indicating that the membrane proteins of the two cells have mixed together. Other studies on the behaviour of membrane lipids have confirmed that the whole membrane, not just the proteins, flow together. (You will learn later that membrane fusion both between and within cells of the same species sometimes takes place under *normal* circumstances and underlies a number of biological processes.)

113

A technique that is used to analyse the fluid nature of membranes in a more quantitative manner is known as FRAP (Fluorescence Recovery After Photobleaching) and is described in Box 3.2. Using this technique, lateral movement of either membrane protein *or* lipid molecules can be monitored.

BOX 3.2   MEASURING MEMBRANE FLUIDITY USING FRAP

This technique relies on the labelling of specific membrane protein or lipid molecules with a fluorescent indicator. The indicator becomes dispersed over the whole of a cell surface and essentially 'lights up' the cell. A small area on the cell surface is continuously monitored for fluorescence (Figure 3.6a) but is then 'bleached' with a powerful laser beam focused on the spot (Figure 3.6b). The fluorescence of the spot area is further monitored. Over a short period of time, the fluorescence in the previously bleached spot recovers (Figure 3.6c and d). The fluorescence recovers because unbleached, i.e. actively fluorescing, molecules diffuse back into the small region (the spot) that is being observed (Figure 3.6c). The rate of this diffusion indicates how fluid the membrane is. Theoretically, the fluorescence should recover to the same magnitude it was before the bleaching laser beam treatment, but it rarely does so. This behaviour is now thought to point to a more sophisticated model of membrane structure, in which there are relatively rigid regions within a predominantly fluid matrix, of which more will be said in Section 3.12.

Figure 3.6 FRAP (fluorescence recovery after photobleaching). Particular kinds of lipid or protein molecules in the cell membrane are labelled with a fluorescent marker. (a) A small area of the cell surface is illuminated, giving maximal (100%) fluorescence. (b) The spot is then 'bleached' with a powerful laser flash, so the fluorescence falls to zero (0%). (c) Active (i.e. unbleached) fluorescent molecules diffuse into the bleached area and the fluorescence of the spot recovers. (d) The rate of recovery indicates the diffusion rate of the labelled (lipid or protein) molecules and is thus a measure of membrane fluidity.

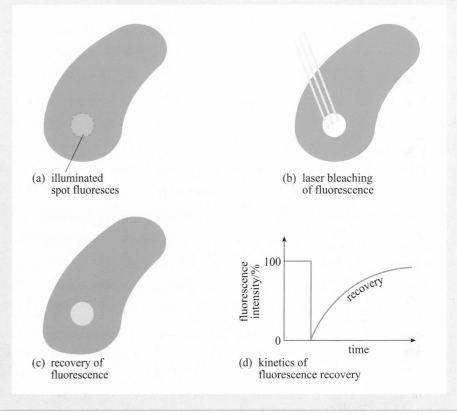

(a) illuminated
     spot fluoresces

(b) laser bleaching
     of fluorescence

(c) recovery of
     fluorescence

(d) kinetics of
     fluorescence recovery

SUMMARY OF SECTIONS 3.1 AND 3.2

1   Membranes are fundamental to cell function; they support protein molecules involved in a variety of cellular activities and, in eukaryotes, they divide the cell into functionally distinct compartments.

2   Membranes are bilayers of amphipathic lipid molecules with interspersed proteins, all held together by weak, non-covalent interactions.

3   Membrane stability is temperature-dependent and is related to lipid composition.

4   Both lipid and protein molecules move freely in the plane of the membrane.

3.3 COMPOSITION OF MEMBRANES

We now go on to study in some detail the chemical structure of the main membrane constituents, first the amphipathic lipids and then the proteins. These topics provide the background for understanding membrane functions.

3.3.1 MEMBRANE LIPIDS

Membranes are made up of several chemically different types of amphipathic lipids, but in the great majority of membranes, **phospholipids** are the most abundant lipid component. They all have a phosphate group, which contributes to the polar head of the molecule, and two long hydrocarbon chains (the hydrophobic tails). There are two kinds of phospholipids, one (the most familiar) based on the small molecule glycerol, the other derived from a much larger molecule known as sphingosine. The only difference between the two kinds of phospholipids that you need to note is in the source of hydrocarbon tails. Phospholipids derived from glycerol (called glycerophospholipids or simply *glycerolipids*) have two long-chain acyl groups attached by ester linkages to the glycerol 'core' (in fact they are often made in the cell from triacylglycerols, TAGs). Sphingolipids have one 'in-built' hydrocarbon chain and the second is acquired by acylation (of the sphingosine amino group) with a long-chain fatty acid.

Figure 3.7 (overleaf) shows the simplified structure of some common membrane lipids from the two groups and the relationships between them. Notice that the 'X' (attached to the negatively charged phosphate) is always a polar group (and can be positively charged) and that the names of the glycerophospholipids are simply phosphatidyl-'X', e.g. phosphatidylethanolamine, phosphatidylinositol (PI). Derivatives of PI are involved in cell signalling, which you will learn about in Chapter 6. The nomenclature of the sphingolipids is generally less related to their chemical structure than to the name of the tissue in which they are abundant (see below). You can see from Figure 3.7 that some membrane lipids have one or more sugar chains attached; these are called **glycolipids**.

Why are there all these different types of membrane lipids? The size and polarity of the head groups influence the properties of the membrane surface, e.g. its interactions with other molecules, including the various membrane proteins. We will return to this topic later in the chapter. Particular lipids are characteristic of

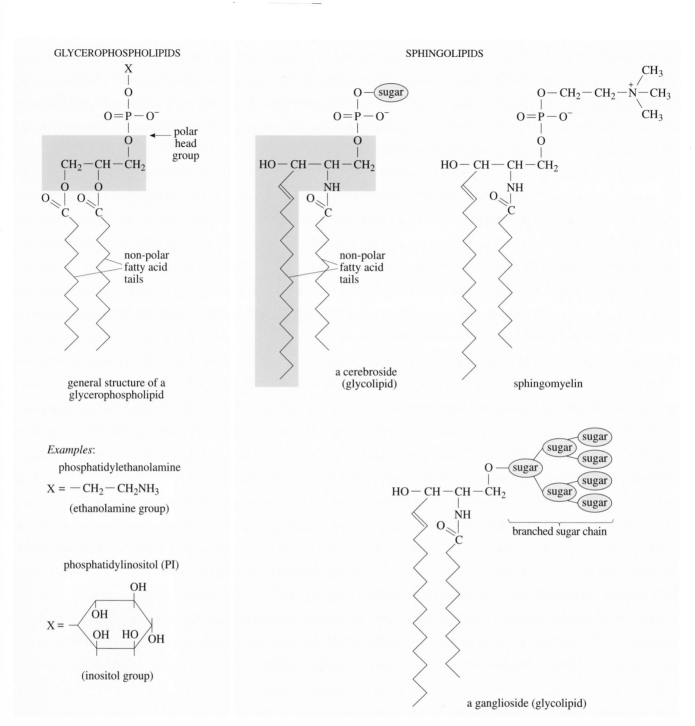

GLYCEROPHOSPHOLIPIDS

general structure of a
glycerophospholipid

polar head group

non-polar fatty acid tails

Examples:

phosphatidylethanolamine

X = — CH_2 — CH_2NH_3

(ethanolamine group)

phosphatidylinositol (PI)

X =

(inositol group)

SPHINGOLIPIDS

a cerebroside
(glycolipid)

sphingomyelin

non-polar fatty acid tails

branched sugar chain

a ganglioside (glycolipid)

Figure 3.7   Simplified structure of some common membrane lipids. The glycerol and sphingosine skeletons are shown in pink boxes. X represents a polar group.

different cell types, as reflected in the names. For example, sphingomyelin is abundant in the myelin sheath surrounding vertebrate nerve axons and the cerebrosides (glycolipids) are common in the membranes of some brain cells. However, how enrichment of the cell membrane in a particular lipid is related to cell function is not known. Many membrane glycolipids in animals are involved in cell recognition by the immune system (e.g. the ABO blood group determinants on red blood cells).

In prokaryotes too, membrane lipid structure can confer special properties on the cell. Most bacteria have a polysaccharide wall outside the cell membrane and some (the so-called Gram-negative bacteria) also have a second, outer membrane surrounding the cell wall. Abundant in the outer layer, or *leaflet*, of the outer membrane are lipid–sugar chains called, not glycolipids, but lipopolysaccharides (LPS). These molecules stimulate a powerful immune response in mammals and other vertebrates, which is why infection by some Gram-negative pathogens can lead to inflammation and fever. Archaea have a distinctive type of membrane lipid in which each of the long hydrocarbon chains is directly joined to glycerol via an oxygen atom and is branched. This ether linkage contrasts with the ester linkage and linear hydrocarbon chains characteristic of the membrane lipids of the Bacteria and all eukaryotes.

The different types of membrane *within* a eukaryote cell have different lipid compositions. For example, the concentration of sphingolipids is higher in ER membranes than in Golgi, and is highest in the cell membrane.

Eukaryote cell membranes have distinctive outside and inside faces, with the two leaflets differing in lipid (and also protein) composition. For example, glycolipids occur exclusively on the outside face of the membrane. Cell membrane lipid composition may be different in different parts of the cell. In animal epithelial cells (Chapter 1), for example, the apical region, or domain, of the membrane, which faces outwards and is not in contact with other cells, is rich in sphingolipids, while the basolateral domain, the part in contact with neighbouring cells and the extracellular matrix, has more glycerolipids.

○ How is this polarity in lipid composition maintained, given the fluid nature of the cell membrane?

● Tight junctions along the membrane (Chapter 1) prevent mixing of the apical and basolateral domain constituents, both lipids and proteins.

In addition to differences in the polar head groups, there is diversity in the chemical structure of the fatty acyl tails. In membranes from different sources, these fatty acids may differ in both chain length and degree of **unsaturation** (number of double bonds). In animals, the chains are typically unbranched with an even number of carbon atoms, ranging from C_{14} to C_{22}, but generally no longer than C_{18}. For saturated chains (Figure 3.8a, overleaf), the amount of hydrophobic interaction increases with chain length, so membranes with a high proportion of saturated long-chain lipids are more rigid than those with predominantly short chains. A double bond in the chain can be either *cis* ('on this side') or *trans* ('on the opposite side'), depending on the orientation of the groups relative to the bond (i.e. the two parts of the chain either end of it) and is usually in the middle of the chain. Figure 3.8b shows how a *cis* double bond produces a bend in the chain, whereas an unsaturated chain with a *trans* double bond (Figure 3.8c) is almost straight, like its saturated counterpart. Natural unsaturated fatty acids in animal, plant and protoctist membranes nearly always have *cis* bonds (and are therefore known as *cis* fatty acids).

○ How would you expect *cis* unsaturated chains to affect membrane properties?

● Packing would be much looser, so the membrane would be more fluid.

Experiments with artificial lipid bilayers have indeed shown that the higher the proportion of *cis* unsaturated chains, the more fluid the bilayer. Recall the different responses to cooling of cell membranes of fruit native to temperate regions and those of bananas: the membranes of the former have fatty acid chains with a greater proportion of *cis* unsaturated fatty acids, so remain fluid, while the latter have more saturated chains and so 'freeze' at refrigeration temperatures. The same behaviour of *cis* unsaturated fatty acids is also clearly manifest in different properties of fats (solid) and oils (liquid): they are both TAGs, but oils are the more unsaturated.

There are some membrane lipids that have fatty acid chains with two, three or even four *cis* double bonds. An important example of the latter is the C_{20}-fatty acid, arachidonic acid (Figure 3.8d), which is also the precursor of several locally acting regulatory molecules, such as the prostaglandins (Chapter 6).

Figure 3.8 Simplified structure of some fatty acid components of membrane lipids. (a) Palmitic acid, a C_{16}-saturated fatty acid. (b) *cis* oleic acid (C_{18}-unsaturated fatty acid). (c) *trans* oleic acid. (d) Arachidonic acid , a C_{20}-fatty acid with four *cis* double bonds.

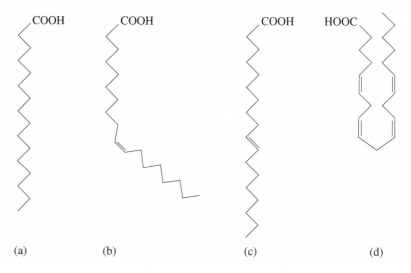

(a) (b) (c) (d)

Finally in our survey of the lipid composition of membranes we come to cholesterol (Figure 3.9a). Chemically, this compound is unrelated to the glycerol- and sphingosine-derived lipids discussed so far but, like them, it is an amphipathic molecule.

○ Why do we describe cholesterol as amphipathic?

● It has a polar head group — albeit a small one (OH) — and the remainder of the molecule is hydrocarbon, therefore hydrophobic.

The hydrocarbon tail of the cholesterol molecule is flexible, but the fused four-ring section is very rigid and its hydrophobic interaction with the surrounding glycerolipid and sphingolipid tails makes that part of the membrane less deformable and so less fluid (Figure 3.9b). For this reason, cholesterol reduces membrane fluidity. Cholesterol is a significant component of animal cell membranes (e.g. nearly 25% by mass of red blood cell membrane lipids) but constitutes a relatively minor proportion of the lipids of intracellular membranes (Table 3.3). For many years the role of cholesterol in membranes was considered to be simply to modulate its fluidity and perhaps add mechanical strength. However, as we shall see in Section 3.12, cholesterol is now thought to have a more sophisticated role in the functioning of the cell membrane.

Plant cell membranes don't have cholesterol but instead have related molecules called phytosterols, and in prokaryote membranes, there are sterol-like molecules called hopanoids.

Table 3.3   Proportion of cholesterol in different cellular membranes in mammalian liver cells. (Notice the increase in cholesterol from ER to Golgi to cell membrane.)

Membrane	Cholesterol (% by mass of total lipids)
ER	6
Golgi	12
Cell membrane	17
Mitochondrion (inner and outer membranes)	3

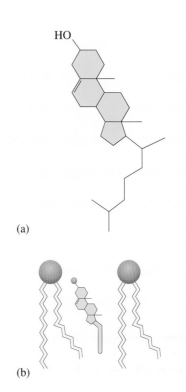

(a)

(b)

Figure 3.9   (a) Simplified structure of cholesterol. The four fused rings are shown in yellow. (b) Diagram illustrating a possible relationship between a cholesterol molecule and surrounding membrane lipids.

Our overview of membrane lipids is now complete. We now go on to consider the proteins within or associated with biological membranes.

3.3.2 MEMBRANE PROTEINS

Many of the properties of membranes are conferred by their complement of proteins and we shall look at some of these properties shortly. First we consider the overall structural aspects of membrane proteins. The proportion of protein relative to lipid is different in different membranes. For example, a typical cell membrane is 50% protein (by mass), while the internal membranes of mitochondria and chloroplasts are around 75% protein. However, protein molecules are, on average, about 50 times larger than lipid molecules, so membrane lipid molecules always far outnumber the proteins present.

Some membrane proteins are *within* the lipid bilayer and protrude on both sides of the membrane (**integral membrane proteins**). Others, however, are attached to either the inside or the outside of the membrane surface (**peripheral membrane proteins**), either covalently linked (usually via a glycolipid molecule) or loosely held by non-covalent interactions with integral proteins (Figure 3.10, overleaf).

Membrane proteins possess all the same levels of organization as the water-soluble proteins described in Chapter 2. A membrane separates two aqueous compartments, so there are three environments into which the structure of an integral membrane protein must be stabilized. These proteins therefore typically possess three structural domains: two polar sections, one on each side of the membrane (*extracellular* and *cytosolic* domains) joined by a non-polar 'torso', the *membrane-spanning*, or *transmembrane*, domain, which is usually folded into

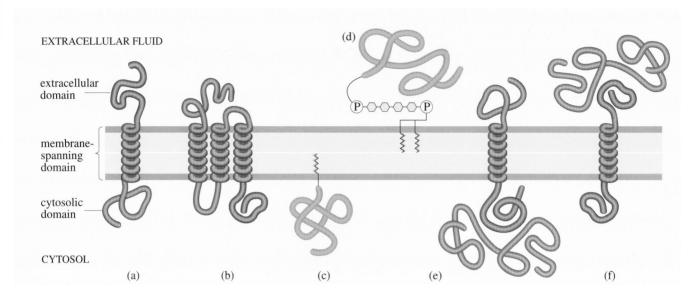

EXTRACELLULAR FLUID

extracellular
domain

membrane-
spanning
domain

cytosolic
domain

CYTOSOL

(a) (b) (c) (d) (e) (f)

Figure 3.10 Different ways in which membrane proteins associate with the lipid bilayer. (a) and (b) Integral membrane proteins, with cytosolic, membrane-spanning and extracellular domains. (c) A protein covalently linked to the cytosolic surface of the membrane. (d) A protein covalently linked to the extracellular surface of the membrane. (P) represents a phosphate group and the green hexagons are sugar units. (e) and (f) Proteins non-covalently attached to an integral membrane protein at either the cytosolic (e) or the extracellular (f) surface.

one or more α-helices and presents non-polar amino acid side chains to the lipid interior. The non-polar surface of the membrane-spanning domain allows the protein molecule to move easily in the plane of the membrane through the fluid matrix of surrounding lipid molecules.

Glycophorin (Figure 3.11) is an integral protein abundant in red blood cell membranes, and has a single membrane-spanning α-helical section about 3 nm long (i.e. just long enough to span the non-polar membrane interior). This section contains about 20 amino acids, many with hydrophobic side chains which face the surrounding hydrophobic lipid chains.

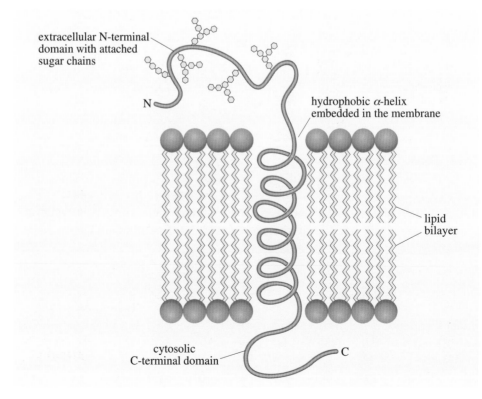

extracellular N-terminal
domain with attached
sugar chains

N

hydrophobic α-helix
embedded in the membrane

lipid
bilayer

cytosolic
C-terminal domain

C

Figure 3.11 Structure of glycophorin, an integral protein of the membrane of vertebrate red blood cells. In common with many cell membrane proteins, glycophorin is a glycoprotein, with sugar chains attached to the extracellular domain.

Some integral membrane proteins have a polypeptide chain which loops back and crosses the membrane several times, forming a bundle of α-helices joined by short extracellular hydrophilic sections. Bacteriorhodopsin is one such **multipass** membrane protein, present in the purple membrane of the archaeon, *Halobacterium halobium*, which is found in salty pools.

It is very difficult to crystallize membrane proteins (as required for their study by X-ray crystallography) because they need to be within the membrane to achieve their native conformation, so not much is known about their 3-D structures. However, the structure of bacteriorhodopsin was relatively easy to work out, because it is concentrated in 'patches' in the membrane (Figure 3.12a). This protein has a light-absorbing pigment molecule (retinal) covalently linked at the centre of a cluster of seven α-helices (Figure 3.12b) and functions in energy transduction (conversion) — see later. A multipass membrane protein that is present in mammalian cell membranes, again with seven α-helices, is a receptor for the hormone adrenalin. It transduces the hormone signal into an intracellular response (you will learn more about this process in Chapter 6).

(a)

Figure 3.12 (a) Schematic drawing of the archaeon *Halobacterium halobium* showing the purple-coloured areas ('patches') of membrane, which contain bacteriorhodopsin. (b) The structure of bacteriorhodopsin, with seven α-helices spanning the membrane. The light-absorbing pigment molecule, or chromophore (retinal), is shown in purple. Like all Archaea, *Halobacterium*'s membranes have ether-linked lipids, which differ from the phospholipids of bacteria and eukaryotes. The proton transfer across the bacteriorhodopsin is associated with energy transduction.

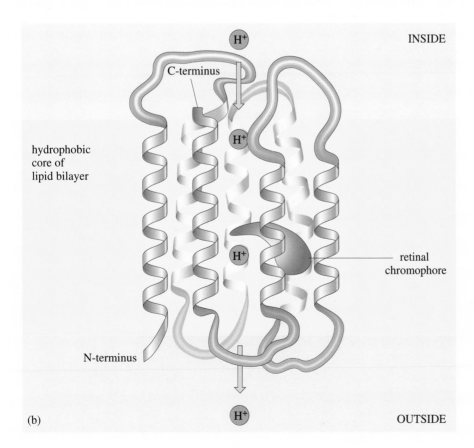

(b)

There are some multipass transmembrane proteins in which the membrane-spanning domains are not α-helices, but lengths of β-sheet, which together form a tubular, barrel-like structure around an aqueous pore; for example the porins in the outer membrane of bacteria, which allow the diffusion of small molecules into and out of the cell. The same structural principle applies as for the multipass α-helices: polar amino acid side chains line the pore and non-polar side chains project from the outside of the 'barrel' to interact with the membrane's lipid interior.

Like membrane lipids, membrane proteins often have sugar chains covalently bound to the extracellular domain, e.g. glycophorin (Figure 3.11).

In the same way as for its lipid components, the cell membrane may be polarized with respect to the particular proteins present. For example, the membrane transport proteins in the apical domain of epithelial cells are different from those in the basolateral domain, which allows the transfer of solutes from one side of the cell to the other.

SUMMARY OF SECTION 3.3

1   Most membrane lipids are phospholipids, with a polar phosphate group and two hydrophobic, fatty acid tails. Glycolipids have sugar chains attached. Some membrane lipids are glycerol esters and others are based on sphingosine.

2   The fatty acid tails of membrane phospholipids differ in both chain length and degree of unsaturation, and in whether their double bonds are *cis* or *trans*.

3   Cholesterol occurs in animal cell membranes and modulates membrane fluidity; similar sterols are found in plant and prokaryote membranes.

4   Membrane proteins are either attached to the surface (peripheral) or span the membrane and protrude on both sides (integral).

5   The membrane-spanning domain of integral membrane proteins has an α-helical or β-sheet secondary structure which interacts with the lipid interior via its hydrophobic side chains.

3.4   OVERVIEW OF MEMBRANE FUNCTIONS

Now that you have a clear idea of the basic structure of membrane lipids and proteins and the physical relationships between them, we can go on to look at the functions of membranes, some of which we have hinted at already. Many of the cell membrane's activities involve specific membrane proteins, e.g. transport of small molecules and ions, cell signalling, energy transduction. The function of such membrane proteins can be studied in a controlled way by isolating them (using techniques described in Chapter 2) and incorporating them in synthetic liposomes (Figure 3.3a). Protein engineering (Box 2.4) can be used to produce specific amino acid substitutions, so that the role of particular side chains in the normal function of the protein can be explored.

Some membrane functions involve the *whole* of the cell membrane, rather than specific membrane proteins, for example the maintenance of cell shape. Yet other functions require the controlled movement (through budding and fusion) of areas of membrane, in fact the coordinated activity of both the cell membrane and the intracellular membrane systems (ER and the Golgi) and associated vesicles (introduced in Chapter 1). Such activities include the transport of large molecules into and out of the cell, and between cell compartments, in particular, protein trafficking (or targeting) to the correct destination, either within the cell or to the exterior.

We now discuss in more detail the main functions of membranes, beginning with the structural role of the outer (cell) membrane.

3.5   A MECHANICAL ROLE FOR THE CELL MEMBRANE

You learned in Chapter 1 about the cytoskeleton, a network of protein filaments which provides eukaryote cells with a flexible internal scaffolding. Some of the cytoskeletal filaments are attached (non-covalently) to certain cell membrane proteins (Figure 3.13). This attachment helps to maintain the shape of the cell and also contributes to the strength of the membrane, which is particularly important for cells that are subjected to mechanical stress. Red blood cells, for example, are forced through narrow capillaries during their passage through the circulation.

Figure 3.13 (a) Diagram of a red blood cell showing the relationship between the inner surface of the membrane and the cytoskeleton. Notice the link proteins which attach the membrane proteins to the spectrin filaments. (b) Electron micrograph showing spectrin filaments in red cell ghosts.

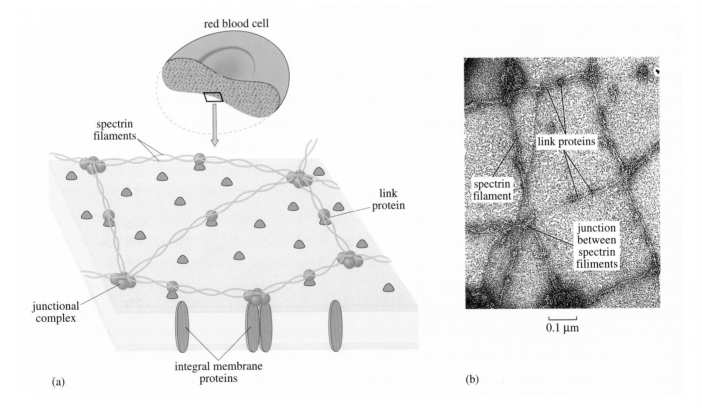

(a)

(b)

The cell membrane–cytoskeleton assembly forms the characteristic biconcave disc shape of red blood cells and also acts as a molecular 'shock-absorber', allowing the cells to tolerate mechanical stresses that would damage many other cells.

Membrane-bound cytoskeletal protein filaments can be seen in EM photos of red cell 'ghosts' (the remains of the cells after lysing (rupturing) them to release their contents), hence the name of this protein, *spectrin*. Spectrin is a cytoskeletal protein that cross-links actin filaments. When spectrin is dissociated from the ghosts, the membrane breaks up into small, spherical vesicles, demonstrating the importance of the cytoskeletal association to the integrity of the red blood cell membrane.

○ Why would people who produce abnormal spectrin have spherical red blood cells and be anaemic?

● Without functional spectrin, the correct cell shape cannot be maintained and, because the unsupported cell membrane is fragile, the cells are easily ruptured and destroyed. Anaemia results if red blood cells are destroyed faster than they can be replaced.

A similar network of spectrin-like filaments is found associated with the cell membrane in other eukaryotic cells too, but their organization and functions are less well understood than they are in red blood cells.

○ The structure of which organelle is maintained by an interaction between a bounding membrane and internal protein filaments?

● The structure of the nucleus depends on an internal network of lamins, the nuclear lamina, which links chromatin to the nuclear envelope (Chapter 1).

3.6 CELL–CELL INTERACTIONS

In all cells, the cell membrane is the outermost structure whose components are frequently exchanged with the cytosol. (The cell wall in bacteria, fungi and plants is inert, extracellular material.) As such, it mediates all the interactions that take place between adjacent cells in all multicellular organisms, between animal cells and the extracellular matrix, and also between cells and pathogens. First we describe the different types of intercellular junctions and their properties and then examine what it is about membranes that enables cells to recognize and adhere to each other or to the matrix, a property that is essential for both embryonic development and the maintenance of tissues.

3.6.1 JUNCTIONS BETWEEN CELLS

As described in Chapter 1, many cells in tissues are linked to each other and the surrounding matrix by distinct regions of contact, or junctions. There are four structurally and functionally distinct types of cell junction: tight junctions, anchoring junctions (also known as desmosomes and hemidesmosomes), adherens junctions and gap junctions.

TIGHT JUNCTIONS

The molecular structure of **tight junctions** is still uncertain, but from microscopic observation, they appear to be made up of strands of protein that span adjacent membranes to form a tight seal between them (Figure 3.14). Tight junctions prevent the lateral movement of other membrane proteins, such as those that transport specific small molecules across the membrane, thus allowing different regions of the cell membrane to have different transport properties. For example in the epithelial cells lining the gut, apical–basolateral polarization of the cell membrane permits unidirectional transport of the soluble products of digestion (e.g. sugars and amino acids) from the gut to the bloodstream.

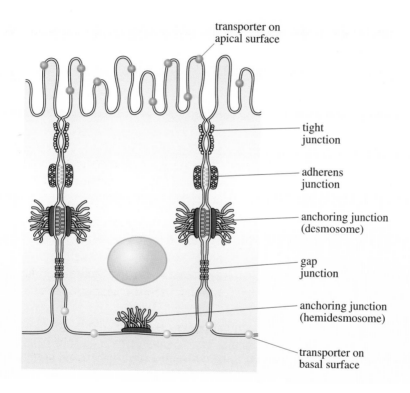

Figure 3.14 Schematic drawing of the different types of junctions between cells. Epithelial cells of the intestine (shown here) possess all these types of junction. Other cell types may only have some types of junction.

ANCHORING JUNCTIONS (DESMOSOMES AND HEMIDESMOSOMES)

Anchoring junctions are present in many types of animal tissues and serve to hold the constituent cells to each other and to the surrounding extracellular matrix. Anchoring junctions all have a common general structure, consisting of transmembrane protein molecules known as **cadherins**. The extracellular domains of cadherins interact with their counterparts on other cells; their cytosolic domains interact with intracellular proteins. The latter in turn are bound to a type of intermediate cytoskeletal filament known as keratin (in much the same way as described for the spectrin scaffold in red blood cells). See Figure 3.15a–c (overleaf).

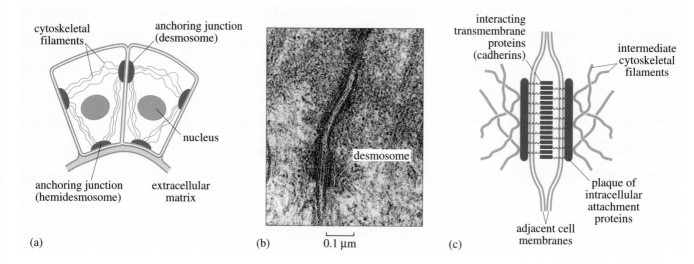

Figure 3.15 Anchoring junctions (desmosomes and hemidesmosomes). (a) Schematic drawing of anchoring junctions between epithelial cells (desmosomes) and between epithelial cells and the extracellular matrix (hemidesmosomes). (b) Electron micrograph of a desmosome. (c) Schematic diagram of the molecular arrangement at a desmosome.

ADHERENS JUNCTIONS

Adherens junctions are similar to anchoring junctions — they also link cytoskeletal components of adjacent cells via intracellular proteins and cadherins. However, the cytoskeletal components linked are, in this case, actin filaments, not intermediate filaments.

GAP JUNCTIONS

Adjacent cells in tissues exchange molecules (to coordinate their activities) via connecting 'tunnels' called **gap junctions**. Gap junctions are about 1.5 nm in diameter and allow the passage of almost any molecule of relative molecular mass less than about 1000 down its **concentration gradient**, i.e. from high to low concentration. Thus, for example, proteins and nucleic acids cannot pass through them, but sugars, amino acids and small peptides can. Gap junctions are widely distributed in many different animal tissues. In electron micrographs, the membranes at gap junctions appear to be separated by a uniformly narrow gap. However, they are not actually separate, but held together by special, multisubunit proteins, called *connexons*, which span the membrane and are aligned with the connexons in the membrane of the adjacent cell, thereby providing aqueous channels linking cells together (Figure 3.16a). Each connexon is made up of a ring of six identical subunits, called *connexins*, arranged symmetrically around a central pore. Gap junctions between plant cells, or **plasmodesmata**, are membrane-lined channels which cross the walls (Figure 3.16b), whereas gap junctions between animal cells are not lined by membrane.

3.6.2 CELL–CELL RECOGNITION AND CELL ADHESION

There are many charged groups on the surfaces of membranes, arising from both positive and negative charges on the constituent proteins, lipids and sugar chains. By and large, cell membranes have a net negative charge on their surface, but its magnitude may be modified by the incorporation of a greater or lesser percentage of charged phospholipids or charged proteins into the membrane.

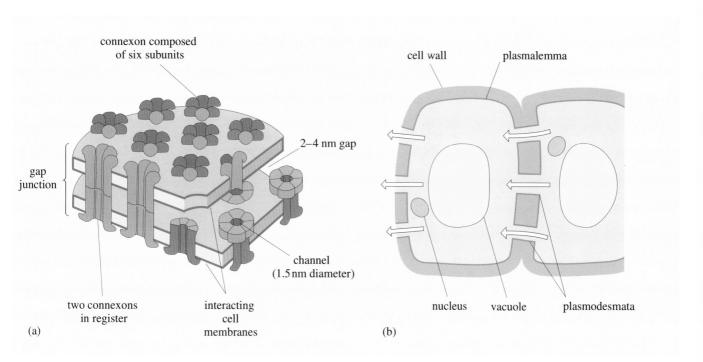

connexon composed
of six subunits

cell wall   plasmalemma

2–4 nm gap

gap
junction

channel
(1.5 nm diameter)

two connexons
in register

interacting
cell
membranes

nucleus   vacuole   plasmodesmata

(a)

(b)

The importance of this cellular property for cell adhesion is demonstrated by the transmembrane glycoprotein, glycophorin (Figure 3.11), of red blood cells. Attached to the extracellular domain of the glycophorin molecule are units of a negatively charged sugar called sialic acid, which make the entire red cell surface negatively charged. The strong repulsion between these negatively charged sugar groups helps to prevent red cells from sticking together, behaviour that is potentially life-threatening because it can lead to thrombosis (clots) and stroke. The amount of sialic acid attached to glycophorin is reduced during disease conditions such as diabetes, so the red blood cells of diabetic individuals become aggregated more easily. As you will learn in Section 3.11, the chemical modification of proteins to form glycoproteins takes place within the ER and Golgi, and much is now known about the sequence of transformations involved. However, why the sialic acid content of glycophorin changes during diabetes is not yet understood.

In vertebrates, sugar chains on both membrane proteins and lipids play a key role in distinguishing self from non-self in the immune response.

Cell–cell recognition and adhesion are particularly important during the course of embryonic development, when cells have to group together in the right place (with the right neighbours) and at the right time. Eventually, the various types of junction characteristic of the different tissues of the mature animal become fully functional, but before this state is achieved, the appropriate cell–cell recognition and adhesion processes have to occur.

If a piece of tissue from an animal embryo is placed in a medium lacking calcium and magnesium ions and containing a substance that effectively *removes* calcium and magnesium ions from the solution (by binding to and hence inactivating them), the tissue dissociates into its constituent cells. If these cells are then placed

Figure 3.16 (a) Diagram of gap junctions between adjacent animal cells. (b) Diagram of plasmodesmata between adjacent plant cells. The plasmodesmata are narrow channels lined by the plasmalemma (cell membrane).

in fresh calcium- and magnesium-containing medium, they may reassemble into a structure that looks like the original tissue. Moreover, if samples of cells from two different organs (e.g. kidney and liver) are mixed together, cells of the same type preferentially adhere together.

Such selective cell–cell recognition and adhesion is mediated by transmembrane glycoproteins. One type are the transmembrane proteins that contribute to adherens junctions and anchoring junctions in mature tissues, collectively called cadherins. Figure 3.17 shows, schematically, the structure of a cadherin molecule and its relationship to intracellular proteins.

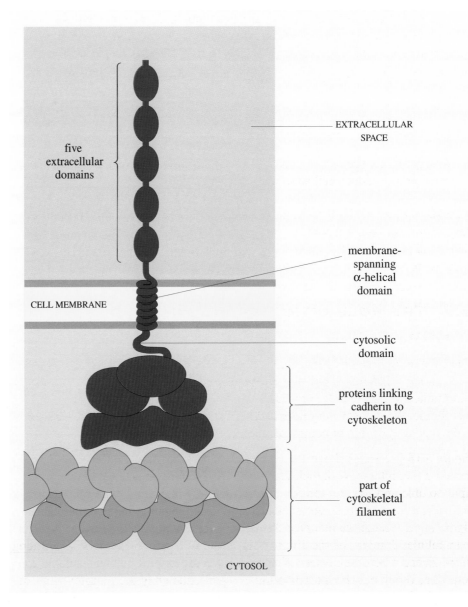

Figure 3.17 General structure of a typical cadherin molecule. Note that the extracellular part is actually made up of five domains, three of which each bind a calcium ion. In anchoring junctions, cadherin is linked to intermediate cytoskeletal filaments via several intracellular proteins.

Adhesion to other cells occurs by the specific, non-covalent interaction between the outermost domains of cadherin molecules in adjacent cells. As evidenced by the cell dissociation studies mentioned above, calcium ions are essential for this process.

While cadherins provide strong binding between cells, there is another type of cell adhesion protein which appears to fine-tune cell–cell interactions during animal development. These molecules have been studied mostly in developing neural (nervous system) tissue, hence the name **neural cell adhesion molecules** or **N-CAMs** for short (other 'CAMs' are expressed by other cell types). These molecules differ from the cadherins in that their adhesive properties are independent of calcium ions. Like cadherins, though, they are membrane glycoproteins with an extracellular region made up of several domains, the outermost of which bind to similar domains of the N-CAMs on the surface of adjacent cells. The sugar components of N-CAMs are chains of sialic acid (as in glycophorin).

○   What property do the sialic acid chains confer on the membrane surface and how does this property influence cell adhesion?

●   A negative charge, which causes N-CAMs on adjacent cells to *repel* each other and so reduce cell adhesion.

As with mature red blood cells, the degree of adhesion between embryonic cells depends in part on the amount of sialic acid in the N-CAM molecules; the fewer sialic acid units, the stronger the adhesion. In fact, changes in N-CAM sialic acid content are believed to be important in embryonic development.

3.7   THE ROLE OF MEMBRANES IN CELL COMMUNICATION

The cells of multicellular organisms coordinate their activities by exchanging a wide variety of chemical and electrical messages. Most intercellular communication depends on processes that take place at or within the cell membrane. We will say very little about these processes here, because Chapter 6 is devoted to the topic of communication between cells.

Figure 3.18 (overleaf) shows the two levels at which extracellular signals are received (i.e. interact with their receptors). A few hormones (e.g. steroids) are lipid-soluble and so enter the cell directly by diffusing through the lipid bilayer before binding to their receptors which are inside the cell. Water-soluble signalling molecules cannot pass through the lipid bilayer. They bind to the extracellular domains of specific receptor proteins in the cell membrane. Binding of the ligand molecule causes a change in the receptor protein that results in a response, which may be the activation of a particular enzyme, commonly one at the beginning of a sequence of reactions. Some receptors are channel proteins and binding of the ligand is what causes the channel to open and allow passive entry of a particular ion (down its electrochemical gradient — see later).

Figure 3.18 Membrane-bound and intracellular receptors. Lipid-soluble ligands pass unaided through the membrane and bind to their receptors in the cytoplasm (or nucleus).

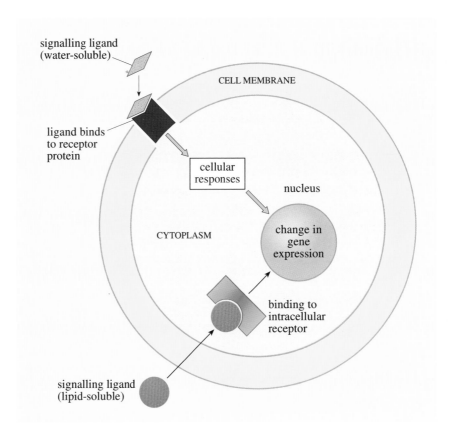

SUMMARY OF SECTIONS 3.4 TO 3.7

1   Some membrane functions are attributable to specific proteins, while others also involve membrane budding and fusion.

2   The cell membrane is attached to the cytoskeleton; this association strengthens the membrane and confers cell shape.

3   Direct interactions between cells in tissues are mediated by several types of junctions: tight junctions, anchoring junctions (desmosomes and hemidesmosomes), adherens junctions and gap junctions.

4   Gap junctions in plants (plasmodesmata) are lined by membrane; those in animal tissues are not.

5   Cell recognition and cell adhesion are particularly important in embryonic development and are mediated by non-covalent interactions between specific cell membrane glycoproteins, some of which are modulated by calcium ions.

6   Most intercellular communication involves processes at or within the cell membrane, e.g. ligand–receptor binding.

3.8   CROSSING MEMBRANES

Cells need to regulate their internal environment, so there has to be selective and controlled transfer of materials across the cell membrane both into and out of the cell. For example, metabolic processes require entry of nutrients (and usually oxygen) and the exit of waste products. Response to some external signals requires the passage of the signalling molecule into the cell or involves specific, transitory ion movements across the cell membrane. In addition, cells may secrete molecules (e.g. extracellular enzymes, hormones) into the external medium or take up large molecules or particles. Controlled transfer of specific molecules and ions across intracellular membranes also occurs and is important in the movement of materials between intracellular compartments.

There are three main routes by which substances traverse the cell membrane.

1   PASSIVE DIFFUSION

The simplest route is passive diffusion between the membrane lipid molecules, without any interaction with specific membrane components. In other words, the membrane behaves as a (protein-free) lipid bilayer. The passive permeability of a lipid bilayer to a particular substance depends partly on its size and partly on how polar it is (Figure 3.19).

Figure 3.19 The relative permeability of a synthetic lipid bilayer (i.e. one devoid of transport proteins found in natural cell membranes) to different types of molecules and ions. The straight arrows denote relatively high permeabilities; curved arrows denote very low permeabilities.

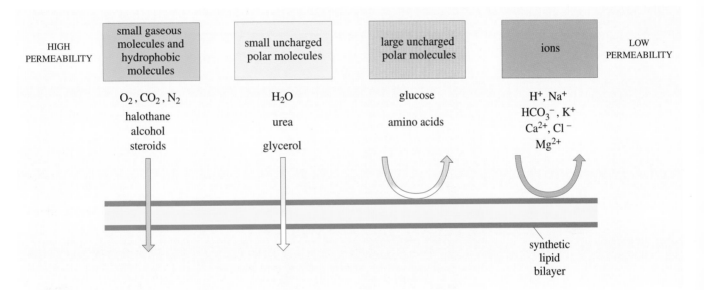

For example, oxygen molecules are both non-polar and small, so diffuse through a lipid bilayer rapidly. Non-polar organic molecules can be relatively large, yet still diffuse readily through the cell membrane. For instance, steroid hormones enter cells in this way.

There are several familiar, exogenous organic molecules whose access to animal tissues is due to their membrane lipid permeability. Alcohol (ethanol, see margin), for example, readily traverses the stomach wall and acts on nerves and muscles within minutes of being ingested. Gaseous inhalable anaesthetics such as halothane (see margin) work fast and effectively because they are lipid-soluble, passing quickly through the membranes of the cells lining the lungs, into the bloodstream and thence through further membranous barriers into the brain, where they disrupt nerve function enough to induce unconsciousness. Fortunately, the liver immediately sets about extracting the foreign substances from the blood and inactivating them, eventually removing enough for the brain to recover, and the patient wakes up again. The organic solvents in glue alter mood by similar processes, and, if inhaled repeatedly, cause liver damage.

ethanol

halothane

131

Water molecules are polar but small, so they too pass easily across a lipid bilayer. Glucose molecules, however, are both relatively large and polar, so a lipid bilayer is much less permeable to glucose, and likewise to small organic polar molecules, such as amino acids.

As for inorganic ions, such as Na^+ and Cl^-, you might reason that their small size might offset the effect of their charge on lipid permeability. However, ions have a surrounding shell of water molecules, which makes their *effective* size very much larger, and explains the very low permeability of a lipid bilayer to ions.

2   TRANSPORT INVOLVING MEMBRANE PROTEINS

Transfer of water-soluble (polar) organic molecules and inorganic ions across the hydrophobic membrane interior is through the agency of specific membrane proteins. Transfer occurs both into and out of the cell and between intracellular compartments, and may be against a concentration gradient.

3   TRANSPORT INSIDE MEMBRANE-DERIVED VESICLES

Macromolecules and particulate matter are too big to pass through membranes. Transfer of such materials involves their sequestration within vesicles that bud off from one membrane (endocytosis; Chapter 1) and subsequently fuse with another.

In the next section we look at our route category 2, focusing mainly on transport processes at the cell membrane. Later, in Section 3.11, we discuss the membrane processes responsible for the 'trafficking' of specific macromolecules within, out of and into cells (i.e. category 3).

3.9   TRANSPORT OF IONS AND SMALL WATER-SOLUBLE MOLECULES

The 'policing' of molecular and ionic traffic across the cell membrane (and across its internal membranes too) is essential to the integrity of every cell, and to the role it plays in the whole organism. The membrane proteins that determine what substances enter and leave the cell are of two main types, classified on the basis of the mechanism by which the material is transferred across the membrane: **carriers** (or **transporters**) and **channels** (Figure 3.20). The relative abundance of different types of carriers and channels may confer unique properties on particular tissues or groups of cells within a single tissue. Both types solve the problem of lipid impermeability to polar substances, by masking either the polarity of the molecule or ion to be transported (by combining it with a membrane-soluble carrier protein) or the non-polarity of the membrane interior (by forming a polar channel through it). Structurally, carriers and channels are both multipass transmembrane proteins that present a hydrophobic surface towards the membrane's lipid interior and a hydrophilic surface towards the aqueous environment.

A carrier, as the name implies, binds to a solute molecule (or ion) and releases it on the other side of the membrane. For example, the glucose carrier protein in mammalian cell membranes binds glucose present in the extracellular fluid, where it is at a higher concentration than in the cell, and releases it into the cytosol for use in metabolism. The carrier is specific for glucose; that is, it does not bind other sugars (or binds them much less strongly).

The binding of the specific solute molecule to be transported alters the conformation of the carrier protein in such a way that its binding site, now occupied by the solute molecule, becomes exposed on the opposite side of the membrane, so the carrier can then release its 'cargo' into the right compartment (Figure 3.20a).

The other type of membrane proteins that transfer hydrophilic substances, in this case usually ions, across membranes are the protein channels. These proteins provide a pore in the membrane through which solutes can pass (Figure 3.20b). Like carriers (transporters), channels are very specific, i.e. only selected ions or molecules are allowed through. Protein channels open in response to a particular signal, so are involved in communication between cells. The feature that most clearly distinguishes the operation of a carrier from a channel is the rate of solute transfer — ion channels are at least 100 times faster than ion carriers. Another difference is in the effect of temperature: lowering the temperature has a much more marked effect on carrier transport than on channel transport.

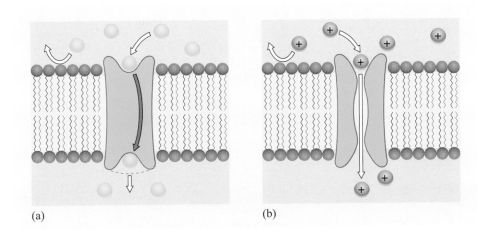

(a)   (b)

Figure 3.20 Model of membrane transport by (a) carrier proteins and (b) protein channels. The red arrow in (a) denotes movement of the solute binding site to the other side of the membrane. The 'cargo' is shown as yellow balls.

Transport across membranes can be either active or passive. In passive membrane transport, or **facilitated diffusion**, a membrane protein (carrier or channel) allows a substance to cross the membrane in the direction from high to low concentration, i.e. down its concentration gradient, and without any input of energy.

In cases where a substance is transported *against* its concentration gradient, i.e. **active transport**, the energy required is provided either directly or indirectly from ATP (described in Section 3.9.3). Note that channels allow only *passive* movement of solute, whereas solute movement via carriers can be either passive or active.

3.9.1 KINETICS OF FACILITATED DIFFUSION

Rates of passive movement, or diffusion, of substances across a permeable membrane and down a concentration gradient, can be predicted using **Fick's law**. This equation relates the difference $(C_H - C_L)$ between the higher, C_H, and the lower, C_L, concentrations of the substance, the area (A) and the thickness (x) of the membrane and a constant D, called the diffusion coefficient, the value of which depends on the nature of the diffusing substance (e.g. its size and polarity) and the temperature, i.e.

$$\text{diffusion rate} = \frac{DA(C_H - C_L)}{x} \tag{3.1}$$

○ What would a graph of the diffusion rate of a small lipid-soluble substance across a permeable membrane against $(C_H–C_L)$ look like?

● It would be a straight line. The diffusion rate increases in proportion to the concentration gradient because small lipid-soluble molecules freely cross cell membranes.

Now look at Figure 3.21. Plot A shows the result of an experiment in which human red blood cells were incubated in glucose solutions of different concentrations. The glucose was radioactively labelled so that the rate of glucose entry could be calculated from measurements made of the amount of radioactivity inside the cells. As you can see the glucose influx (uptake rate) is linear at very low concentrations, but is much greater than the rate predicted for uptake by diffusion alone (plot B). As external glucose concentration increases the uptake rate levels off.

○ Look back at Figure 2.33 in Chapter 2 and suggest an explanation for the shape of curve A in Figure 3.21.

● Like Figure 2.33, plot A in Figure 3.21 is a hyperbolic plot, showing kinetics that are consistent with there being limited number of glucose transport protein molecules in the membrane with which the glucose molecules interact.

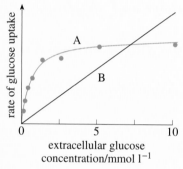

Figure 3.21 Plot A: influx rates of glucose into red blood cells against extracellular glucose concentration. Plot B: theoretical line predicted from Fick's law.

At low, non-saturating, glucose concentrations transport is enhanced by increasing concentrations, but at high concentrations the transport protein molecules become saturated, which explains the upper limit to the rate of transport.

Not surprisingly then, the kinetics of transport of molecules across membranes are described by an equation of the same form as the Michaelis–Menten equation:

$$J = \frac{J_{max}[S]}{K_t + [S]} \tag{3.2}$$

where J is the rate of transport, or *flux*, J_{max} denotes the maximum rate of transport and K_t (not K_M) is a measure of the affinity of the transport protein for the substance, S, being transported. A high value of K_t indicates low affinity; low

K_t indicates high affinity. As in enzyme kinetics, the two transport parameters, J_{max} and K_t, are readily obtained from linearized plots, e.g. J against $J/[S]$.

Channel transport has the same kinetics as passive carrier-mediated transport, which is perhaps puzzling, as passive movement through a protein-lined channel might be expected to be indistinguishable kinetically from passive diffusion. The preceding discussion has implied that there is a clear-cut distinction between carriers and channels. However, this grouping is actually too simplistic. It is now recognized that the selectivity shown by ion channels is associated with binding of the ion to a region of the protein pore, followed by its dissociation and passage across the membrane, i.e. more of a carrier-type mechanism. Accordingly, channels and carriers are no longer considered be two discrete groups; instead the two mechanisms described above are now regarded as the two extremes of a continuum of facilitated diffusion mechanisms.

3.9.2 MEMBRANE POTENTIAL

What drives the diffusion of uncharged molecules across the membrane is simply the concentration difference between the two sides. For charged solutes, however, things aren't quite that simple, because there is an electrical potential gradient (voltage) across cell membranes, the **membrane potential**; the inside is negative with respect to the outside. Membrane potentials range from −10 to −100 millivolts (mV), with a value of −70 mV being typical of many mammalian cell types.

○ In terms of relative ion concentrations inside and outside the cell, what does the charge imbalance on either side of the cell membrane mean?

● That there is a slight excess of positively charged ions over negatively charged ions outside, and a slight deficit inside the cell.

The membrane potential is actually the result of the combined effect of *all* the selective ion movements across the membrane, both passive flow (facilitated diffusion) and active transport (discussed below). In particular, it is the potassium ion (K^+) concentration difference that contributes most to the cell membrane potential. The proportion of ions involved is minute though. Consider, for example, a typical animal cell of 20 μm diameter, which contains around 6×10^{11} K^+ ions. It has been calculated that the movement of only a few million K^+ ions out of the cell would carry enough charge to change the membrane potential by about 100 mV. Thus even small changes in ion concentrations can have very significant effects on membrane potential.

The membrane potential (inside negative) enhances the entry of positive ions and impedes the entry of negative ions. The tendency of a particular ion to be passively transported across the membrane thus depends on the *net* effect of its concentration gradient and the existing membrane potential, i.e. the **electrochemical gradient** for that ion. Thus, for example, for chloride ions (Cl^-) to be transported into a cell by facilitated diffusion, the concentration gradient (high $[Cl^-]$ outside, low $[Cl^-]$ inside) must be large enough to overcome the opposing electrical gradient.

3.9.3 ACTIVE TRANSPORT ACROSS MEMBRANES

As you have seen, membrane proteins (carriers and channels) mediate the transmembrane movement of solutes down their electrochemical gradients, a process that is passive, i.e. does not require energy. However, cells also transport certain solutes across their membranes 'uphill', i.e. *against* an electrochemical gradient. This process is active transport and it requires an energy source, usually ATP, either directly or indirectly, and is always mediated by carrier proteins.

THE CELL MEMBRANE SODIUM PUMP

The concentration of potassium ions (K^+) in cells is between 10 and 20 times as high inside the cell as it is outside, and there is a similar differential in Na^+ concentration, but in the opposite direction (Table 3.4).

○ In what direction must Na^+ ions and K^+ ions be actively transported to maintain the concentration gradients for these ions shown in Table 3.4?

● Na^+ ions must be pumped out and K^+ ions pumped in.

In fact, both these ionic gradients are maintained by the activity of the Na^+–K^+ ATPase or **sodium pump**, a membrane carrier protein that uses the energy of ATP hydrolysis to pump out Na^+ ions and at the same time pump in K^+ ions. The evidence that ATP hydrolysis provides the energy to drive the pump has come from studies on resealed red cell ghosts (Section 3.5) in which the cytoplasm was replaced by solutions of known composition. Ion and ATP concentrations were controlled, specific inhibitors (such as ouabain, a toxin extracted from certain African plants that blocks Na^+ extrusion) were added and the effects on the operation of the pump recorded. A simple schematic model of the mechanism of the sodium pump is illustrated in Figure 3.22. As you can see, for every molecule of ATP hydrolysed, 3 Na^+ ions are pumped out of the cell and 2 K^+ ions are pumped in.

Table 3.4 Concentrations of ions inside and outside a typical mammalian cell.[*]

Ion[†]	Concentration inside cells/ mmol l^{-1}	Concentration outside cells/ mmol l^{-1}
Na^+	5–15	145
K^+	140	5
Mg^{2+}	0.5	1.2
Ca^{2+}	10^{-4}	1–2
Cl^-	5–15	110

[*]The total number of positive charges must balance all the negative charges; the apparent deficit in negatively charged ions is made up by the other inorganic ions such as phosphates and bicarbonate and intracellular macromolecules carrying phosphate and carboxyl groups.

[†]While most of the cell's sodium, potassium and chloride are free in the cytosol, most of the cell's magnesium and calcium are not: Mg^{2+} ions are bound to proteins and most of the intracellular Ca^{2+} ions are concentrated inside organelles.

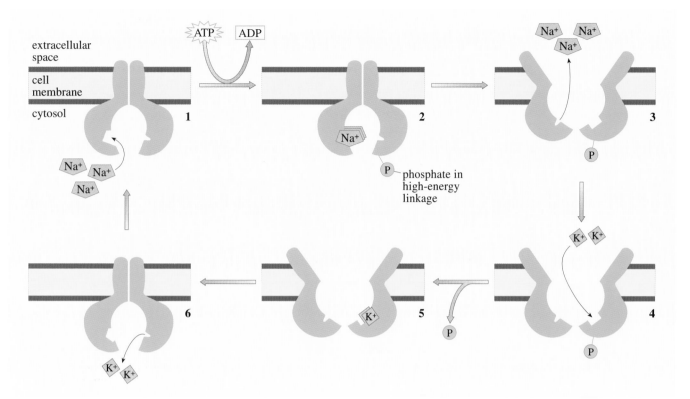

The sodium pump is present in virtually all animal cell membranes and consumes up to 30% of the cell's energy — 70% in the case of nerve cells! It is an example of an *energy transducer*: chemical energy is converted (transduced) into a transmembrane ion gradient. This gradient is a form of stored energy.

Figure 3.22 A scheme showing the sodium pump which extrudes 3 Na⁺ for every 2 K⁺ taken up.

Animal cells have other ATP-driven pumps that function in *intracellular* membranes; for example, the Ca^{2+} pump in ER membranes and the proton (H^+) pump of lysosomal membranes required for acidification of the lysosome's interior (Chapter 1). Plant cells don't have a sodium pump but have both a Ca^{2+} pump and a proton pump in the plasmalemma (cell membrane).

All the ion pumps discussed so far use ATP directly and carry out what is known as **primary active transport**.

COUPLED TRANSPORT OF SOLUTES

The sodium pump produces a steep gradient of Na^+ ions across the cell membrane. The dissipation of this gradient, i.e. the flow of Na^+ ions back down their electrochemical gradient, may be coupled to the simultaneous, 'uphill' transport of *another* solute. This sort of process is sometimes called **secondary active transport** or **cotransport**. The building up of the ion gradient in the first place is primary active transport. Cotransport of solutes in the *same* direction, or **symport**, is the mechanism by which glucose and amino acids are taken up by the epithelial cells lining the gut. Na^+ ions flow in 'downhill', and the dissipation of the ion gradient provides the energy for the other solute to be *pumped* into the cells, in the direction from low to high concentration (see Figure 3.23a).

○ Why would facilitated diffusion (which occurs in all other cells of the body) not suffice for glucose and amino acid uptake from the gut?

● Much of these organic nutrients would be lost from the gut, as there would only be net uptake when the gut concentrations exceeded intracellular concentrations. Diets and meals vary in content and frequency, so gut concentrations of digestion products fluctuate correspondingly. It is important that the maximum amount of nutrients are absorbed.

An Na^+-powered glucose transporter is present in the membranes of cells lining vertebrate kidney tubules, where it reabsorbs ('rescues') glucose after filtration of the blood. Without active reabsorption of glucose from the filtrate, huge quantities would be lost from the blood into the urine.

Passive influx of Na^+ ions can also be coupled to the pumping of another solute in the *opposite* direction, i.e. out of the cell. This cotransport mechanism is called **antiport**. For example, most animal cells have an Na^+–H^+ exchanger that pumps out the excess of H^+ ions produced in the acid-forming reactions of cell metabolism, thus regulating intracellular pH (keeping it at about 7.2). (See Figure 3.23b.)

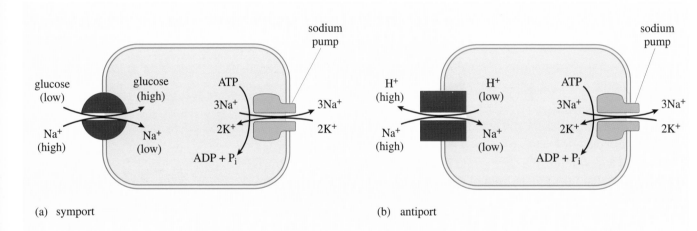

(a) symport

(b) antiport

Figure 3.23 (a) Symport: the Na^+–glucose cotransport system. (b) Antiport: the Na^+–H^+ cotransport system.

It is important to remember that the Na^+-gradient-powered cotransport systems discussed above can only operate because the Na^+–K^+ ATPase (also shown in Figure 3.23) continuously pumps out Na^+ ions, thus maintaining the required gradient of Na^+ ions (low inside, high outside).

Both microbial and plant cell membranes have an H^+ ATPase which generates a proton gradient across the membrane. In root cells, dissipation of this proton gradient is coupled to the uptake of mineral ions from the soil against their concentration gradient.

3.9.4 ION GRADIENTS AND ATP SYNTHESIS

Ion gradients not only drive active transport, they can be used to make ATP.

○   What would happen if resealed red cell ghosts (see Section 3.5) were prepared with the ion concentration gradients reversed (i.e. low $[K^+]$ and high $[Na^+]$ inside and high $[K^+]$ and low $[Na^+]$ outside)?

●   The ions would flow down their gradients of concentration to make the ATPase reaction happen in reverse, i.e. to *synthesize* ATP from ADP and P_i.

Of course, reversal of the sodium pump is an artificial situation. However, ion gradients are the agency of the almost universal, naturally occurring, membrane-based processes that transduce an external energy source into ATP, the cell's 'energy currency'. In fact, the energy is stored most commonly as a transmembrane gradient of not sodium ions but *protons*, and ATP is made as these H^+ ions flow back across the membrane.

There are several proton pumps that are driven by light energy. The simplest of them has been mentioned already (Section 3.3.2) — the protein bacteriorhodopsin, present in the purple patches of the membrane of *Halobacterium halobium* (Figure 3.12). Bacteriorhodopsin contains a light-absorbing pigment, retinal (the same as in the retina of the vertebrate eye), and has a channel that is specific for protons. Light is absorbed by the retinal, which is thereby activated. As the activated form returns to its initial state, protons are pumped through the protein channel in the lipid membrane, setting up a gradient, which is used to drive ATP synthesis.

Most organisms generate their ATP using much more complicated energy-transducing membrane systems than that of *Halobacterium*. A number of different membrane proteins in a precise array (and other membrane associated molecules) are involved and proton pumping is separate from ATP synthesis. In very general terms: light energy or chemical energy (e.g. from food molecules) is used to power electron transport along a series of carriers in a specialized membrane. The electrons flow down an energy gradient, strictly a *chemical potential gradient*. The electron flow is coupled to 'uphill' proton transport from one side of the membrane to the other, as shown in Figure 3.24a. In other words, the chemical potential energy is transduced into a proton gradient. The higher concentration of protons on one side of the membrane makes that side more positive than the opposite side. The proton concentration gradient and charge gradient together constitute the proton electrochemical gradient, or *proton-motive force*, which drives the synthesis of ATP as the protons flow back down their electrochemical gradient via special enzymes called ATP synthases integrated into the membrane (Figure 3.24b).

The linking of ATP synthesis to a proton gradient (or, more generally, a gradient of any ion) is the basis of the **chemiosmotic hypothesis**, which was first proposed by the biochemist Peter Mitchell in 1961 (Figure 3.25).

(a)

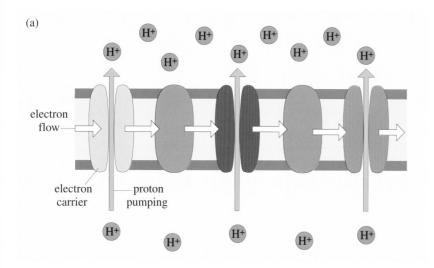

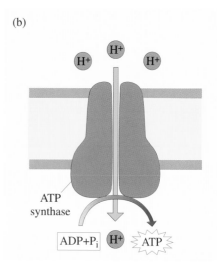

(b)

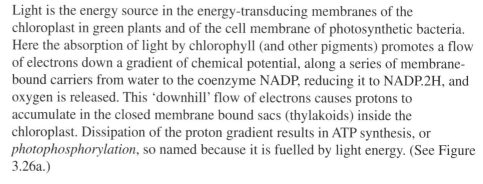

Figure 3.24 (a) As electrons are transferred along the membrane by series of carriers, protons are pumped from one side to the other. Protons flow back across the membrane down their electrochemical potential gradient, through special channels, ATP synthases. (b), which harness the energy of this flow to the formation of ATP.

Light is the energy source in the energy-transducing membranes of the chloroplast in green plants and of the cell membrane of photosynthetic bacteria. Here the absorption of light by chlorophyll (and other pigments) promotes a flow of electrons down a gradient of chemical potential, along a series of membrane-bound carriers from water to the coenzyme NADP, reducing it to NADP.2H, and oxygen is released. This 'downhill' flow of electrons causes protons to accumulate in the closed membrane bound sacs (thylakoids) inside the chloroplast. Dissipation of the proton gradient results in ATP synthesis, or *photophosphorylation*, so named because it is fuelled by light energy. (See Figure 3.26a.)

The inner membrane of mitochondria also contains chains of electron carriers, along which electrons flow down a chemical potential gradient, and at the same time protons are pumped from one side of the membrane to the other, from the mitochondrial matrix (the interior of the mitochondrion) into the space between the inner and outer membranes. Here, though, the starting point for electron flow is the reduced coenzyme NAD.2H and the end-point is oxygen, which is reduced to water. As in the chloroplast, when the protons flow back across the membrane down their electrochemical gradient, ATP is produced. This process is called *oxidative phosphorylation*, as the energy is derived from the oxidation of food molecules. (See Figure 3.26b.)

Figure 3.25 Peter Mitchell (1920–1992), working in a private laboratory in Cornwall in 1961, produced a concept of how electron transport causes ATP synthesis. At that time, Mitchell's chemiosmotic hypothesis was so novel that it was not taken seriously, but it was eventually accepted and acknowledged by the award of a Nobel prize in 1978.

You will learn more about electron transport and ATP synthesis in both chloroplasts and mitochondria in Chapter 5.

We have now looked at a variety of energy-exchange systems in membranes. The primary *energy source* can be ATP, light or reduced coenzymes. This energy is transduced into a transmembrane *ion gradient* (of Na^+ or H^+ ions). The energy stored as the ion gradient is transduced into an *energy sink*, either active solute transport (e.g. glucose or another ion) or ATP synthesis. Figure 3.26 summarizes the basic similarities between these processes.

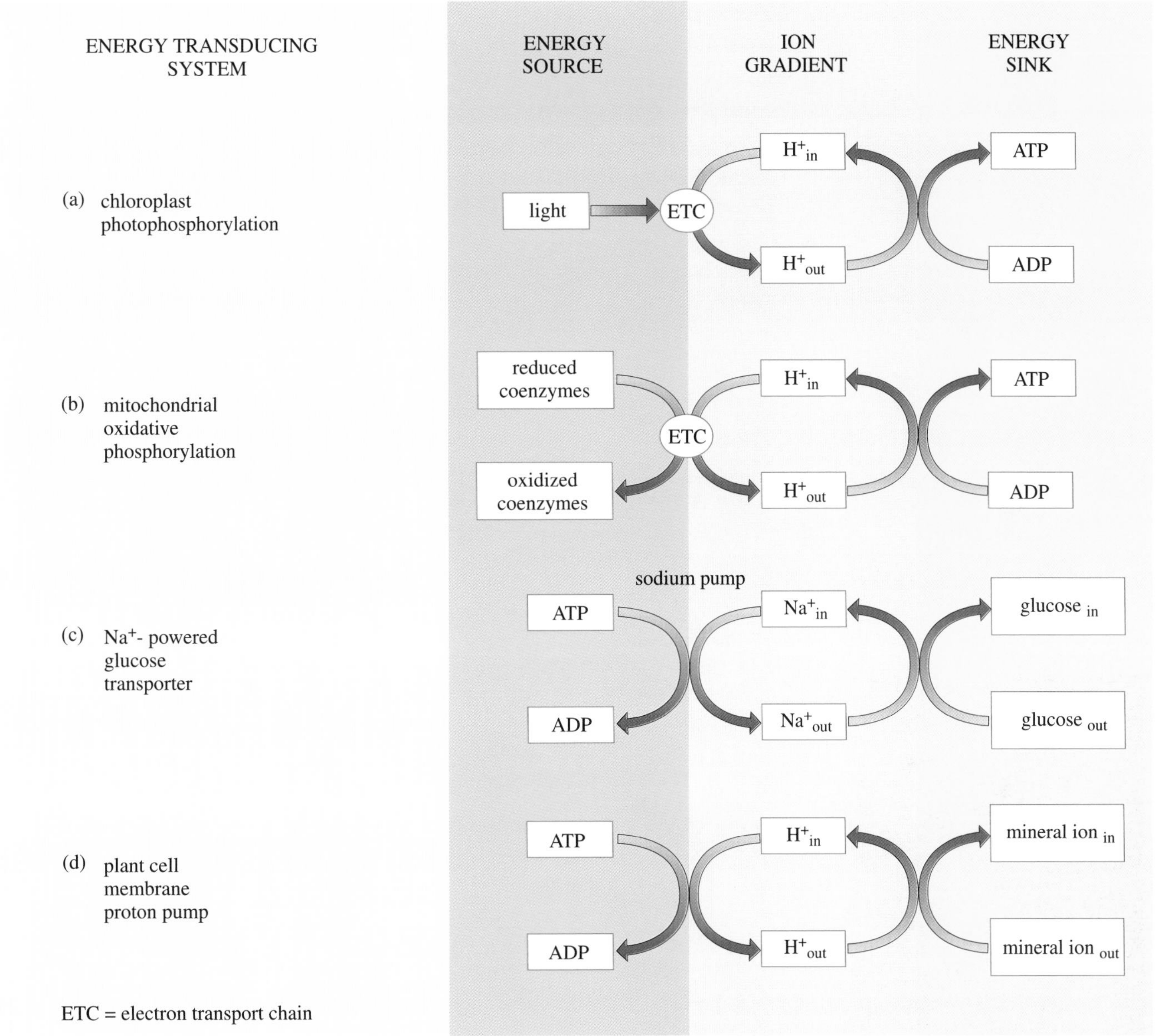

Figure 3.26 Simplified scheme showing some energy exchange (transduction) systems that use transmembrane ion gradients. Note the different energy sources and energy sinks (ATP synthesis or active transport). (a) Photophosphorylation at the inner chloroplast membranes (thylakoids). (b) Oxidative phosphorylation at the inner mitochondrial membrane. (Recall that these membranes contain 75% protein, much of which is electron carriers and ATP synthase.) (c) Active transport of glucose into intestinal epithelial cells of animals, powered by the sodium pump. (d) Active transport of ions into plant root cells powered by the membrane proton pump.

SUMMARY OF SECTIONS 3.8 AND 3.9

1   Substances enter cells in one of three ways: passive diffusion, via the agency of membrane proteins, or by endocytosis.

2   The linear relationship between rates of passive diffusion and concentration gradient is described by Fick's law.

3	Membrane carriers and channels are proteins that transfer ions and small polar molecules across membranes.

4	Passive carrier-mediated and channel transport take place down a concentration gradient and are termed facilitated diffusion.

5	The kinetics of facilitated diffusion are similar to those of enzyme-catalysed reactions, implying binding to a limited number of transport molecules which become saturated at high concentrations of the transported substance.

6	The membrane potential — inside negative and outside positive — together with the concentration gradient of an ion determine the total driving force, or electrochemical potential, for facilitated diffusion of that ion across the membrane.

7	Active carrier-mediated transport requires ATP and moves materials against a concentration gradient. Channel transport is passive only.

8	The sodium pump in animal cell membranes uses the energy of ATP hydrolysis to transport Na^+ ions out and pumps K^+ ions in, and is an example of primary active transport.

9	In secondary active transport (cotransport), discharge of an ion gradient produced by primary active transport is coupled to 'uphill' transport of another solute, either in the same direction (symport) or in the opposite direction (antiport).

10	ATP synthesis powered by a proton electrochemical gradient (chemiosmosis) occurs in both mitochondrial and chloroplast inner membranes.

11	All membrane energy-exchange systems link an energy source to an energy sink via a transmembrane ion gradient.

## 3.10	Water movement across membranes

### 3.10.1	Osmosis and water potential

In the preceding discussion of the movement of small molecules and ions across membranes, we have said almost nothing about water. While membranes are essentially impermeable to polar and charged solutes (as we have seen, their transport requires special mechanisms), they are relatively permeable to water. For this reason they are described as **semipermeable**, or **differentially permeable**.

The recovery of a wilted plant after watering and the bursting of red blood cells when placed in water containing few or no ions are both caused by trans-membrane water movement into cells. In plant cells, the presence of a rigid cell wall sets a limit on water uptake and the cells become stiff, or turgid. (Turgor is important for support in non-woody plant tissues.) The same limitation applies to most bacterial cells, which also have a cell wall. However, in the case of animal cells, bounded only by their delicate membrane, water continues to enter, until the outward pressure on the cell membrane causes it to rupture. Red cell ghosts (Section 3.5) are produced by bursting intact cells by soaking them in dilute aqueous solution.

What causes movement of water into, or out of, cells? The driving force in the above examples is the difference in the *total* solute concentration either side of the membrane. The nature of the solutes doesn't matter. If there is a gradient in total solute concentration, then in the absence of other forces (to be described shortly), water moves across the membrane from the region of low solute concentration to the high concentration compartment. This process is known as **osmosis**. The total solute concentration gradient thus corresponds to an **osmotic gradient** and the movement of water across the membrane is a consequence of this gradient.

But for plant cells, the osmotic gradient is not the only factor that determines whether water moves in or out. Irrespective of the size of the osmotic gradient, entry of water cannot continue beyond a certain point that is determined by the mechanical properties of the cell wall.

Let's now consider the water relations of cells in a quantitative way. Look at Figure 3.27, which represents two adjacent cells (compartments) separated by a differentially permeable membrane. Water 'tries' to move across the membrane from compartment A (low solute concentration) into compartment B (higher solute concentration). The opposing hydrostatic pressure (i.e. pressure due to water, symbol P) that has to be applied to compartment B to prevent entry of water from compartment A has the same numerical value as the **osmotic pressure**, which has the symbol π (pi). Osmotic pressure and hydrostatic pressure are the two components of the net driving force for water movement between cells, or **water potential** (symbol Ψ, psi, pronounced 'sigh'), i.e.

$$\Psi = P - \pi \tag{3.2}$$

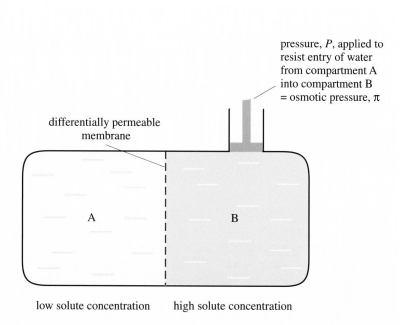

differentially permeable membrane

pressure, P, applied to resist entry of water from compartment A into compartment B = osmotic pressure, π

A

B

low solute concentration   high solute concentration

Figure 3.27 Illustration of the relationship between osmotic pressure (π), hydrostatic pressure (P) and water potential (Ψ). Here, osmosis, the movement of water from compartment A into compartment B across a differentially permeable membrane, driven by the gradient in osmotic pressure, cannot occur because of the equal and opposite hydrostatic pressure applied to compartment B. In this case, therefore, $\Psi = 0$.

Water moves *down* gradients of water potential, from regions of higher to those of lower Ψ. So if you know the water potential of two cells, you can predict whether water can move from one to the other, and the driving force is the difference in water potential between them.

In the situation illustrated in Figure 3.27, π and P are equal in magnitude. Therefore, from Equation 3.2, $\Psi = 0$, which is just a mathematical expression of the statement that there is no net driving force for water movement.

For typical animal cells, there is no inward pressure (above atmospheric) on the cell contents, i.e. $P = 0$, so the water potential gradient depends *only* on the osmotic pressure gradient. This gradient is generally very small, as the cell membrane ion pumps ensure that the total intracellular ion concentration is virtually the same as that of the cell's environment, which is why animal cells don't swell to a spherical shape and burst, as they would do if placed in water.

The presence of a rigid cell wall makes the situation very different for plant cells, however. Entry of water by osmosis is opposed by the internal hydrostatic pressure (usually called *turgor pressure*) exerted by the cell wall on the cell contents. In the model in Figure 3.27, if P were to fall (i.e. the wall became more elastic), then Ψ would decrease (Equation 3.2) so water would enter compartment B, even though there has been no change in the osmotic gradient. Water potential gradients between living plant cells are very important as they enable water to move through the plant (e.g. across the root and along the phloem).

One process in vascular plants that depends on a gradient of water potential is the opening of the gas exchange pores (stomata) in the surface of leaves (Figure 3.28a). The membrane of the guard cells surrounding each stoma contain ion-specific channels. The channels open in response to a stimulus, causing the total solute concentration to increase several-fold. Water then rushes in by osmosis, until limited by the turgor pressure of the guard cells. Thus the cells swell up and become more rigid (turgid), so causing the pore to open (Figure 3.28b).

Figure 3.28 (a) Stomata in the surface of a leaf of lemon balm. (b) Opening of a stoma as a result of entry of water into surrounding guard cells, driven by a gradient of water potential.

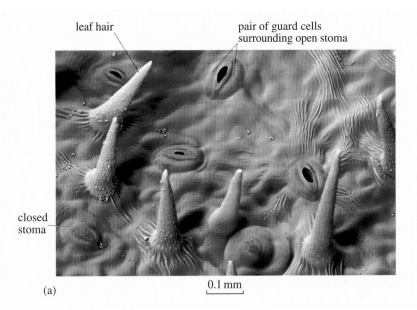

leaf hair

pair of guard cells surrounding open stoma

closed stoma

0.1 mm

(a)

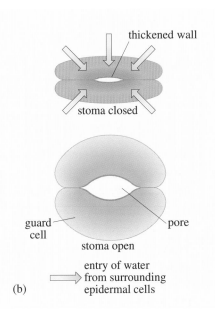

thickened wall

stoma closed

guard cell

pore

stoma open

entry of water from surrounding epidermal cells

(b)

3.10.2 FACILITATED DIFFUSION OF WATER

Permeability of membranes to water used to be ascribed to passive diffusion alone, driven by water potential gradients as described above. However, water flow rates across the membranes of red blood cells have been measured that are more than twice as large as could be accounted for by diffusion, and are inhibited by protein-binding chemicals.

○ What does this evidence suggest?

● That there is a facilitated route for water transport which is mediated by transport proteins.

Indeed, it was subsequently found that there is family of integral membrane proteins called **aquaporins**, all of which are channel proteins that are highly selective for water. Slightly different aquaporins are found in animals, plants, fungi and bacteria, At least ten distinct aquaporins (AQPs) have been identified in mammals and the number is even higher in plants.

The importance of aquaporins is demonstrated in several diseases of humans in which the aquaporin of a particular tissue is functionally defective, for example, in the mammalian kidney, where a reduced ability to reabsorb water from the collecting ducts (after filtration of the blood) results in the production of copious amounts of watery urine, a condition called diabetes insipidus. Water transport is also a major activity of the gut: fluid is secreted from salivary glands, stomach and small intestine and much of it is absorbed again from the colon. Several aquaporins are involved in this water transport, for example AQP4 in colonic surface epithelium facilitates water uptake from the colon into the bloodstream.

In plants, aquaporin channel activity has been demonstrated in the membrane that surrounds the vacuole (the tonoplast). The abundance of aquaporins in plants is probably related to the need for control of water movement during growth and development and in the face of fluctuating environmental conditions. For example, aquaporin genes are expressed in response to water stress (caused by either drought or salinity).

Aquaporins may not be the sole mechanism of facilitated water transport, however. For example, there is recent evidence that the Na^+-powered glucose transporter (Figure 3.23a) may cotransport water molecules.

SUMMARY OF SECTIONS 3.9 AND 3.10

1 Membranes are differentially permeable (i.e. permeable to water and very small non-polar molecules, but not to polar and charged solutes).

2 Osmosis is the passage of water across a differentially permeable membrane from a solution of low concentration to a high-concentration solution, i.e. down an osmotic pressure gradient.

3 Water potential (Ψ) is the net driving force for water movement and depends on both osmotic pressure (π) and hydrostatic pressure (P). For animal cells $P = 0$ and in plant cells P = the turgor pressure, which depends on the properties of the cell wall.

4   Some of the water flow across membranes is mediated by channel proteins called aquaporins and some (possibly) by cotransport with solute molecules.

3.11   MEMBRANE TRAFFICKING: AN OVERVIEW

The title of this section reflects the dynamic nature of cellular membranes — not just the outer cell membrane (which has been our main focus so far) but also the membrane-bound compartments within the eukaryotic cell. Most of the properties of membranes discussed above can be directly related to the activities of specific proteins within them, properties that can be described without reference to the fluid nature of the membrane. However, there are some basic cell activities that rely on the dynamic flux of membrane material through the cell, a process that depends on budding of *vesicles* — small membrane-bound sacs — from one membrane-bound compartment, their movement through the cytosol and their fusion with another membrane. Figure 3.29 summarizes the membrane-trafficking routes within the cell. As you can see, there is transfer in both directions, both out to and inwards from the cell membrane, as well as internal two-way traffic.

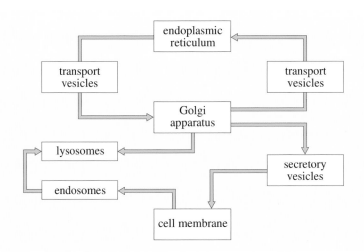

Figure 3.29 Intracellular membrane traffic 'map'.

3.11.1   PROTEIN TARGETING

We examine first the route outward from the ER to the Golgi and thence to the cell membrane or to lysosomes, which is called the *secretory pathway* as it transfers proteins synthesized on the ER to the cell exterior. Figure 3.30 shows in three dimensions the structure of the intracellular compartments that make up the secretory pathway, and their interrelationships. While some cells are specialized for secretion, by no means do all proteins that enter the secretory pathway end up outside the cell. Some end up in lysosomes and, as we shall see shortly, some get no further than the interior of cellular membranes.

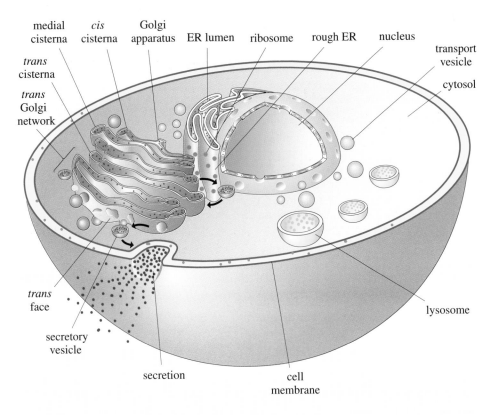

Figure 3.30 A 3-D cut-away view of the secretory pathway.

The ER and Golgi act sequentially to target many newly synthesized proteins to the correct destination within the cell, a process called **protein sorting** (or targeting). In prokaryotes, there are no ER or Golgi and only two alternative destinations: inside the cell or the exterior, by secretion. In eukaryotes, however, targeting is a much more complex process, due to the number and variety of internal compartments and, in some cells (such as epithelial cells and neurons), to the polarized nature of the cell membrane.

○ List the main intracellular compartments.

● Cytosol, nucleus, ER, Golgi, lysosomes, mitochondria, chloroplasts, peroxisomes, vacuole(s) (see Table 3.1).

A mammalian cell makes about 10^4 different proteins. To become functional, they must all end up in the right compartment. Cytosolic proteins (e.g, cytosolic enzymes, cytoskeletal proteins) do not need to be guided to a particular destination. However, those that are secreted, destined for the interior of organelles or incorporated into membranes all have to be directed from their site of synthesis to the right place in the cell. Box 3.3 outlines how intracellular protein targeting can be investigated *in vitro*.

BOX 3.3 INVESTIGATING PROTEIN TARGETING

The sorts of experiment that are carried out to establish the intracellular destination of a particular protein involve using a purified mRNA that encodes the protein of interest, in a cell-free system (a homogenate that contains all the enzymes needed for translation, and all the organelles) using radioactively labelled amino acids. The protein synthesized is then radioactively labelled and so becomes distinguishable from all the other proteins present. One method used to find out whether a subcellular fraction (e.g. mitochondria) contains the labelled protein is centrifugation (Figure 3.31a; centrifugation was described in Chapter 1, Box 1.1). If the protein is within a particular organelle, then the labelled protein co-fractionates with that organelle during centrifugation. Another method involves testing the accessibility of the protein to protease digestion. If addition of protease releases radiolabelled amino acids only after detergent treatment (which disrupts membranes so that externally applied enzymes can enter — see Section 3.2) then the protein must have been within the organelle being investigated (Figure 3.31b).

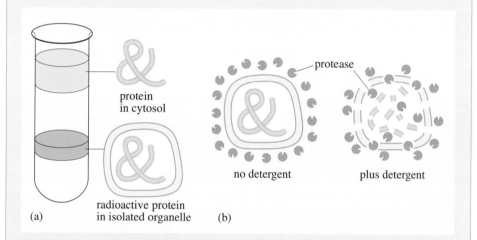

Figure 3.31 Two methods used to find out whether a particular protein is translocated into a particular organelle, both of which determine the fate of radioactively labelled protein. (a) Centrifugation to separate the organelle from the liquid fraction. (b) Addition of protease, with and without prior detergent treatment.

The ER–Golgi processing route is one of two basic types of protein targeting pathway, and begins as the protein is being synthesized, i.e. it is **co-translational**. Mitochondria, chloroplasts and peroxisomes are outside the secretory pathway, so targeting of proteins to these organelles requires a different route and mechanism. This process occurs after translation is complete, i.e. it is **post-translational**. Figure 3.32 shows the two types of targeting pathway.

In this section we describe co-translational protein targeting, and then in Section 3.11.2, go on to look at the whole process of membrane biogenesis, with which co-translational targeting via the secretory pathway is inextricably linked. We then look briefly at post-translational targeting (Section 3.11.3) before going back to complete the membrane trafficking picture depicted in Figure 3.29, with a discussion of the pathway taken by material ingested into cells by endocytosis (Chapter 1), the so-called endocytic pathway (Section 3.11.4).

Figure 3.32 The basic
intracellular targeting pathways.

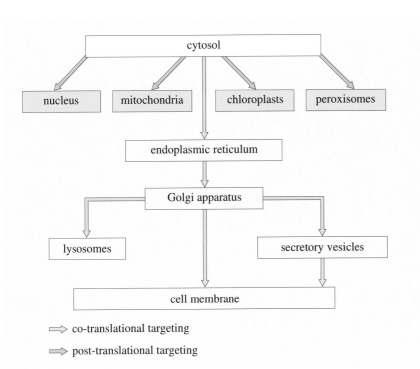

⇒ co-translational targeting

⇒ post-translational targeting

Figure 3.32 The basic intracellular targeting pathways.

Co-translational targeting is quite complex and is summarized in Figure 3.33. The mechanism was worked out from experiments done in the 1970s using vesicles derived from isolated rough ER membranes (*microsomes*). mRNA coding for a particular secreted protein was used in a cell-free protein-synthesizing system (i.e. all the components required for protein synthesis were present) with or without microsomes. In the absence of microsomes a slightly larger protein was made than when microsomes were present. The extra length is due to the presence of a short, N-terminal sequence, which is cleaved off at the ER membrane when synthesis is complete. Further studies established that the N-terminal sequence ('sorting signal' or **signal sequence**, attached to the ribosome, is recognized by a *signal recognition particle (SRP)* in the cytosol. Translation is then halted until the SRP recognizes and binds to a so-called docking protein on the cytosolic face of the ER and the signal sequence is inserted into the membrane. Translation is resumed and the growing polypeptide chain is pushed through the ER membrane. The signal sequence is removed by hydrolysis and the free polypeptide then folds up in the ER lumen, with the assistance of a chaperone protein (Chapter 2). Translocation of the protein through the ER membrane as it is being synthesized ensures that the protein doesn't fold up in the wrong compartment (the cytosol).

○ What kind of molecule would be synthesized in an artificial system containing microsomes and a synthetic mRNA encoding a cytosolic protein, but with a signal sequence attached?

● Synthesis of a protein with a signal sequence at its N-terminus would begin and the growing chain would enter the microsomal (ER) lumen and lose its (artificial) signal sequence.

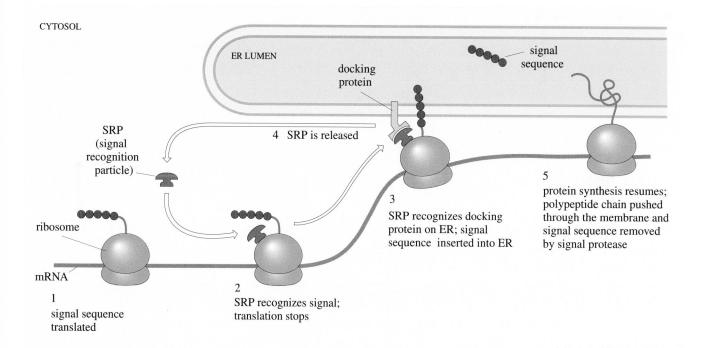

CYTOSOL

ER LUMEN

signal sequence

docking protein

SRP (signal recognition particle)

4   SRP is released

ribosome

3
SRP recognizes docking protein on ER; signal sequence inserted into ER

5
protein synthesis resumes; polypeptide chain pushed through the membrane and signal sequence removed by signal protease

mRNA

1
signal sequence translated

2
SRP recognizes signal; translation stops

Figure 3.33 Stages (1–5) in the process of co-translational insertion of proteins through ER membranes.

In other words, if this system were a living cell the protein normally found in the cytosol would end up inside the ER, the wrong compartment.

The destination of the newly synthesized protein in the ER lumen can be either the interior of an organelle derived from the ER (e.g. Golgi, lysosomes) or the exterior of the cell, if the protein is secreted. The intracellular membranes are *not* continuous from ER to Golgi, to cell membrane. The structural discontinuity is bridged by **transport vesicles** — small membrane-bound sacs that bud off from one membrane, move through the cytosol and fuse with another.

The secretory pathway is much more than just a protein delivery system. Entry into the co-translational targeting pathway is just the first of many steps in the channelling of proteins to the correct destination. Specific, post-translational modification of the newly synthesized proteins takes place in both the ER and the Golgi. In fact the pathway is more appropriately called the **biosynthetic–secretory pathway**.

○   What type of post-translational process modifies proteins in the Golgi?

●   Glycosylation, the covalent addition of sugar chains to reactive side chains on certain amino acids (Chapter 1).

The Golgi apparatus is not a homogeneous stack of membrane-bound sacs but is structurally and functionally compartmentalized, with four main regions (known as the *cis* cisternae, medial cisternae, *trans* cisternae and *trans* Golgi network; Figure 3.30), in each of which particular protein-processing enzymes are concentrated. The functional differences between the Golgi regions were discovered using two methods: (a) fractionation of the Golgi apparatus and assay of the separate fractions for a particular enzyme activity; and (b) use of immunocytochemistry to locate specific enzymes in EM preparations. For example, galactosyltransferase, the original marker enzyme for the Golgi, which adds galactose units to proteins, has been localized to the *trans* cisternae.

The Golgi 'sorts out' the mix of proteins and 'sends' them out in transport vesicles which deliver their contents to the correct destination, e.g. the cell membrane or lysosomes, or back to the ER in the case of the protein-modifying enzymes that 'belong' there (ER-resident enzymes). The return vesicle transport between individual Golgi cisternae and the *cis* face of the Golgi and the ER is not shown in Figure 3.30. What determines where proteins from the ER lumen end up? For enzymes destined for the lysosomes, the 'address label' is the carbohydrate part of the molecule (see below). In most cases, though, a specific amino acid sequence is recognized. For example, ER-resident proteins that end up in the *cis* cisternae have a sorting sequence that is four amino acids long and binds to a receptor in the lumenal face of the Golgi membrane. Any proteins that have this 'retention signal' are thus captured and then repackaged into vesicles that return to the ER.

The vesicle budding and fusion model described above for the movement of proteins through the stationary Golgi system was accepted until the latter part of the 20th century, but there is currently some controversy about it. Evidence has accumulated in support of an alternative, cisternal progression or maturation model (a hypothesis that was proposed in the 1950s and subsequently rejected), which visualizes the Golgi as a 'bottling station': cisternae are formed on the *cis* (entry) face and move sequentially towards the *trans* (exit) face. The currently favoured model is a hybrid, according to which outward transport of proteins being processed occurs by cisternal progression and the Golgi processing enzymes are returned to the cisternae via vesicular transport.

Proteins destined for secretion are packaged into vesicles that bud off the Golgi and then migrate to and fuse with the cell membrane, to release their contents to the exterior, by exocytosis (Chapter 1). Secreted proteins are numerous and diverse: they include fibrils of collagen for the extracellular matrix of vertebrate tissues, algal scales, some animal hormones (such as insulin), cytokines and digestive enzymes in animals, fungi and carnivorous plants. The exocytosis of some proteins is continuous ('constitutive'), for example proteins secreted into the bloodstream by liver cells. Alternatively, exocytosis may be regulated, occurring only in response to a specific stimulus. In such cases, continuous release would be wasteful, as for secretion of digestive enzymes into the gut, or even disastrous; for example, the release of signalling molecules, such as hormones and neurotransmitters, is tightly controlled.

TARGETING OF INTEGRAL MEMBRANE PROTEINS

Integral membrane proteins of eukaryotic cells are synthesized in much the same way as those entering the ER lumen, but the translocation process is more complex. Some sections of the polypeptide chain, instead of passing through the membrane, become anchored within it. We won't go into the details of how this association is achieved, but just note that as for the soluble ER proteins, it is the amino acid sequence that determines whether and how a protein is inserted. The sequential effects of appropriate 'start transfer' and 'stop transfer' sequences ensure that integral proteins are correctly inserted into the ER membrane.

Because integral membrane proteins always enter the membrane from the cytosolic side, then all molecules of the same protein, e.g. a particular receptor or transporter, face the same (correct) way in the membrane. This polarity is fixed, which means that all membranes derived from the ER by the budding and fusion events of the biosynthetic–secretory pathway have their integral proteins in the right orientation to carry out their function. If proteins are dissociated from a membrane, isolated and then mixed with phospholipids, vesicles are formed in which some of the proteins face inwards and others face outwards. This result demonstrates the crucial role of the insertion process in ensuring that membrane proteins have the right orientation.

In Section 3.3.2, we distinguished between integral and peripheral membrane proteins, and noted that some of the latter are covalently linked to the membrane via a glycolipid. The translocation of such proteins is similar to that of the soluble proteins in the ER lumen: the entire chain (except for a short hydrophobic anchor sequence) crosses the membrane (Figure 3.34a), the anchor sequence is cleaved off, but then, instead of the protein being released into the lumen, it is then covalently attached to a lipid called glycosylphosphatidylinositol (GPI for short) whose fatty acids hold it onto the membrane surface (as shown in Figure 3.34b).

○ From what you learnt in Section 3.3.1, what sort of lipid is GPI?

● The 'glycosyl' tells us it is a glycolipid, i.e. has a sugar chain as part of its structure, the 'phosphatidyl' means it is also a glycerophospholipid. (The presence of inositol suggests it might be a precursor of a signalling molecule.)

Figure 3.34 Origin of glycosylphosphatidylinositol (GPI)-anchored peripheral cell membrane proteins. (a) Newly synthesized protein in ER lumen, anchored in membrane by a short, C-terminal sequence of hydrophobic amino acids called the anchor sequence. (b) Cleavage from the anchor sequence and simultaneous attachment to GPI. Its two fatty acid tails are embedded among the phospholipids and hold the whole molecule onto the membrane.

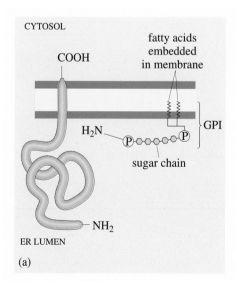

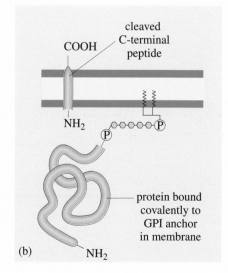

3.11.2 MEMBRANE BIOGENESIS

The synthesis of membrane proteins is part of **membrane biogenesis**, the production of new membrane material. The synthesis of new membrane *lipid* also takes place at the ER. Thus all the cell's new membrane originates from the ER via the secretory pathway.

The process of making membrane lipids begins with phospholipid synthesis in the leaflet facing the cytosol.

○ How can this process lead to growth of the lipid *bi*layer?

● Phospholipid molecules must be transferred from the cytosolic to the lumenal side of the membrane.

The transfer of phospholipid molecules from one layer to the other does not occur spontaneously (Section 3.2). However, in ER membranes there is rapid transmembrane 'flipping' of phospholipid molecules, catalysed by a specific translocator protein, resulting in two equal leaflets (Figure 3.35).

As well as phospholipids, the ER also makes the precursors of other amphipathic membrane lipids. Further modifications, such as glycosylation (to glycolipids), are carried out by enzymes in the Golgi lumen.

○ From what you know about the process of membrane biogenesis, can you explain why sugar chains only appear on the extracellular face of the cell membrane?

● Growth of the cell membrane occurs by the fusion of vesicles which budded off from the Golgi, so the lumenal surface of the vesicle becomes the extracellular face of the cell membrane derived from it. Since sugar chains are added inside the Golgi, they appear on the extracellular face of the cell membrane.

The cell membrane, Golgi apparatus and intracellular vesicles all form part of the same membrane system derived from the ER. But much less is known about how the organelles that are not part of this system — chloroplasts, mitochondria and peroxisomes — get their membrane material required for growth and proliferation. Post-translational trafficking of proteins made in the cytosol provides many of the membrane proteins and the soluble proteins of these organelles (to be described below). However, little is known about the delivery of membrane lipids to them. Lipids are insoluble in water, so their transfer through the aqueous interior of the cell requires the agency of a (water-soluble) carrier protein. *In vitro* experiments have shown that there are phospholipid carrier proteins in the cell which randomly transfer phospholipid molecules from one membrane to another, so this process would result in net transfer of lipids from a lipid-rich to a relatively lipid-poor membrane. However, it is likely that there are other, more specific, mechanisms for delivering lipids to organelles that are outside the secretory pathway.

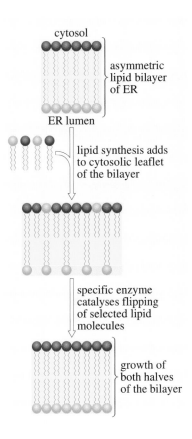

cytosol

asymmetric lipid bilayer of ER

ER lumen

lipid synthesis adds to cytosolic leaflet of the bilayer

specific enzyme catalyses flipping of selected lipid molecules

growth of both halves of the bilayer

Figure 3.35 Membrane lipid synthesis in the cytosol-facing leaflet of the ER, and the subsequent equilibration between the two layers by translocator-catalysed flipping of phospholipid molecules into the leaflet facing the ER lumen.

3.11.3 POST-TRANSLATIONAL PROTEIN TARGETING

The other basic form of protein targeting pathway is very different in that it does *not* involve translocation through the ER membrane followed by transfer via the biosynthetic–secretory pathway. Instead, protein molecules are synthesized on *free* ribosomes and released into the cytosol, from where they are targeted to their specified destination. For example, although mitochondria and chloroplasts both contain their own DNA, ribosomes and other protein-synthetic machinery, the majority of their proteins are synthesized in the cytosol, so post-translational targeting is crucial to the growth and functioning of these organelles.

Mitochondria and chloroplasts have external and internal membranes, so to reach the right compartment, their proteins must cross one or more membranes. For example, some electron transport proteins (Section 3.8.4) have to cross the outer membrane before they can take up residence within the internal membranes of the organelle, while the soluble matrix enzymes have to cross both outer and inner membranes.

To traverse a membrane, a newly synthesized protein must be prevented from folding up. Chaperones (Chapter 2) attach themselves to the protein, keeping it in an extended form while it is in the cytosol. As in the co-translational route, post-translational protein targeting to the right location in a particular organelle involves recognition of specific leader (signal) sequences in the protein chain which are removed by proteolysis when the protein has reached its intended destination.

NUCLEAR TARGETING

The mechanism by which macromolecules are transported across the nuclear envelope is very different from the transport mechanisms involved in the transfer of proteins across the membranes of other organelles. Not only do proteins enter the nucleus, but RNAs and ribosomes are transported out of the nucleus, i.e. molecular traffic is two-way and does not consist exclusively of proteins.

○ By what route does macromolecular traffic enter and leave the nucleus?

● Transport into and out of the nucleus is via nuclear pores (Chapter 1).

There are between 3000 and 4000 nuclear pores in the nuclear envelope of a typical mammalian cell. They are not just passive holes. Each one is formed by an elaborate structure made up of over 100 different proteins, called the **nuclear pore complex**. The pore diameter is relatively large in comparison to the protein molecules that pass through it. But protein influx is selective. Selectivity is via recognition of a signal sequence on the protein, a short chain of positively charged amino acids (*nuclear localization signal*), by a receptor on the pore. The transport process also involves the binding of cytosolic proteins and requires energy (provided by ATP hydrolysis). It is thought that proteins are transported through nuclear pores in their fully folded conformation.

○ How does transport through nuclear pores differ from protein transport into other organelles?

● In other organelles (e.g. mitochondria, chloroplasts and peroxisomes) the protein molecules have to be in an unfolded state to enable them to be 'threaded' across the lipid bilayer.

PROTEIN TARGETING IN PROKARYOTES

Prokaryotes secrete certain proteins — in fact their ability to do so is exploited in genetic engineering for the production of 'foreign' protein. Because these organisms don't have intracellular membranes, the route from the site of synthesis to the cell exterior is much simpler than in eukaryotes. As in eukaryote protein targeting, prokaryote proteins intended for export have the required 'address label', i.e. a signal sequence, to direct them to the right destination, in this case the cell membrane. The passage of prokaryote proteins across the cell membrane occurs *after* translation is complete, i.e. targeting is post-translational, and chaperones prevent the protein from folding before it has passed through the membrane. See Figure 3.36.

○ What protein delivery process in eukaryote cells does prokaryote protein secretion most resemble?

● Protein delivery to chloroplasts and mitochondria.

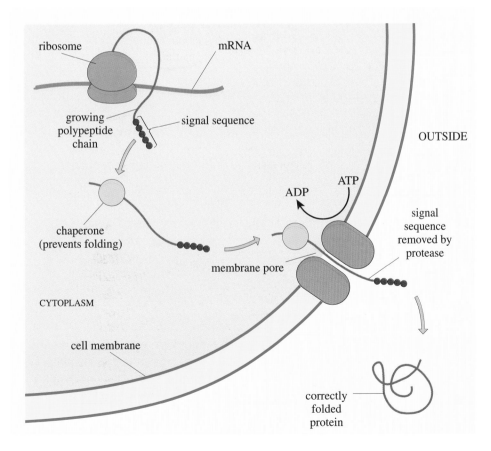

Figure 3.36 Prokaryotic protein targeting (secretion). The chaperone protein binds to the growing polypeptide chain and prevents premature folding, which would make transport across the cell membrane impossible. The unfolded polypeptide is threaded through a (narrow) pore in the membrane, a process that is energy (ATP)-requiring. Once the protein has passed through the pore, the signal sequence is cleaved off by an extracellular protease.

3.11.4 ENDOCYTOSIS: TRAFFICKING FROM CELL MEMBRANE TO CELL INTERIOR

After that brief digression into trafficking of proteins that don't take the eukaryo ER to Golgi route, we now return to complete our study of intracellular membrane trafficking, via the biosynthetic–secretory and endocytic pathways. S far, we have discussed the translocation and processing of proteins for secretion and the associated process of membrane biogenesis, activities that involve net vesicular trafficking from the ER via the Golgi to the cell membrane. Obviously there must be a return of cell membrane material, otherwise the cell's surface would go on increasing! In fact, endocytosis of the cell membrane occurs all the time (i.e. it is constitutive), and is part of the general process of recycling membrane material back into the cell (Figure 3.37), thereby keeping the structu in good working order, and enabling frequent adjustments to the array of receptors, carrier and channel proteins that it supports. It also means that new fatty acids from the diet can be incorporated into membrane lipids.

Figure 3.37 The biosynthetic–secretory and endocytic pathways in a eukaryotic cell. The compartments illustrated correspond to the boxes shown on the flow diagram earlier (Figure 3.29).

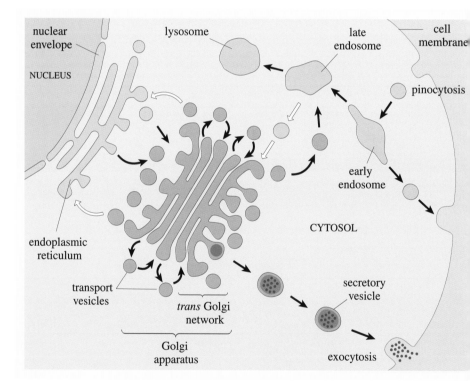

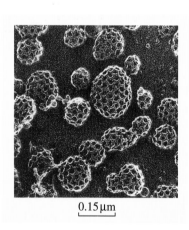

0.15 µm

Figure 3.38 Electron micrograph showing clathrin-coated pits and vesicles beneath the cell membrane of cultured human fibroblasts (connective tissue cells). To prepare the specimen for microscopy, the cells were quickly frozen, fractured and etched to expose the cytoplasmic face of the membrane (see Box 3.1).

This sort of endocytosis is referred to as **pinocytosis** ('cell drinking'), as extracellular fluid is taken into the cell as the vesicles are pinched off from the cell membrane — in cultured fibroblasts, at a rate estimated at 2500 vesicles per minute. The vesicles are derived from invaginations, or 'pits', in the cell membrane which are surrounded by a cage of small protein molecules called **clathrin** (Figure 3.38). The clathrin cage appears to stabilize the formation of th pits. As soon as a clathrin-coated vesicle has been pinched off it loses its coat (Figure 3.39) and can then fuse with other intracellular vesicles called *early endosomes*. The possible fates of early endosomes are shown in Figure 3.37. As you can see, some generate vesicles which return material directly to the cell

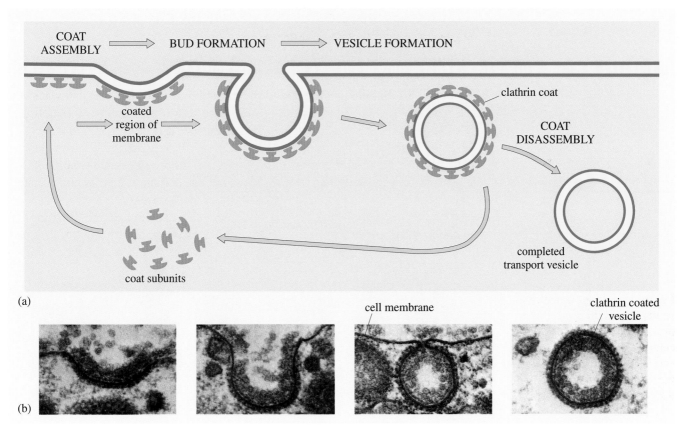

COAT ASSEMBLY ⟹ BUD FORMATION ⟹ VESICLE FORMATION

coated region of membrane

clathrin coat

COAT DISASSEMBLY

completed transport vesicle

coat subunits

(a)

cell membrane

clathrin coated vesicle

(b)

Figure 3.39 (a) Sequence of events in the formation of a clathrin-coated vesicle followed by loss of the clathrin coat. (b) Electron micrographs showing clathrin-coated vesicle formation.

membrane by exocytosis, while others develop into late endosomes, from which material is directed either to lysosomes (where it is digested) or recycled back to the Golgi.

Certain eukaryotic cells are specialized to engulf and subsequently digest particulate matter by phagocytosis.

○ State two major functions of phagocytosis.

● Nutrition: phagotrophic protoctists and some animal cells engulf particles of food (and expel the indigestible remains). Defence: nearly all animals have phagocytic cells that engulf invading microbes.

Phagocytes in vertebrates also have a scavenging role, ingesting huge numbers of dead cells and cell debris. For example, in an adult human more than 10^{11} worn-out red blood cells are phagocytosed in the liver every day.

Phagocytosis is similar to pinocytosis in that it involves invagination of an area of the cell membrane and the formation of a vesicle. However, the vesicles formed are much larger. The size (and shape) depend on the dimensions of the particle being ingested (see Figure 3.40). Another difference is that for material to be phagocytosed by cells known as macrophages it must first bind to specialized receptors on the cell surface. Phagocytosis is triggered following this binding process. After phagocytosis, the particle is subjected to intracellular digestion within lysosomes and the digestion products are released into the cytosol.

Lysosomes have an important role in all eukaryotic cells, not just those that ingest extracellular materials.

○ Can you recall, from Chapter 1, what lysosomes do?

● They dispose of worn-out organelles.

For example, the mitochondria in liver cells have an average lifetime of about 10 days. Lysosomes containing, and presumably digesting, mitochondria (as well as other organelles) can be seen in EM images of liver cells. This process of recycling obsolete parts of the cell is called **autophagy** ('self-eating').

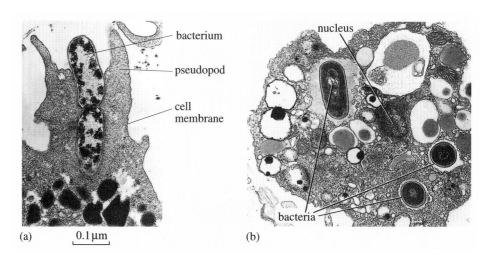

(a) 0.1 μm   (b)

Figure 3.40 (a) Electron micrograph of a phagocyte extending pseudopods to form a vesicle that engulfs a bacterium (which is in the process of dividing). (b) Electron micrograph of a phagocyte from a tunicate, the sea squirt *Ciona intestinalis*, containing three bacteria inside lysosomes.

RECEPTOR-MEDIATED ENDOCYTOSIS

You have seen in earlier sections that some quite large molecules (such as polypeptide chains) move across membranes. However, very large molecules are not able to squeeze through. As we have seen, one solution to this transport problem is to use membrane pores (e.g. plasmodesmata (Figure 3.16b) or nuclear pores), but another is endocytosis. In fact, particular macromolecules and macromolecular complexes are taken up selectively by **receptor-mediated endocytosis** (RME). As the name implies, this process involves specific receptor proteins at the cell surface that recognize and bind the macromolecular ligand (Chapter 2). The occupied receptors are able to float about freely in the plane of the cell membrane, but subsequently they become clustered together in clathrin-coated pits. The next phase of the transport process is pinching off the coated pit from the membrane into the cytosol, i.e. endocytosis. Thus, RME gets around the problem of passing the molecules to be transported through the membrane bilayer by transporting the ligand *and* the receptor together with part of their surrounding membrane into the interior of the cell. Concentration of the ligand in the coated pits means that a specific molecule can be taken into the cell in large amounts without also taking in a large volume of fluid.

An example of RME is the uptake of low-density lipoproteins (LDL) by animal cells. LDL are large macromolecular complexes of protein, phospholipid and cholesterol molecules (Figure 3.41). The endocytosed LDL particles are delivered to lysosomes where enzymatic hydrolysis releases the cholesterol for use by the cell (Figure 3.42).

○   What do all animal cells use cholesterol for?

●   They incorporate it into membranes (see Table 3.3).

The LDL receptor proteins are recycled back to the cell membrane via endosomes. The structure of LDL is reminiscent of the enveloped viruses, such as HIV, which enter animal cells in the same way, but instead of meeting their end in lysosomes, they go on to proliferate.

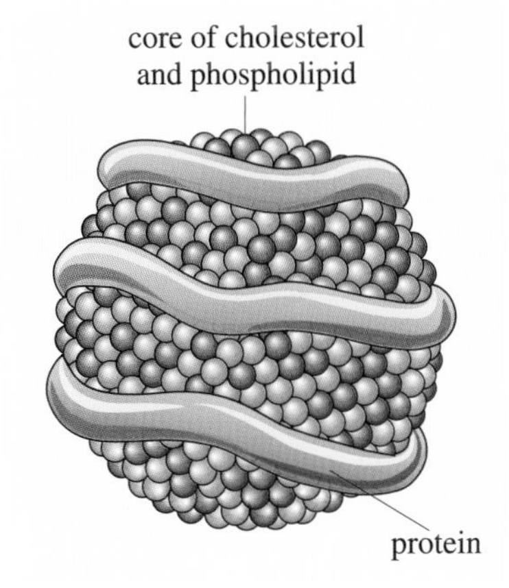

Figure 3.41 Structure of a low-density lipoprotein (LDL) particle, typically 180–250 nm in diameter.

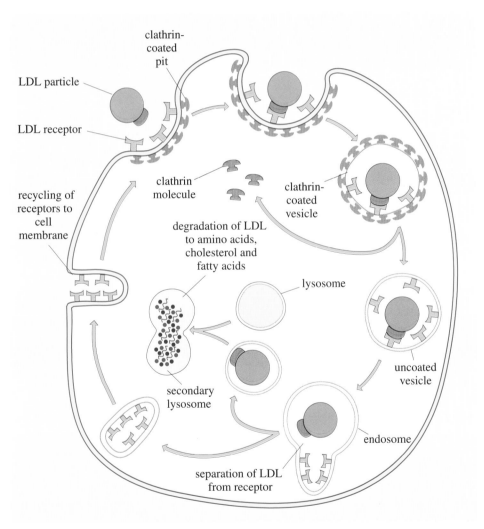

Figure 3.42 Receptor-mediated endocytosis of LDL. After a sequence of several steps the LDL particle ends up in a lysosome, where hydrolases release the cholesterol, which then diffuses out into the cytosol. The now-free LDL receptors are delivered back to the cell surface via endosomes which fuse with the cell membrane.

In some types of cells (e.g. mammalian epithelial cells and smooth muscle cells), there is an alternative mechanism of receptor-mediated endocytosis that does not involve clathrin. Ligands are thought to bind to receptors located in flask-shaped invaginations of the cell membrane, 70–100 nm in diameter, called **caveolae** (Figure 3.43), which undergo endocytosis to form endocytic vesicles. Caveolae and the endocytic vesicles derived from them contain a structural protein called **caveolin**, which may have a similar role to that of clathrin in stabilizing the vesicle. However, caveolin is a transmembrane protein, unlike clathrin, which is a peripheral protein. Numerous cell signalling proteins have been localized to caveolae (using immunohistochemical techniques). Also, isolated caveolin-rich membrane fractions are found to be associated with several signalling proteins. Such evidence strongly implicates caveolae in cell signalling.

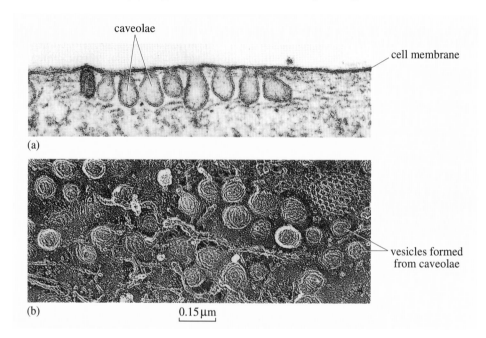

Figure 3.43 Caveolae at the cell membrane of cultured human fibroblasts. (a) Electron micrograph showing caveolae in cross-section. (b) Electron micrograph of the cytoplasmic face of the membrane (prepared by freeze-etching), showing the external appearance of the caveolae.

3.11.5 VESICLE FORMATION AND TARGET RECOGNITION

The vesicles involved in transport at different steps along both the secretory and endocytic pathways have protein coats, of which there are several types, COPI and COPII (COP = coat protein), as well as clathrin, which was mentioned above. COPI- and COPII-coated vesicles are involved in transport between ER and Golgi, while clathrin-coated vesicles are involved in both transport of lysosomal enzymes between Golgi and endosomes and in endocytosis.

Vesicles need to be selective as to the target membrane with which they fuse. Therefore, they must have specific surface markers that carry the information about both their origin and their contents, and which are recognized by receptors on the right target membrane. This currently favoured model is the so-called SNARE hypothesis[1] summarized in Figure 3.44. Recognition by specific integral vesicle (v) and target (t) membrane proteins, v-SNAREs and t-SNAREs, is thought to apply to most of the vesicular transport steps along both the secretory and endocytic pathways.

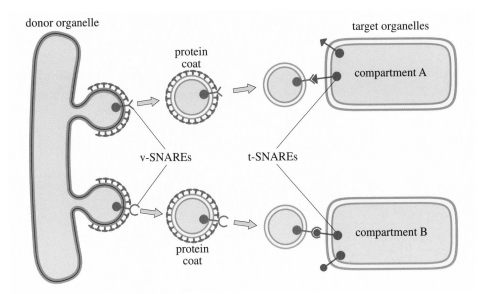

Figure 3.44 The proposed role of SNAREs in vesicle targeting. Complementary pairs of v-SNAREs and t-SNAREs ensure binding (docking) to the appropriate membrane. SNAREs are best characterized in neurons, in which they are believed to mediate the docking of synaptic vesicles to the cell membrane, prior to exocytosis of the vesicle contents (Figure 3.30).

SUMMARY OF SECTION 3.11

1   Membranes are dynamic structures: lipid and protein material is cycled in both directions between the outer (cell) membrane and internal membranes by vesicle budding and fusion.

2   Targeting of proteins to the correct compartment is either co-translational (synthesis and processing occurring via the ER and Golgi) or post-translational (synthesis occurring on free ribosomes in the cytosol and delivery to membrane-bound organelles).

3   Both types of targeting involve recognition of one or more specific signal sequences (usually a short chain of amino acids), which are later removed.

4   Proteins entering the biosynthetic–secretory pathway have several alternative destinations: the exterior (via secretion), lysosomes or the membrane itself (integral proteins).

5   The synthesis of membrane lipids as well as proteins (membrane biogenesis) occurs via the biosynthetic–secretory pathway.

6   Proteins cross or enter mitochondrial and chloroplast membranes as linear polypeptide chains and are folded into their tertiary structure once in place; proteins that enter the nucleus, via nuclear pores, are already folded.

[1] The term 'SNARE' is an acronym — *Soluble N*-ethylmaleimide-sensitive factor *A*ttached *RE*ceptor — which summarizes the properties by which receptors of this type are characterized.

7 Secretion of proteins in eukaryotes is post-translational and folding occurs after passage through the membrane.

8 There are several types of endocytosis (invagination of cell membrane to form vesicles).

8 Pinocytosis constantly recycles cell membrane as small clathrin-coated vesicles.

9 Phagocytosis is used to engulf food particles (nutrition) and pathogens (defence).

10 Receptor-mediated endocytosis (RME) occurs following ligand–receptor binding. In RME that takes up specific large molecules, the membrane invaginations and vesicles derived from them are clathrin-coated; another type of RME uses caveolae (caveolin-containing pits and vesicles), which are thought to be involved in signal transduction.

11 Various types of protein coat surround vesicles at different steps of the secretory and endocytic pathways. Vesicle targeting involves specific surface proteins that (a) identify the vesicle's origin and contents and (b) are recognized by receptors on the target membrane.

3.12   MEMBRANE FLUIDITY REVISITED

Singer and Nicholson's fluid mosaic model of membrane structure is now believed to be too simple, for membrane proteins do not always float freely in the lipid matrix. You learnt in Section 3.5 that membrane proteins anchored to the cytoskeleton have restricted lateral movement. As we have seen, within epithelial cell membranes there is polarization into apical and basolateral domains, which differ in lipid and protein composition. Evidence is now accumulating of a much finer degree of **lateral organization** within cell membranes in general, not just those of cells that have tight junctions.

Detergent treatment of membranes has identified a resistant fraction rich in glycosphingolipids containing saturated fatty acids, cholesterol and various GPI-anchored proteins.

○ Why are regions of the membrane with the composition described above relatively resistant to detergent treatment?

● These regions resist fragmentation by detergents because both saturated fatty acid tails and cholesterol contribute to strong hydrophobic interactions within the lipid bilayer.

There is much controversy about what this detergent-resistant membrane (DRM) fraction actually corresponds to *in vivo*. An attractive idea is that it represents semi-rigid microdomains, or 'rafts', which float within the largely fluid matrix of the membrane. In addition to particularly strong hydrophobic interactions, adjacent glycosphingolipids could hydrogen bond via their glycosyl OH groups, thus contributing to the lateral stability of putative rafts. DRMs include caveolae, but can be isolated from cells that don't have caveolae.

A number of fluorescence studies of living cells support the **raft hypothesis**. Particular membrane proteins and lipids are labelled with fluorophores (molecules that fluoresce) and the fluorescence emission is measured. From the results obtained, the proximity of membrane components is deduced. Regions of close proximity are taken to imply concentration in rafts. In another method, the lateral mobility (i.e. in the plane of the membrane) of individual membrane molecules is followed by attaching a fluorophore to the component of interest. The results obtained are consistent with the raft concept.

A further type of investigation that has provided evidence for clustering of particular membrane proteins uses chemicals that cross-link molecules when they are sufficiently close together. These studies have also shown that clustering is inhibited by cholesterol removal. A variety of membrane proteins, such as transporters, receptors and signalling molecules have been found in detergent-resistant membrane fractions, which has led to the suggestion that rafts, of which caveolae appear to be a subset, might be 'hot spots' for signalling. Concentration of membrane receptors in rafts might increase their sensitivity to chemical signals and might result in the selection or channelling of signalling pathways so that particular signalling sequences can be activated. However, the existence of rafts is not accepted by all. A few fluorescence microscopy studies have found no evidence to support the raft hypothesis; however, it is possible that these negative results are due to disruption of the rafts by the fixation or labelling procedures. In summary, there is now strong evidence for the existence of rafts but we have still a lot to learn about their size, composition and functions.

SUMMARY OF SECTION 3.12

1   According to the raft hypothesis the cell membrane possesses semi-rigid microdomains.

2   Membrane rafts, of which caveolae appear to be a subset, may modulate signal transduction by concentrating particular membrane proteins.

CONCLUSION

Detailed studies of membranes have revealed their complex structure and varied topography. They are fundamental to cellular dynamics, being key players in the regulation of the cell's internal environment, energy transduction, and the processing and transfer of materials. This last role involves continuous recycling of membrane material. Relationships between the apparent structural differentiation in the cell membrane at the molecular level and membrane functions such as signal transduction are now beginning to be unravelled. This topic is an area of very intense research interest and we can look forward to some exciting revelations in the future.

FURTHER READING

Alberts, B., Bray, D., Lewis, J., Raff, M., Roberts, K. and Watson, J. D. (1994) *Molecular Biology of the Cell* (3rd edn), Garland Publishing Inc. [A detailed, comprehensive text, with several chapters dealing with different aspects of membrane structure and function.]

Elliott, W. H. and Elliott, D. C. (1997) *Biochemistry and Molecular Biology*, Oxford University Press. [The chapter on membranes is a good introduction to the subject.]

Heymann, J. B. and Engel, A. (1999) Aquaporins: phylogeny, structure and physiology of water channels, *News in Physiological Sciences*, **14**, pp. 187–193. [A review of evolutionary relationships of the aquaporins, their molecular structure and mode of action.]

Jacobson, K. and Dietrich, C. (1999) Looking at lipid rafts?, *Trends in Cell Biology*, **9**, pp. 87–91. [A balanced appraisal of the raft hypothesis.]

Simons, K. and Toomre, D. (2000) Lipid rafts and signal transduction, *Nature Reviews: Molecular Cell Biology*, **1**, pp. 31–39. [A comprehensive review of the evidence of the role of rafts in signal transduction, complete with glossary.]

Trends in Cell Biology (1998), **8**. [Entire issue devoted to the Golgi: history and review of current research.]

METABOLISM

4.1 INTRODUCTION

4.1.1 METABOLIC PATHWAYS

Within every living cell, a continual series of chemical reactions takes place, either breaking down complex fuel molecules to provide energy, or else building up complex molecules with specialized functions, e.g. proteins, nucleic acids, steroid hormones, complex carbohydrates, glycoproteins and many other molecules. Each particular **metabolic pathway** or sequence of reactions is thus either part of *anabolism*, the biosynthesis of complex molecules from small building blocks, or part of *catabolism*, the breakdown of complex molecules to provide energy and building blocks.

Many of these reactions are carried out simultaneously, forming a huge network of interconnecting chemical reactions. Figure 4.1 shows a small corner of this network and immediately begs the question, what controls this seemingly chaotic set of reactions? What channels a particular chemical down a particular pathway

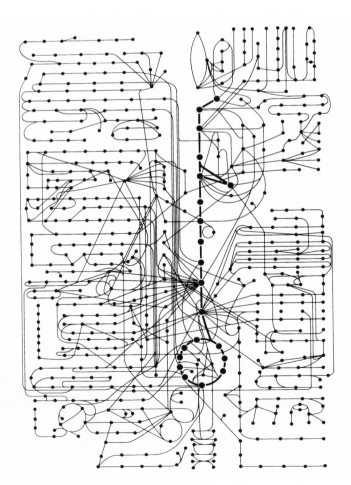

Figure 4.1 Network of metabolic pathways.

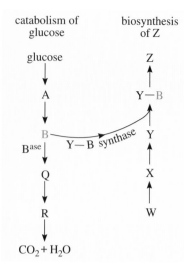

Figure 4.2 Two metabolic pathways: a catabolic pathway involving the breakdown of glucose to carbon dioxide and water, and a biosynthetic pathway that produces substance Z. Note how an intermediate from one pathway can be used in another.

into a specific end-product? The answer is that all metabolic reactions are catalysed by enzymes, most of which are highly specific, reacting with selected molecules from a sea of others, and catalysing their conversion into the next compound (intermediate) in a pathway, e.g. forming B in the oxidation (breakdown) of glucose (Figure 4.2). The new intermediate B may then bind to the active site of either enzyme 'B^ase' and be further broken down, or to enzyme 'YB synthase' and be converted into YB. Either way, the route taken depends on the enzymes available.

4.1.2 CELL HOMOGENATES

Most of the enzymes of metabolism do not need an intact cell to continue working; they can be extracted from living cells and studied in isolation (*in vitro*) after various degrees of purification, e.g. as crude cell extracts or as single purified proteins. A major breakthrough in the history of biochemistry came in 1897, when Edward Buchner showed how the whole set of enzymes catalysing the early stages in glucose oxidation could be extracted as a unit from yeast cells. This crude preparation could break down glucose in the same way as intact yeast cells — but only if supplied with inorganic phosphate, which was used up as the glucose broke down. Not long after, experimenters found first a phosphorylated sugar that accumulated in the yeast extract, and then an enzyme that acted upon it, converting it into another sugar derivative. With this kind of approach, the enzymes and intermediates of glycolysis were painstakingly identified, and maps of the glycolytic pathway as we know it began to take shape.

In this chapter we look at one catabolic pathway in detail, the oxidation of glucose to CO_2 and H_2O, which releases energy. We describe how fats and amino acids can act as alternative fuels by feeding into specific points partway down the glucose oxidation pathway. We also describe briefly how fatty acids are synthesized from acetyl CoA, and how amino acids can be interconverted.

We then turn to biosynthesis, describing how glucose and polysaccharides can be synthesized by reverse-glycolysis. We discuss how biosynthesis can drain central pathways of key intermediates, and how these intermediates can be topped up from alternative sources, e.g. the glyoxylate cycle. We show how intermediates from the oxidation pathways can also be channelled into biosynthesis.

Finally, we discuss the basic control mechanisms that determine the rate at which molecules flow through a pathway.

However, we begin with three features that characterize chemical reactions that take place in biological systems, namely the role of *enzymes* and *coenzymes*, and the specialized mechanisms for *energy transfer* between biomolecules.

4.2 BASIC PRINCIPLES OF METABOLISM

4.2.1 NAMING OF ENZYMES

The key properties of enzymes have already been described (Chapter 2), but you will also find it useful to know how their names reflect the type of reaction they catalyse. All enzyme names end in -ase, except those discovered a long time ago, e.g. the digestive enzymes pepsin (in stomach) and trypsin (in intestine). In metabolism, you often come across the synthase enzymes, which catalyse the synthesis of larger molecules by joining together two small molecules. A molecule of water is released as in Equation 4.1:

$$A-OH + B-H \longrightarrow A-B + H_2O \qquad (4.1)$$

The opposite reaction, **hydrolysis**, is catalysed by a *hydrolase* enzyme, which cleaves a bond in the middle of a molecule, adding H or OH to the exposed bonds on either side, as in Equation 4.2:

$$A-B + H_2O \longrightarrow A-H + B-OH \qquad (4.2)$$

Kinase enzymes use ATP to add phosphate groups to carbon intermediates, in a reaction known as **phosphorylation**. In contrast, *phosphatase* enzymes catalyse the reverse reaction and remove phosphate. An *ATPase* hydrolyses ATP (giving ADP and an **inorganic phosphate** ion, usually abbreviated to P_i).

Slightly less clearcut are the *oxidases*, which catalyse oxidation reactions, i.e. the addition of O atoms or removal of H atoms, or sometimes just the removal of electrons. Oxidases that catalyse the transfer of electrons to coenzymes are known as *dehydrogenases*. Many of these enzymes catalyse reactions that are reversible under physiological conditions, and are therefore involved also in reduction reactions, where H atoms or electrons are added to a carbon intermediate, or O atoms are removed.

4.2.2 COENZYMES

Coenzymes or group transfer molecules take part in many enzyme-catalysed reactions, bringing in or removing small groups of atoms, e.g. NH_2, 2H or phosphate groups. The 2H group removed during oxidation of lactate for example (Figure 4.3) is temporarily attached to **coenzyme NAD**, which binds close to it in the active site. The resulting NAD.2H diffuses away, carrying the 2H 'passenger'

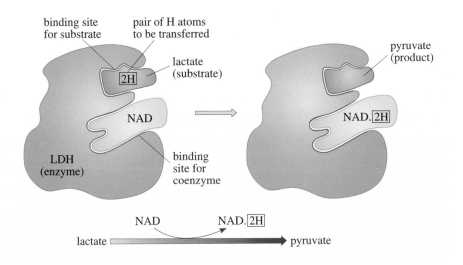

Figure 4.3 Diagram illustrating the role of coenzyme NAD in the enzyme-catalysed oxidation of lactate by lactate dehydrogenase (LDH).

group to another enzyme whose active site also binds tightly and specifically to NAD (or NAD.2H). This recognition of particular coenzymes by enzymes catalysing related reactions is vital to their role in transferring groups, and is made easier by the sheer bulkiness of most coenzyme molecules (see Figure 4.4). Most are much bigger than the small carbon intermediates of metabolism, and so bind only to large, specifically 'landscaped' crevices in the enzyme active site. Indeed most of the coenzyme structure is adapted for recognition by particular enzymes. Note how the same nucleoside substructure [adenine-sugar-] is found in all but one of the common coenzymes shown in Table 4.1 and Figure 4.4.

Table 4.1   Coenzymes commonly used in metabolism.

Coenzyme	Full name	Group transferred
NAD	nicotinamide adenine dinucleotide	2H
NADP	nicotinamide adenine dinucleotide phosphate	2H
FAD	flavin adenine dinucleotide	2H
CoA	coenzyme A	CH_3CO (acetyl)
pyridoxal phosphate		NH_2
ADP*	adenosine diphosphate	$H_2PO_3^-$ (phosphate, P_i)
UDP*	uridine diphosphate	six-carbon sugars

*ADP and UDP are included here as they do fulfil a coenzyme role, but they are also more commonly classified as nucleotides (as are ATP and UTP).

Note also the small but all important *attachment site* in each coenzyme, e.g. at the terminal phosphate in the short phosphate chain of ADP and at the free **SH group** of coenzyme A. The latter behaves much like the OH group in alcohols, and you have already met it in the amino acid cysteine (Chapter 2). The aromatic ring attachment site of NAD is slightly more complex, and accommodates only two electrons and one proton from the 2H passenger group. This group dissociates as in the equation: $2H \rightleftharpoons 2H^+ + 2e^-$.

○ If you imagine each hydrogen in the 2H group split into proton plus electron ($H^+ + e^-$), what part of the 2H group is not bound to NAD, but remains behind in solution?

● One proton, H^+.

Usually this ion just joins the large pool of protons resulting from dissociation of water ($H_2O \longrightarrow H^+ + OH^-$), but it may be directed towards a particular site in the cell, adding to the proton imbalance needed for chemiosmotic coupling — see Chapter 5.

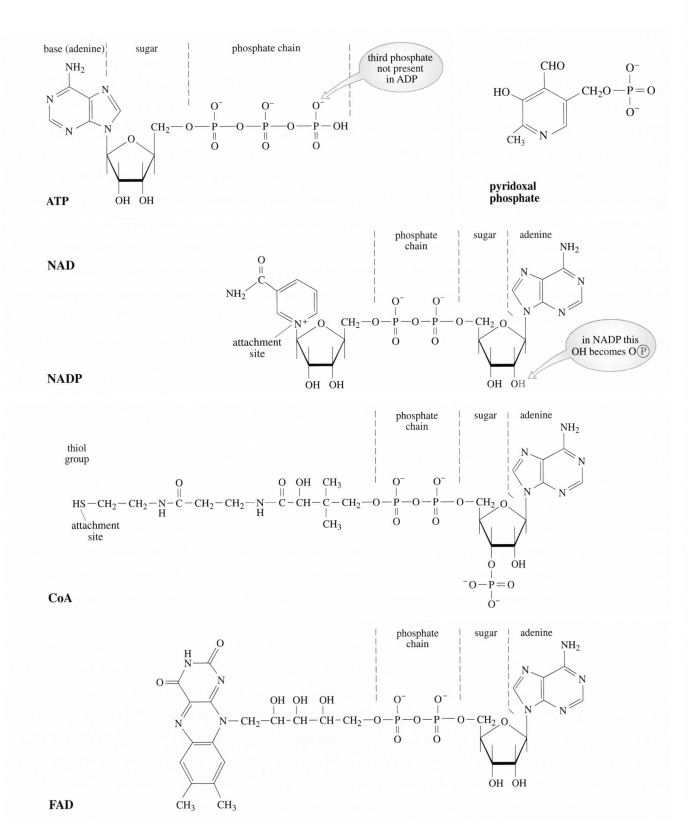

Figure 4.4   Structures of common coenzymes. Note the convention used here with sugars, in which ring C atoms and substituent H atoms are omitted from the ring formulae. You have to imagine a C atom wherever bonds meet in the sugar ring, and an H atom at the end of each 'empty' bond shown pointing above or below the ring.

The coenzymes in Table 4.1 are the main ones you will meet here. All but pyridoxal phosphate have a further very important role. They transfer energy between carbon compounds as well as transferring chemical groups. This is because the two forms of the coenzyme molecule — loaded-up and passenger-free — have very *different free energies* (see Box 4.1).

For reasons we shall come to shortly, the 'loaded-up' form of a coenzyme is less stable, and therefore has a higher free energy. So there is a strong compulsion for it to give up its passenger group, releasing the extra free energy as it does so. Loaded-up coenzymes are sometimes referred to as *activated carrier molecules* or even, as with ATP, as *short-term energy stores*.

These concepts are useful, but it can be misleading to think that energy is associated with just a single bond, between say coenzyme A or ADP and their respective passenger groups. There is nothing special about such bonds. In the case of acetyl CoA, the bond is simply a covalent link (actually a thioester bond) between the acetyl group and the SH attachment site of coenzyme A. In the case of **ATP**, it is simply a covalent link between the third phosphate and the

---

BOX 4.1   FREE ENERGY

The first law of thermodynamics states that energy can be neither created nor destroyed. From this it follows that in a chemical (or biochemical) reaction, energy may change form (typically between chemical bond energy and heat energy), but the total amount of energy remains the same. Many chemical reactions release energy as heat (*enthalpy, H*) as new bonds are made, for example, when coal burns in air.

However, in this case, there is not only a change in chemical bonding, but also in the disorder of the system. In solid coal, the carbon atoms are regularly arranged, whereas in carbon dioxide gas, each forms part of a randomly moving molecule. The change from coal to CO_2 is accompanied by a loss of regularity, or an increase in disorder. In general, reactions tend towards a decrease in order. Disorder is represented as the thermodynamic quantity *entropy, S*. The second law of thermodynamics states that a reaction occurs spontaneously only if it is accompanied by a global increase of entropy (loss of order). A good example is when ice melts to water, and the regular arrangement of water molecules in ice gives way to the much more fluid arrangement in liquid water.

When coal burns to give CO_2, the reaction is spontaneous because there are favourable changes in both *H* and *S*. Enthalpy (*H*) is released and molecular disorder (*S*) increases. These terms can be combined in the term **free energy (G)** which can be looked upon as the energy released during a (biochemical) reaction that is available for doing work. This free energy depends on the two factors promoting the reaction, enthalpy and entropy, which are linked by the equation:

$$\Delta G = \Delta H - T\Delta S \qquad (4.3)$$

where Δ ('delta') is a symbol meaning 'change in', and *T* is temperature in K (which is usually constant in the cell). Biochemists are normally concerned with *changes* in *G*, *H*, and *S* when a biochemical change takes place, rather than with their absolute values.

The important point to remember when studying metabolism is that **reactions occur spontaneously only in the direction in which ΔG is negative.** They may be very slow unless enzymes are present to speed them up, but enzymes can still only catalyse reactions in the direction in which ΔG is negative. Thus reactions are favoured where heat is given out (ΔH negative) and/or the disorder of the system increases (ΔS positive). These changes depend on the chemical and physical nature of the reactants and products. For example, if the product has stronger bonds than the reactants, heat is given out; if the product is a gas and the reactant a solid, disorder increases. Entropy, and hence ΔG, can also be affected by concentration. For example, a small amount of product mixed with a large amount of reactant is more disordered than if the amounts are roughly equal.

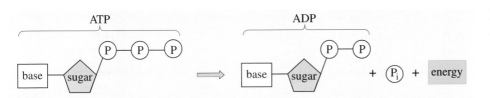

Figure 4.5   The breakdown of ATP to ADP releases energy.

rest of the molecule (see Figure 4.5). The energy stored in ATP lies not in this particular bond, but in the number of different ways that electrons can be arranged in the starting compound ATP, compared with the combined products ADP and P_i. There are fewer arrangements for ATP, which means it is inherently less stable and has a higher free energy than its breakdown products. So conversion of ATP into ADP releases energy. Similar arguments can be applied to the free-energy differences between acetyl CoA/CoA, NAD.2H/NAD and some other coenzymes. The details need not concern us; the important point is that free energy differences between loaded/unloaded forms of some coenzymes can be used to drive energy-requiring reactions in the cell by a process that can be visualized as **coupling**.

4.2.3 COUPLED REACTIONS

Reactions that release energy have a negative ΔG value and take place spontaneously. Conversely, reactions with positive ΔG values need energy, and cannot proceed unless energy is supplied from elsewhere. A unique aspect of cell chemistry is that proteins — usually enzymes — can 'couple' two such reactions together, allowing an energy-requiring reaction to be driven by an energy-releasing reaction. The link can be shown as follows:

1   energy-*releasing* reaction; occurs spontaneously
   e.g. ATP $\longrightarrow$ ADP + P_i: ΔG negative   (4.4)

2   energy-*requiring* reaction; impossible unless energy supplied
   e.g. x + y $\longrightarrow$ x—y: ΔG positive   (4.5)

3   coupled reaction; occurs spontaneously
   ATP + x + y $\longrightarrow$ ADP + P_i + x—y: net ΔG negative   (4.6)

There is of course one proviso in this scheme; the energy released as ATP $\longrightarrow$ ADP must exceed the energy needed for x + y $\longrightarrow$ x—y i.e. the *net* energy change must still be negative.

Because of their structure, enzymes and other proteins are uniquely designed to bring about coupling, by holding interacting molecules together in adjacent binding sites on the protein surface (Figure 4.3 earlier).

○ How many specific binding sites would be needed for an enzyme to couple reactions 4.4 and 4.5 above?

● Three; one each for ATP, x and y.

Although the cell may have many millions of coenzyme molecules of any one kind, each must be rapidly recycled. In the above example, ADP must be

Figure 4.6 Energy-releasing and energy-requiring reactions linked by ATP.

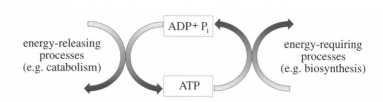

re-phosphorylated to ATP, in a separate energy-*requiring* reaction, that is itself driven by coupling to another energy-*releasing* process (see Figure 4.6).

○ From your background knowledge of cell biology/biochemistry, name the energy-releasing processes most commonly used to drive ATP synthesis (i.e. ADP phosphorylation).

● Oxidative phosphorylation and photophosphorylation. (More details are given in Chapter 5.)

ATP has been variously called a high-energy intermediate, an energy transfer molecule, or even 'energy currency'. During its conversion into ADP it can drive not only biosynthetic reactions (as in the example earlier) but a wide range of energy-requiring activities, such as muscle contraction (Chapter 7) or ion pumping (Chapter 3). Myosin (Figure 4.7) is a large protein consisting of a long fibrous tail and two enzymatic heads which, when associated with actin and other cofactors, acts as an ATPase in muscle contraction. In ion pumping, a membrane-bound protein may couple ATP breakdown to the movement of ions such as H^+. Since these positively charged ions are all transported to the same side of the membrane against a concentration gradient, this process requires energy.

Figure 4.7 Structure of the muscle protein, myosin.

Energy-requiring reactions in metabolism may use **coenzyme A** or other coenzymes, rather than ATP. Fatty acids, for example, need to be 'activated' before they can enter metabolism, forming a **thioester** group as in acetyl CoA (Figure 4.8).

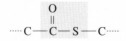

Figure 4.8 Structure of the thioester group.

SUMMARY OF SECTIONS 4.1 AND 4.2

1 Metabolism is the sum of the chemical reactions occurring in the cell. Each reaction is catalysed by a specific enzyme.

2 *Coenzymes* are group transfer molecules, usually larger than the carbon intermediates of metabolism. Much of their structure is required for *recognition* at specific binding sites near the enzyme active site. For some

coenzymes (e.g. ATP and coenzyme A) the attachment site for passenger groups is particularly clear.

3 A coenzyme acts as an activated carrier molecule or short-term energy store, when in its loaded-up form. It releases energy as its passenger is removed (e.g. as ATP $\longrightarrow$ ADP + P$_i$).

4 Enzymes can *couple* energy-releasing reactions (e.g. ATP $\longrightarrow$ ADP) with energy-requiring reactions, so long as the net ΔG is negative.

4.3 STRUCTURE OF CARBON INTERMEDIATES

To understand the chemical changes that take place during metabolism, we need to think a little about the structure of glucose and its derivatives.

Look ahead briefly to Figures 4.17–4.20 which show details of the glucose oxidation pathway. Carbon intermediates in each step are shown with full chemical formulae, but you should focus on the *small changes* that take place to *specific regions* of each structure, as metabolism proceeds from step to step. Try also to pick out particular functional groups attached to particular, numbered carbons in each structure. (In numbering, there are rules governing which carbon in a chain is numbered C-1. It is usually the carbon in, or attached to, the functional group and it is normally shown towards the top of the page.)

Glucose, for example, is a six-carbon chain with a **hydroxyl** group (OH) on all except C-1, which carries a **carbonyl** group C=O. In solution, glucose exists mainly as a six-membered ring formed by five carbons and an oxygen (Figure 4.9). Fructose is another sugar with six carbons, but they are usually arranged as a five-membered ring (see Figure 4.10). To enter a metabolic pathway, sugars are

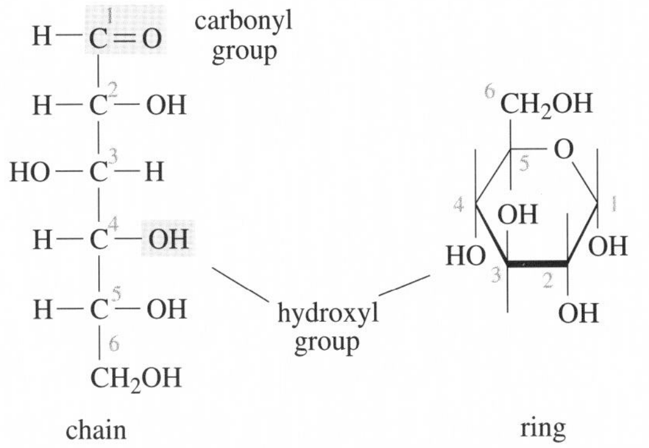

Figure 4.9 Chain and ring structures of glucose. In solution each molecule spends only a very small proportion of its time as a chain. At any one time, most of the glucose molecules are rings. Recall the convention used here, in which ring C atoms and substituent H atoms are omitted from the ring formula; imagine a C atom wherever bonds meet in the ring, and an H atom at the end of each 'empty' bond shown pointing above or below the ring.

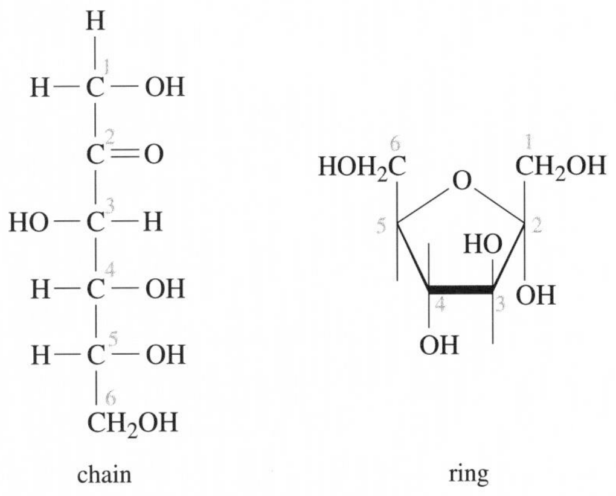

Figure 4.10 Chain and ring structures of fructose.

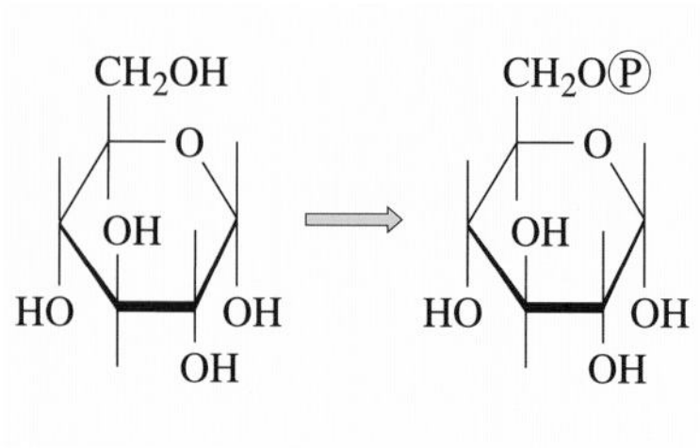

Figure 4.11 Phosphorylation of glucose to glucose 6-phosphate (G6P); the symbol Ⓟ represents a phosphate group, usually derived from ATP.

activated by *phosphorylation*, e.g. on carbon-6 (C-6) of glucose, the $-OH$ group i replaced by a negatively charged phosphate group, resulting in a structure usually abbreviated to $-O$Ⓟ. Depending on the pH in its immediate vicinity, this $-O$Ⓟ group can have zero, one or two negative charges (see Figure 4.11 and 4.12a).

Most of the other carbon intermediates in glucose oxidation are *carboxylic acids*, i.e. their functional groups include a **carboxyl** group, COOH. At cell pH, the carboxyl group is usually ionized, as you can see for pyruvic acid and its pyruvate anion in Figure 4.12b. Similarly, glyceric acid in Figure 4.12c is ionized to glycerate.

Note how pyruvate can be described as a 3-carbon chain, each C forming part of a different functional group; the CH_3 is a **methyl** group and the $C=O$ a carbonyl group. Other functional groups you may encounter in metabolism are **acetyl** (CH_3CO) and NH_2 (**amino**) groups; *in vivo*, this last is usually in its charged form as NH_3^+.

A saturated carbon in the middle of a chain has to be $-CH_2-$ rather than $-CH_3$ as at the end of a chain. You will find plenty of these $-CH_2-$ groups in the long-chain **fatty acids**. Figure 4.13 should remind you how fatty acids combine with **glycerol** to make **triacylglycerols** (TAGs).

○ Why can a fatty acid be described as a long-chain carboxylic acid?

● It is a carboxylic acid because of its carboxyl group (COOH), and long-chain because of its string of $-CH_2-$ groups.

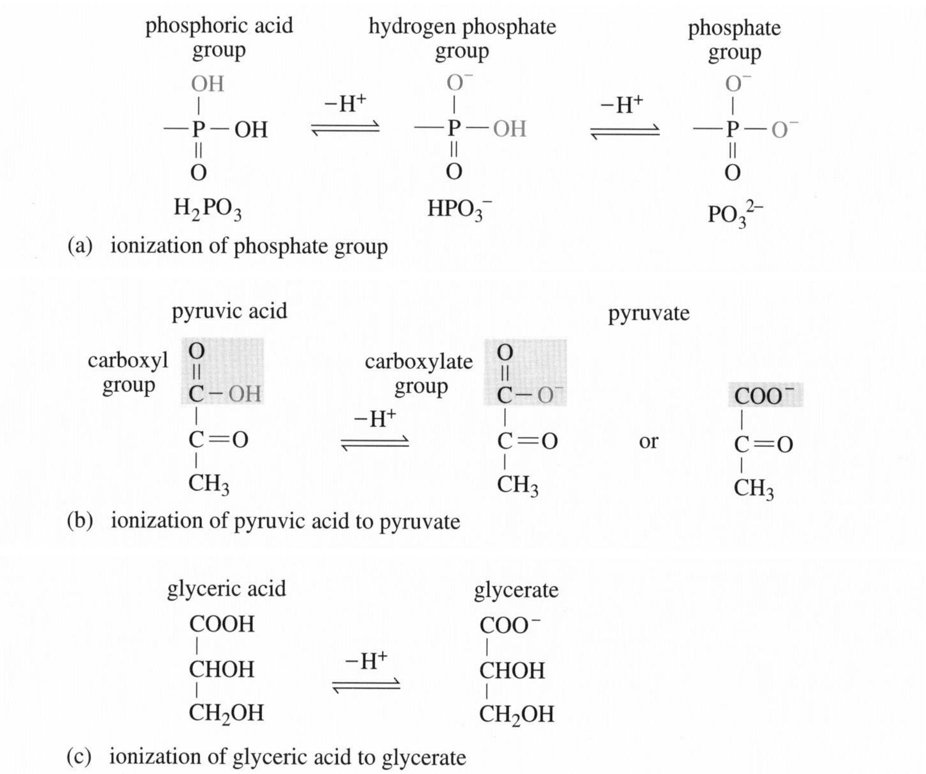

(a) ionization of phosphate group

(b) ionization of pyruvic acid to pyruvate

(c) ionization of glyceric acid to glycerate

Figure 4.12 (a) Ionization of a phosphate group; (b) ionization of pyruvic acid to pyruvate; (c) ionization of glyceric acid to glycerate.

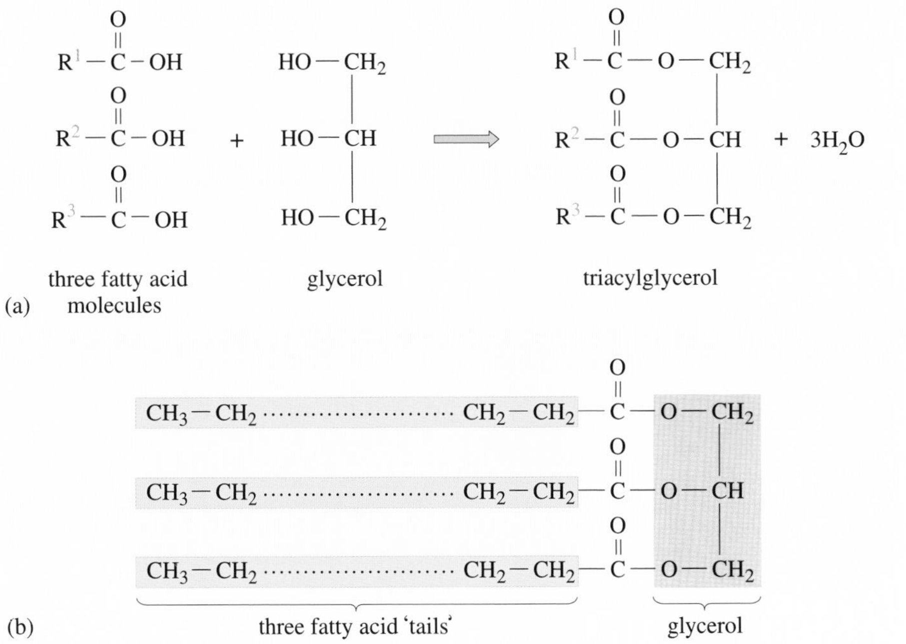

Figure 4.13 (a) Formation of a triacylglycerol (TAG).
(b) Extended structure of a TAG showing the three fatty acid tails. R^1, R^2 and R^3 represent different *saturated* carbon chains, i.e. $-(CH_2)_n-$, or *unsaturated* carbon chains, e.g. $-(CH_2)_7CH=CH(CH_2)_7-$.

To check that you can follow our descriptions of metabolic pathways, try this question.

○ If C-1 of glycerate (shown on the left of Figure 4.14) is part of the carboxyl group, is the compound on the right of Figure 4.14 best described as: 1-phosphoglycerate, 2-phosphoglycerate or 3-phosphoglycerate?

● As 3-phosphoglycerate, because the bottom carbon atom is C-3.

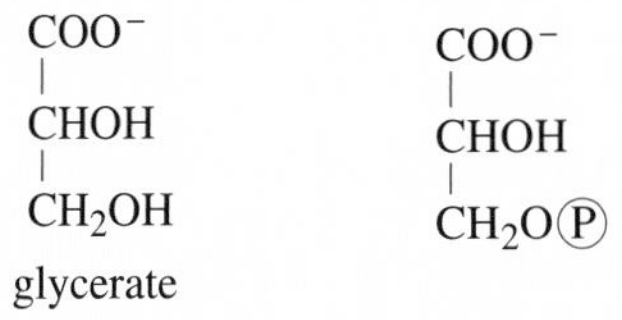

Figure 4.14 Formulae of glycerate and phosphoglycerate for in-text question.

SUMMARY OF SECTION 4.3

The *functional groups* most commonly encountered in metabolism are acetyl (CH_3CO), hydroxyl (OH), carbonyl (C=O), amino (NH_2), carboxyl (COOH), methyl (CH_3) and methylene ($-CH_2-$) groups.

4.4 GLUCOSE OXIDATION PATHWAYS

4.4.1 OVERVIEW

In all eukaryotes and many prokaryotes, glucose oxidation pathways lie at the centre of metabolism. We describe the oxidation as starting from glucose, although other sugars, fatty acids and amino acids can also be oxidized by entering the pathway at different points — wherever there is an intermediate of similar structure (see later). This is one advantage of having so many small steps to achieve *in vivo* what can be done *in vitro* simply by burning glucose in air; this one-step oxidation is shown in Equation 4.7:

$$C_6H_{12}O_6 + 6O_2 \longrightarrow 6CO_2 + 6H_2O \qquad (4.7)$$

In this chapter, we describe the metabolic reactions that convert the six glucose carbons into six CO_2 molecules, and remove the twelve glucose hydrogens as five NAD.2H (and one FAD.2H). This takes us through glycolysis, the link reaction and the TCA cycle (Figure 4.15). The re-oxidation of reduced coenzymes and the input of oxygen via the electron transport chain (ETC) are left till Chapter 5.

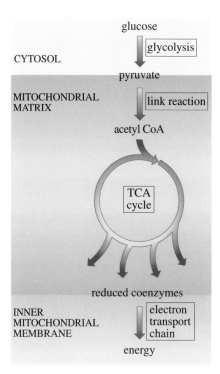

Figure 4.15 Overview of glucose oxidation pathway.

In each step of glucose oxidation, a different enzyme catalyses a chemical change in the carbon intermediate, often just adding or removing small groups of atoms such as H_2O, CO_2, NH_2, phosphate, 2H, etc.

○ Which of these groups arrive or leave bound to a specific coenzyme?

● All except H_2O and CO_2.

Other steps may involve *isomerization,* where the total number of C, H, O and P atoms is unchanged, but the atoms are rearranged into different functional groups. In some steps a C—C bond is broken. To achieve this and other chemically demanding feats under the mild conditions of cell chemistry, the pathway may take a circuitous route, manoeuvring the carbon intermediate into a particularly reactive configuration, e.g. so that activating C=O groups come to lie next to resistant bonds. The C=O (carbonyl) group can withdraw electrons from such bonds because of its strongly electronegative (electron-attracting) oxygen atom; a C=O group occurs for example in compounds activated by coenzyme A. The details of these reactions are less important than the take-home message that they allow complex chemical transformations to take place under mild conditions, without contravening the laws of simple organic chemistry!

4.4.2 GLYCOLYSIS

The glycolytic pathway is a very ancient route for glucose breakdown, found in all living organisms apart from certain specialized microbes. It takes place in the cytosol, and in animals the starting point is usually taken as glucose, which is supplied to cells via the blood. However, it could equally well start a little lower down (see Figure 4.16) with **glucose 6-phosphate (G6P)** or **fructose 1,6-bisphosphate (FbisP)** from the breakdown of the plant storage compounds, starch and sucrose (see later).

The pathway ends with pyruvate, though under anaerobic conditions this compound is further metabolized as described in Section 4.4.5. In Figure 4.16 you see an overview of the whole of glycolysis, with only the names of carbon intermediates and the points where coenzymes are involved. In referring to important carbon intermediates, you may find it easier to use the abbreviations shown here; we shall do this throughout the chapter. Note that in Figure 4.16, acids are shown as anions (i.e. pyruvate not pyruvic acid; phosphoglycerate not phosphoglyceric acid) because they occur predominantly as anions in the cell.

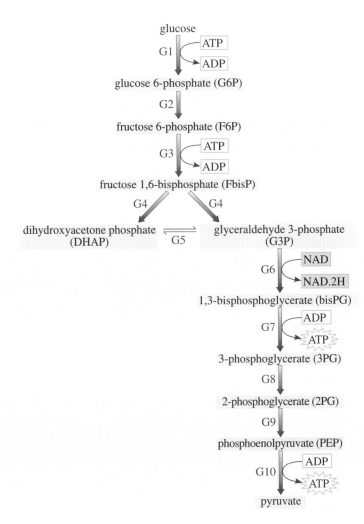

Figure 4.16 Outline of glycolysis. Only the names of carbon intermediates are given, and the points where coenzymes are involved. Numbers beside arrows refer to consecutive reactions in the glycolytic sequence (G1, G2 etc.). Reactions are often easier to visualize if abbreviations are used, as shown here.

Figure 4.17 shows the 'early' glycolytic reactions G1–G4 in more detail. The full formulae of the intermediates in the pathway are shown. However, you should pay particular attention to the chemical changes taking place and the coenzymes involved. Together reactions G1–G4 achieve the breakdown of 6C glucose into

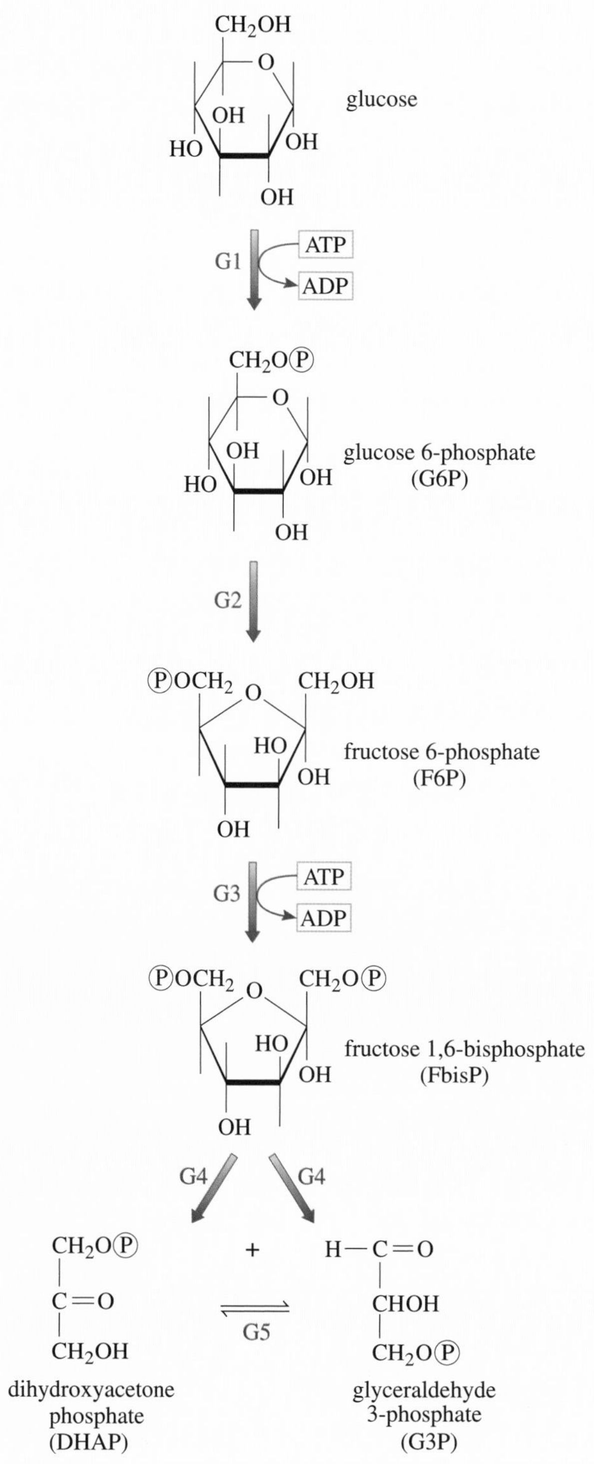

Figure 4.17 Details of glycolysis: early reactions.

two 3C compounds, the products of reaction G4. The activating reactions that precede G4 involve two *phosphorylations* (G1 and G3) each using an ATP. There is also an *isomerization* which you might like to note just for interest (see reaction G2); it converts a glucose derivative into a fructose derivative.

In the 'late' glycolytic reactions G6–G10 (Figure 4.18), one of the 3C products of reaction G4 (G3P) is manoeuvred through a series of steps into two reactive intermediates, first bisPG (1,3-bisphosphoglycerate) and later **PEP (phosphoenolpyruvate)** which are the respective products of reactions G6 and G9. Each then loses a phosphate to make ATP in two reactions G7 and G10, which are known as **substrate-level phosphorylations**. (This name distinguishes them from oxidative phosphorylations, that involve molecular oxygen. We return to this point in Chapter 5, so do not worry about it now).

Reaction G6 is a good example of *coupling*, where an energy-releasing reaction (oxidation) drives an energy-requiring reaction (phosphorylation). To couple two such reactions, the enzyme catalysing G6 must be large enough for three specific binding sites. This enzyme is known as glyceraldehyde 3-phosphate dehydrogenase or GAPDH ('gap'-D-H) for short. The product bisPG is a 'high energy' intermediate, and its breakdown in reaction G7 releases enough energy to make ATP.

○ Name the three compounds that must bind to specific sites on the enzyme GAPDH.

● The carbon intermediate G3P, phosphate and the coenzyme NAD.

Finally, note that all the 'late' glycolytic reactions happen *twice* for every glucose molecule oxidized because *both* the 3C products of reaction G4 go through to the end of glycolysis. For this to happen, the left-hand product of reaction G4 (DHAP) must first isomerize into the right-hand product G3P; see reaction G5. You may think that isomerization is an unnecessary complication. But when glucose supplies are exhausted, the oxidation pathways are in danger of drying up. One way of preventing this potentially dangerous outcome is for DHAP to be formed from fat, then isomerized into G3P and hence fed down the oxidation route to make vital ATP.

4.4.3 THE LINK REACTION

Under aerobic conditions, the next step in glucose oxidation is the link reaction, which takes place in the mitochondrial matrix. **Pyruvate** formed at the end of glycolysis thus has to pass from the cytosol, through both mitochondrial membranes into the matrix.

○ The outer mitochondrial membrane is freely permeable to small carbon intermediates, but the inner membrane is not. Suggest how a charged intermediate like pyruvate might pass through the hydrophobic bilayer of the inner mitochondrial membrane.

● By attaching to a specific, membrane-bound carrier protein (see Chapter 3). This is known as the pyruvate transporter.

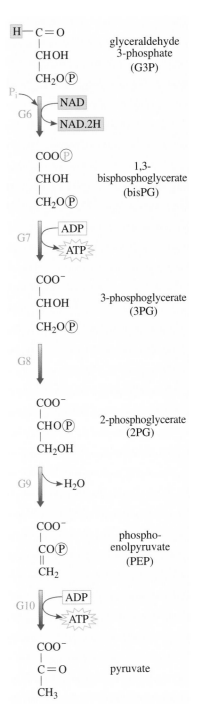

Figure 4.18 Details of glycolysis: late reactions.

Figure 4.19 The link reaction. Note how the H atoms (in red boxes) from pyruvate and from the coenzyme A attachment site are packaged together to form NAD.2H, while the acetyl group (grey box) from pyruvate is transferred to coenzyme A forming acetyl CoA.

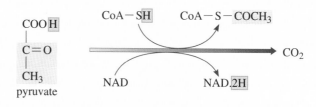

In the **link reaction**, CO_2 is split off from pyruvate, leaving a 2C fragment to be dealt with by the TCA cycle. As shown in Figure 4.19 this fragment is an acetyl group, CH_3CO-. Being too reactive to exist on its own, it becomes covalently bound to coenzyme A through the SH attachment site. The H displaced from here, together with an H from the OH on C-1 of pyruvate, form a 2H package that is picked up by NAD. Thus pyruvate is split up into three products, i.e. CO_2, H, and CH_3CO, the whole reaction being catalysed by multiple copies of three different enzymes, held together in a giant **multienzyme complex** known as **PDC**, the **pyruvate dehydrogenase complex**.

4.4.4 THE TCA CYCLE

The tricarboxylic acid or TCA cycle completes the breakdown of glucose, by fragmenting the acetyl group now attached to coenzyme A. The last two carbons of glucose are released as CO_2, and the H atoms are attached to coenzyme NAD or FAD, forming **reduced coenzymes**. These enter the electron transport chain as the major, energy-carrying products of the TCA cycle. Figure 4.20 — which you should study with the help of Figure 4.21 — shows all the reactions in full. We shall now touch on each reaction briefly by describing how it contributes to the cycle as a whole.

The TCA or *tricarboxylic acid cycle* is named from the three carboxylate groups (COO^-) of *citrate*, the first intermediate in the cycle. In reaction T1 a 2C acetyl group from the link reaction is combined with an important 4C intermediate, **oxaloacetate** or **OAA**, to form 6C citrate (see reaction T1 in Figures 4.20 and 4.21a). The 2C acetyl group only undergoes this reaction because it has already been activated by coenzyme A, into a 'high-energy' thioester intermediate. After an internal rearrangement (see reaction T2, whose details need not concern us), first one and then the other carboxyl group is released as CO_2 (see reactions T3 and T4). The first two molecules of reduced coenzyme are formed at the same time (see the NAD.2H released at these points in Figure 4.20). Reaction T4 is another activation step, and like T1 it uses coenzyme A to form a 'high-energy' intermediate, another thioester known this time as succinyl CoA. The breakdown of this compound in reaction T5 is coupled to the formation of ATP. (In humans and some other species, reaction T5 produces GTP, which then phosphorylates ADP to ATP in a separate reaction.) Apart from reaction T7 (which adds a molecule of H_2O) the remaining steps are concerned with removing hydrogens to form reduced coenzymes (see FAD.2H and then NAD.2H in Figure 4.20).

The whole cycle can be seen as a vehicle for drawing 2C fragments in from the link reaction and releasing them as CO_2. The 4C molecule that results is converted

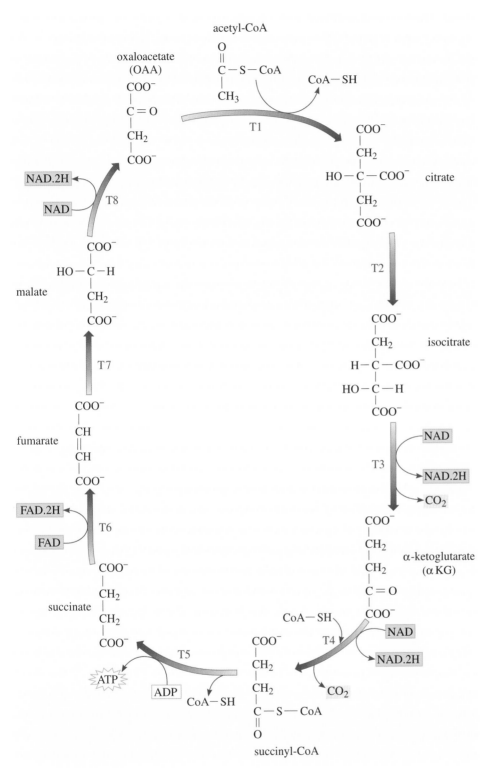

Figure 4.20 Details of the TCA cycle. Numbers beside arrows refer to consecutive reactions in the cycle (T1, T2, etc.).

back into OAA, ready for reaction T1 again. Without OAA, the link reaction cannot connect with the TCA cycle, and the whole of glucose oxidation would grind to a halt. This is a very real danger in the cell, since OAA is an important

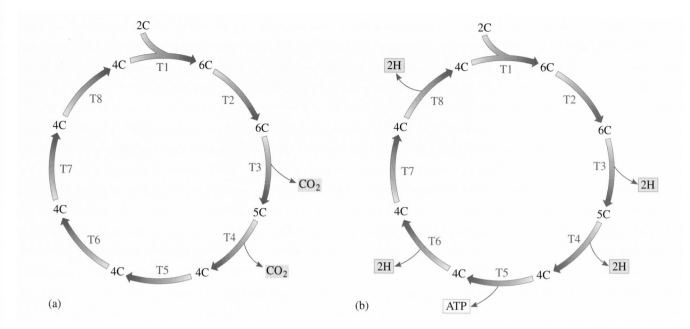

(a)

(b)

Figure 4.21 Summary of the main outcomes of the TCA cycle. (a) Changes in carbon molecules: note how glucose-derived carbon atoms are finally lost as CO_2; (b) energy changes: note the formation of ATP in reaction T5, and the removal of H atoms in reactions T3, T4, T6 and T8 to form reduced coenzymes (not shown).

intermediate, often diverted to other, biosynthetic reactions. So side reactions that top up OAA levels from other sources are vital for central metabolism, as we shall see later.

In terms of cell economy, the TCA cycle serves three useful functions:

1   It uses glucose H atoms to form reduced coenzymes. In the last stage of glucose oxidation (the electron transport chain) these H atoms finally make glucose energy available as ATP, through the process of oxidative phosphorylation (to be described in Chapter 5).

2   It produces a molecule of ATP by substrate-level phosphorylation (reaction T5). Since the cycle turns twice for every glucose oxidized, the yield is 2 ATPs per glucose molecule.

3   It produces carbon intermediates for biosynthesis. This is particularly relevant in plants, where biosynthesis rather than energy production is the main role of the TCA cycle.

4.4.5 GLUCOSE OXIDATION AND OXYGEN AVAILABILITY

When oxygen is plentiful (**aerobic** conditions), large amounts of ATP are made available from glucose oxidation, as reduced coenzymes from the TCA cycle undergo oxidation and produce ATP by oxidative phosphorylation (see Chapter 5). There are in addition some 6 ATPs formed by substrate-level phosphorylation (in reactions G7, G10 and T5). However the net yield (from glycolysis + TCA cycle) is only 4 ATPs/glucose, because of the two ATP-requiring activation steps in early glycolysis (G1 and G3).

This meagre ATP output is overshadowed by the electron transport chain, which raises the yield to around 34 ATPs/glucose. Exact numbers may fluctuate with conditions in the ETC — the important point is that this picture of plenty is very different from the situation in *anaerobic* conditions, when glucose oxidation does not go beyond glycolysis.

○ What is the yield of ATP/glucose in anaerobic conditions?

● Two. Reactions G6 and G10 happen twice for every glucose, together yielding 4 ATPs; but 2 ATPs have already been used in reactions G1 and G3. So the net yield is two (4 − 2).

In anaerobic conditions then, neither the link reaction nor the TCA cycle operate, and glycolysis is the only route for glucose oxidation. However, it goes beyond pyruvate to include various steps that regenerate NAD from NAD.2H.

○ Why does glycolysis grind to a halt without these steps? *Hint*: look at details of the late glycolytic reactions in Figure 4.18.

● Reaction G6 is an oxidation, requiring NAD. So unless the NAD.2H produced in this reaction can be re-oxidized elsewhere, the cytosol runs out of NAD.

Figure 4.22 shows some of the strategies used to regenerate NAD in anaerobic cells. The **LDH (lactate dehydrogenase) reaction** (Figure 4.22a) comes into play, for example, in heavily exercising vertebrate muscle. One reason why a sprinter continues to pant long after the race is finished, is because lactate is being re-oxidized to pyruvate by reversal of the LDH reaction.

Figure 4.22b shows the two-step conversion of pyruvate to ethanol ('alcohol'), as catalysed by enzymes in oxygen-deprived brewers' yeast.

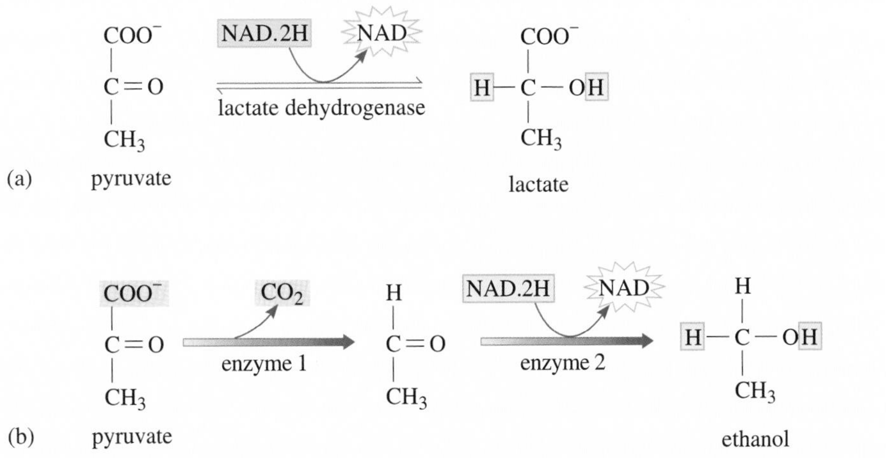

(a)   pyruvate   lactate

(b)   pyruvate   ethanol

Figure 4.22 Fate of pyruvate in anaerobic conditions: Formation of (a) lactate and (b) ethanol.

4.4.6 THE ENZYMES OF GLUCOSE OXIDATION

The three stages of glucose oxidation have been described as if they flow effortlessly from one carbon intermediate to the next. In reality each step is catalysed by an enzyme, with a binding site specific for the carbon intermediate, and for a coenzyme where appropriate. In this chapter, we name only the regulatory enzymes, which are listed in Table 4.2; they also have allosteric sites (Chapter 2) for binding control molecules. (We return to 'control' in the final section.)

Although the full names of the regulatory enzymes are listed in Table 4.2, it is their abbreviations and the reactions they catalyse that we are emphasizing here. You may find it useful to recall that a kinase catalyses transfer of phosphate from ATP and a dehydrogenase transfers H atoms to a coenzyme (see Section 4.2.1).

Table 4.2 Regulatory enzymes of glucose oxidation.

Enzyme	Full name	Reaction catalysed	
		Number	Overall equation
HK	hexokinase	G1	glucose $\longrightarrow$ G6P
PFK	phosphofructokinase	G3	F6P $\longrightarrow$ FbisP
PK	pyruvate kinase	G10	PEP $\longrightarrow$ pyruvate
PDC	pyruvate dehydrogenase complex	link	pyruvate $\longrightarrow$ acetyl CoA
IDH	isocitrate dehydrogenase	T3	isocitrate $\longrightarrow$ αKG
αKG	α-ketoglutarate dehydrogenase	T4	αKG $\longrightarrow$ succinyl CoA

SUMMARY OF SECTION 4.4

1   The 'early' glycolytic reactions convert glucose (6C) into DHAP (3C) and glyceraldehyde 3-phosphate or G3P (3C). Two molecules of ATP are used up for each molecule of glucose oxidized.

2   The chain of 'late' glycolytic reactions converts G3P into pyruvate, and takes place twice for every glucose molecule. Four ATPs (2×2) are formed, by substrate-level phosphorylation. Reaction G6 is a good example of the coupling of energy-releasing and energy-requiring reactions.

3   The link reaction is catalysed by PDC (pyruvate dehydrogenase complex) and converts pyruvate into an acetyl fragment which enters the TCA cycle as acetyl CoA; other products are NAD.2H and CO_2.

4   The TCA cycle converts the acetyl group into CO_2, forming one ATP, one FAD.2H and three NAD.2H. These reduced coenzyme molecules, along with carbon intermediates for biosynthesis, are metabolically the most important products of the cycle.

5   In anaerobic conditions, glucose is not oxidized beyond pyruvate, ATP yields are much reduced, and various NAD-generating reactions convert pyruvate into lactate or alcohol, depending on genetic make-up.

Here is a good point to work through the first three sections of the CD-ROM on *Making ATP* ('Overview', 'Glycolysis', and 'TCA Cycle'). They strongly reinforce what you have read so far in this chapter, drawing everything together in a way that text alone cannot do. They also make full use of the interactive facility, to teach key points about chemical formulae.

4.5   ALTERNATIVE FUELS

4.5.1   OVERVIEW

Because glucose oxidation proceeds through so many small steps, there are a large number of intermediate compounds. Each step represents a possible starting point for oxidizing alternative fuels to provide ATP. It needs only an appropriate enzyme or enzymes to convert the alternative fuel into an intermediate of the oxidation pathway. In this way, fat and protein can be channelled into the pathway when glucose supplies are low, e.g. in the starvation of animals, or the germination of lipid-rich seeds. In higher animals, these alternative fuels are particularly important for sensitive tissues like the brain, which is normally dependent on blood glucose. Under extreme conditions such as starvation, it can use certain alternative fuels to stave off coma and death.

Triacylglycerols (TAGs) make very compact fuel reserves, storing large quantities of energy in a small space. They are laid down in seeds (e.g. nuts) and in adipose tissue, especially in animals about to hibernate or birds about to migrate. Fat deposits can be mobilized when needed by the action of **lipases**. These enzymes hydrolyse TAGs to glycerol and fatty acid, as shown earlier in Figure 4.13. In animals, the lipases are under hormonal control, while in seeds their activation is triggered by germination. In carnivores (cats, owls, snakes, etc. and the many invertebrate predators) and in people (e.g. the Inuit) whose diet consists mainly of meat, amino acids from dietary protein are the major source of energy. However, in other organisms, amino acids from the breakdown of protein are only rarely used for fuel, e.g. in animal starvation.

4.5.2   GLYCEROL FROM TAGS IS OXIDIZED VIA GLYCOLYSIS

Glycerol and fatty acid products of TAG hydrolysis feed into the glucose oxidation pathway at different points.

○   Compare the structure of glycerol (Figure 4.13) with the structures of glucose oxidation intermediates (Figures 4.17–4.20). Which of the following glucose oxidation intermediates are most similar to glycerol?

(a) Products of glycolytic reactions G1–G3;

(b) Products of glycolytic reactions G4–G10;

(c) Products of the link reaction;

(d) TCA cycle intermediates.

●   (b) is correct — these are 3C molecules; (a) is incorrect, because these intermediates are all 6-carbon sugars; (c) is incorrect, because the link reaction product is the 2C acetyl group; (d) is incorrect, because these intermediates all have 4, 5 or 6 carbons.

To narrow down the choice of entry point within the sequence of reactions G4–G10, you need to know that glycerol (like glucose) has to be activated by phosphorylation, before it can enter the glycolytic pathway. This is accomplished

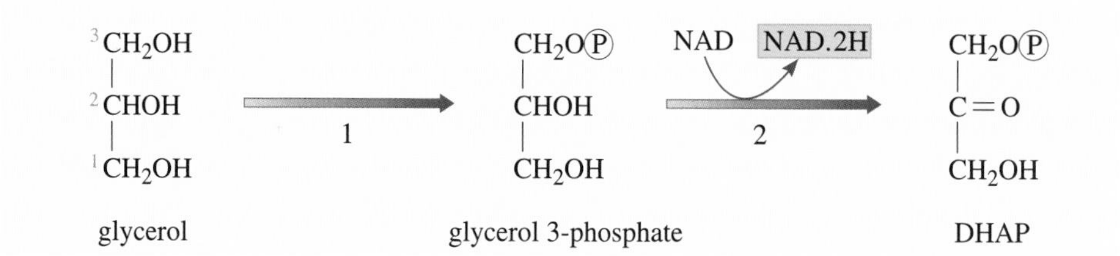

Figure 4.23 The two steps in the conversion of glycerol to DHAP.

$$^3CH_2OH \quad\quad\quad CH_2O\textcircled{P} \quad NAD \;\; \boxed{NAD.2H} \quad CH_2O\textcircled{P}$$
$$^2CHOH \xrightarrow{\quad\quad 1 \quad\quad} CHOH \xrightarrow{\quad\quad 2 \quad\quad} C=O$$
$$^1CH_2OH \quad\quad\quad CH_2OH \quad\quad\quad\quad\quad CH_2OH$$

glycerol   glycerol 3-phosphate   DHAP

by reaction 1 in Figure 4.23, which converts glycerol into glycerol 3-phosphate. The glycolytic intermediate that most closely resembles this activated glycerol is **dihydroxyacetone phosphate** or **DHAP**, the product of reaction G4.

○ What is the structural difference between DHAP and glycerol 3-phosphate?

● The central carbon forms part of a carbonyl group (C=O) in DHAP, but part of a CHOH group in glycerol 3-phosphate.

○ So what type of reaction is needed to convert glycerol 3-phosphate into DHAP?

● A reaction that removes H atoms, i.e. an *oxidation*.

The coenzyme in this reaction is NAD (see reaction 2 in Figure 4.23). In this way, glycerol from hydrolysed TAG stores can be converted in just two steps into the glycolytic intermediate DHAP, and oxidized via glycolysis. Figure 4.24 shows how this alternative entry point allows glycerol, rather than glucose, to be the fuel for oxidation.

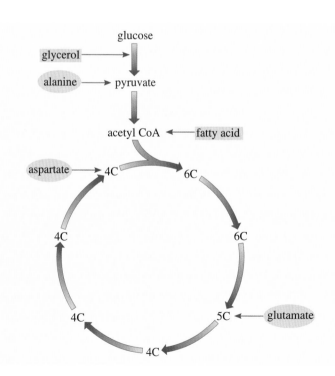

Figure 4.24 Entry points for the oxidation of alternative fuels. Intermediates in grey boxes come from TAGs; intermediates in grey circles come from protein.

4.5.3 FATTY ACIDS ARE OXIDIZED VIA ACETYL CoA

We now turn to fatty acids, the other products of TAG hydrolysis. It would be hard to guess from its formula where one such as palmitate might feed into the oxidation pathway. Aligning its carboxyl end with acetyl CoA (as in Figure 4.25) gives a clue. If this portion could be released as an acetyl group (CH_3CO) attached to coenzyme A, it could be fed into the TCA cycle along with acetyl CoA molecules from the link reaction. In the mitochondrial matrix these reactions chop 2C fragments sequentially from the fatty acid molecules, starting at the carboxyl end. Box 4.2 (p. 189) describes how this fragmentation mechanism was first discovered. It continues until the whole chain has been fed into the TCA cycle as acetyl CoA. For those few fatty acids with an odd number of CH_2 groups in the long fatty chain, a *three-carbon* fragment is left. This is converted into the TCA intermediate *succinyl CoA*, the product of reaction T4 (see Figure 4.20). Hence the oxidation of 3C fragments from odd-numbered fatty acid chains is no problem.

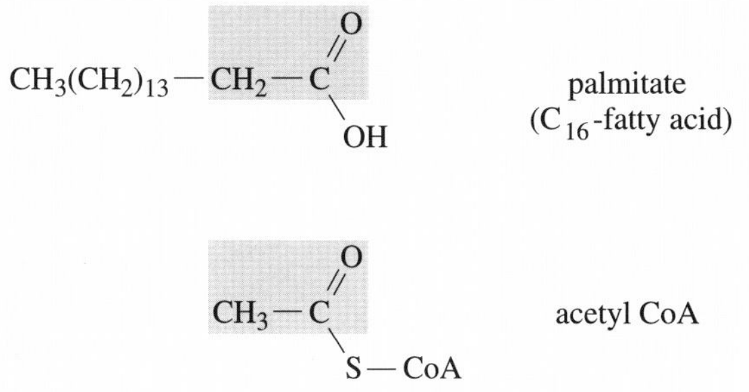

palmitate
(C_{16}-fatty acid)

acetyl CoA

Figure 4.25 Acetyl groups in palmitate and acetyl CoA.

The formation of acetyl CoA from a representative fatty acid — say palmitate — takes place in two stages, activation then oxidation. In *activation*, a thioester bond is formed to coenzyme A as shown in Figure 4.26. This energy-expensive step needs ATP, from which *two* phosphate groups are removed to leave AMP (adenosine *mono*phosphate) rather than the usual ADP. Fortunately, once this costly activation has been done, the activated fatty acid (now called palmitoyl CoA) can be chopped up two carbons at a time, without further activation. The

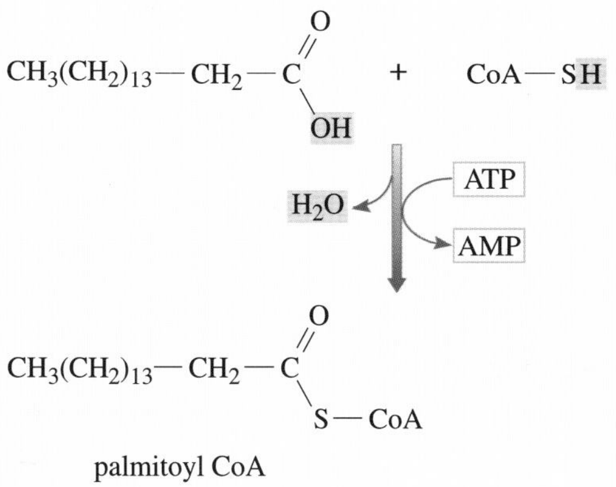

palmitoyl CoA

Figure 4.26 Activation of a fatty acid (palmitate) by coenzyme A.

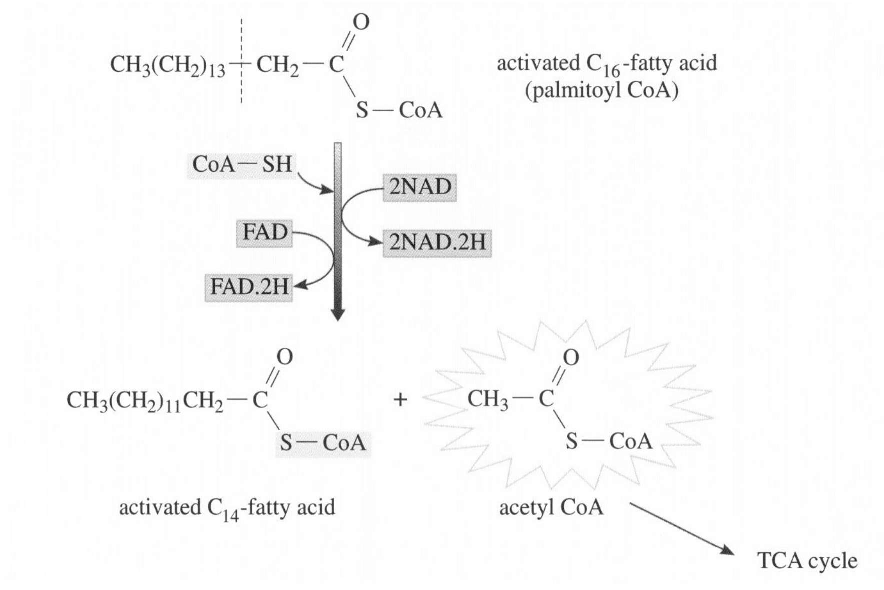

Figure 4.27 Oxidation of an activated C_{16}-fatty acid (palmitoyl CoA) to an activated C_{14}-fatty acid, forming acetyl CoA. *Note*: the extra oxygen required for this reaction comes from water.

$$CH_3(CH_2)_{13} \mid CH_2 - C \overset{O}{\underset{S-CoA}{\big\|}}$$

activated C_{16}-fatty acid (palmitoyl CoA)

CoA—SH

2NAD

FAD

2NAD.2H

FAD.2H

$$CH_3(CH_2)_{11}CH_2 - C \overset{O}{\underset{S-CoA}{\big\|}}$$

$+$

$$CH_3 - C \overset{O}{\underset{S-CoA}{\big\|}}$$

activated C_{14}-fatty acid

acetyl CoA

TCA cycle

'chopping up' is the *oxidation* stage, shown in detail in Figure 4.27. It is catalysed by a series of four enzymes, and a battery of coenzymes is needed. The net result is to convert a C_{16}-fatty acid into a C_{14}- fatty acid, releasing one molecule of acetyl CoA into the TCA cycle, and producing three molecules of reduced coenzyme for ATP formation via the ETC. The remaining C_{14}-fatty acid is still activated, because it has been attached to another CoA during the oxidation reaction. The activated C_{14}-fatty acid can then go straight into another oxidation. By repeating this oxidation seven times, a single C_{16}-fatty acid can produce seven acetyl CoA molecules, not to mention 21 (7×3) molecules of reduced coenzymes. Hence fatty acids are a very good fuel source, when fed into the oxidation pathways as shown in Figure 4.24 earlier.

4.5.4 KETONE BODIES

Under some circumstances, two acetyl CoA molecules combine, forming a 4C compound called acetoacetate. This compound, and two of its simple derivatives are known as **ketone bodies**. They are routinely found in vertebrate blood albeit at low levels, and are a fuel used by heart muscle. Here they are converted back into acetyl CoA, and provide energy for muscle contraction via the TCA cycle. The brain too makes use of ketone bodies, since they are the only fuel compound apart from glucose to cross the *blood–brain barrier,* the arrangement of cells and extracellular matrix that prevents some substances from blood entering the cerebrospinal fluid (CSF) that surrounds the brain.

For acetyl CoA to be oxidized via the TCA cycle, it must first react with oxaloacetate (OAA) in reaction T1 (see Figure 4.20). When, for any reason, OAA levels are too low to cope with all the acetyl CoA generated by fatty acid oxidation, ketone bodies accumulate. In humans (but not in most animals that are adapted to prolonged fasting), the resulting condition, called ketosis, is potentially fatal.

BOX 4.2   PIONEERING STUDIES ON FATTY ACID OXIDATION AND COENZYME A

Long before coenzyme A was known, and before the enzymes of fatty acid activation and oxidation had been isolated, biochemists knew that in whole animals, these alternative fuel molecules were chopped up two carbons at a time, starting from the carboxyl end. In 1904, the German biochemist F. Knoop had labelled two sets of fatty acids with an aromatic ring in place of the terminal CH_3 group (Figure 4.28), the best method of identifying molecules before specific radiolabelled carbon compounds were available. He fed these modified fatty acids to dogs, and then looked in their urine for compounds with this same aromatic ring. Dogs that were given labelled fatty acid with an *odd* number of CH_2 groups, were found to excrete derivatives of compound A. This molecule has a two-carbon chain attached to the aromatic ring and could be formed only by removing CH_2 groups two at a time (starting from the COOH end). Conversely, dogs fed the commoner fatty acids, which have an *even* number of CH_2 groups, then excreted derivatives of compound B. This molecule has *only one* carbon attached to the aromatic label, which again could be produced only if carbons were removed two at a time.

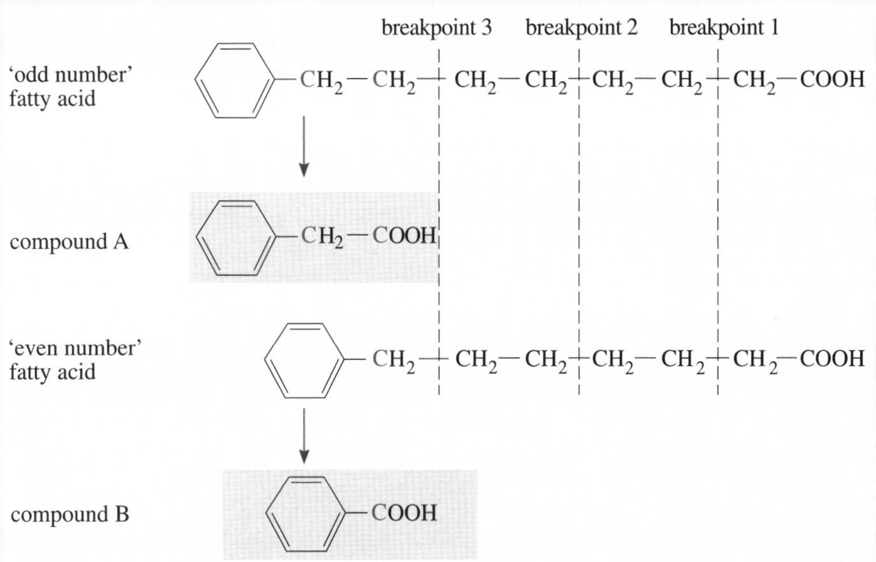

Figure 4.28   Stepwise removal of two-carbon fragments from labelled fatty acids: Knoop's classic experiment of 1904.

This 2C fragment is removed as the acetyl group CH_3CO, and in 1945 several research groups showed that semi-purified enzyme preparations could catalyse the addition of such acetyl groups to biological compounds. However, more highly purified enzyme preparations failed to do this, and eventually it was shown that some other factor from the cell homogenate was also needed. This turned out to be coenzyme A, which was not purified until the early 1950s.

4.5.5 OXIDATION OF AMINO ACIDS

When even fat supplies are low, protein may be hydrolysed to amino acids and used as a source of energy. In general this does not happen in plants, but carnivorous animals routinely oxidize amino acids for energy.

For amino acids with the same carbon backbone as a glycolytic or TCA cycle intermediate, oxidation is simple. A specific **transaminase** catalyses the transfer of NH_2 from the amino acid to the carbon skeleton of a 'receiver' molecule — whose fate we consider later. Figure 4.29 shows, for example, how alanine transaminase converts 3C alanine (a simple amino acid) into 3C pyruvate (the end product of glycolysis). Different transaminases catalyse removal of the NH_2 group from each of the two acidic amino acids, aspartate and glutamate (Table 2.2). In each case the carbon skeleton that remains can be fed into the TCA cycle as either OAA (from aspartate) or αKG (from glutamate) — see Figure 4.20 earlier. The specific transaminases catalysing these reactions have specific binding sites for the amino acid being deaminated and for the receiver molecule. They also need coenzyme **pyridoxal**, which we can imagine as in Figure 4.30 rotating between amino acid and receiver, as it transfers the NH_2 group from one to another. (Pyridoxal is a vitamin for higher animals.)

Figure 4.29 Removal of NH_2 group from alanine, to form pyruvate, and its transfer to a receiver to form glutamate.

alanine   pyruvate

COO⁻   COO⁻
| |
CH—NH_2 C=O
| |
COO⁻   CH₃   CH₃   COO⁻
| |
CH₂   CH₂
| |
CH₂   CH₂
| alanine |
C=O   transaminase   CH—NH_2
| |
COO⁻   COO⁻

'receiver'   glutamate

Figure 4.30 The active site of a transaminase enzyme, showing how the coenzyme pyridoxal transfers an NH_2 group from amino acid to 'receiver'.

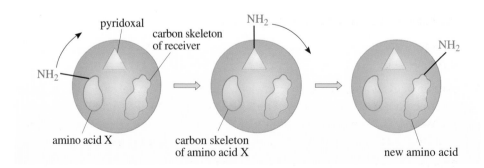

The receiver molecule can now be revealed as αKG (α-ketoglutarate of the TCA cycle), which is converted into glutamate as a result of the various transaminase reactions. As a common amino acid, glutamate can be used for protein synthesis, or converted to other amino acids should they be in short supply (by specific transaminases acting in reverse). Alternatively, when demands for protein are low, the NH_2 group is liberated as NH_3 (ammonia) leaving the carbon skeleton of glutamate (αKG) to be oxidized via the TCA cycle (see Figure 4.31). The enzyme catalysing this reaction is **GDH (glutamate dehydrogenase)**, an abundant mitochondrial enzyme whose activity is carefully controlled, depending on conflicting demands for energy or for amino acids for protein synthesis.

The NH_3 released in the GDH reaction is highly toxic. Being a small and very water-soluble molecule, it can easily diffuse out of microbial cells, and in aquatic animals can be readily removed as water flows over the gills. However, for other animals, major adaptations have evolved for the removal of NH_3, most of which is converted into urea and excreted in the urine. Plants do not deaminate, so have no problems with toxic NH_3.

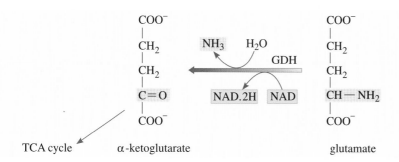

Figure 4.31 The GDH reaction. The enzyme glutamate dehydrogenase (GDH) catalyses deamination of the amino acid glutamate. The reaction is shown going towards the left so that the 'receiver' (αKG) appears in the same position as that shown in Figure 4.29.

SUMMARY OF SECTION 4.5

1   Fats (TAGs) can be oxidized via the glucose oxidation pathways, after hydrolysis to fatty acids and glycerol.

2   Glycerol enters glycolysis, after a two-step conversion into DHAP (product of reaction G4).

3   Fatty acids enter the TCA cycle as acetyl CoA. They are first *activated* (in an energy-expensive reaction in which ATP is converted into AMP), and then a complex *oxidation* releases two carbons as acetyl CoA and forms three reduced coenzymes. This oxidation step can be repeated until the entire fatty acid has been converted to acetyl groups.

4   Ketone bodies, formed by the combination of two acetyl CoA molecules, are a fuel used by heart muscle; they are also oxidized by the brain.

5   Amino acids whose carbon skeletons match those of glycolytic or TCA cycle intermediates (e.g. pyruvate or OAA), can be fed into the glucose oxidation pathways. The NH_2 group is removed by specific *transaminases* that pass it to a 'receiver' compound αKG (α-ketoglutarate), forming glutamate.

6   The important mitochondrial enzyme GDH (glutamate dehydrogenase) can deaminate glutamate to αKG, leaving toxic ammonia for excretion.

Here is a good point to work through the two sections entitled 'Alternative Fuels' and 'Control' in the CD-ROM *Making ATP*.

4.6   BIOSYNTHESIS AND REPLENISHING REACTIONS

4.6.1   THE SCOPE OF BIOSYNTHETIC AND REPLENISHING REACTIONS

The oxidation pathways produce not only energy, but numerous carbon intermediates. Many of these are siphoned off to make other biological compounds, by enzymes at the start of various biosynthetic pathways. Figure 4.32 shows the scope of this undertaking, which of course varies enormously in different organisms — and even in different tissues of the same organism — depending on the enzymes they possess. The very large number of possibilities is what makes the metabolic map so daunting (see Figure 4.1 earlier).

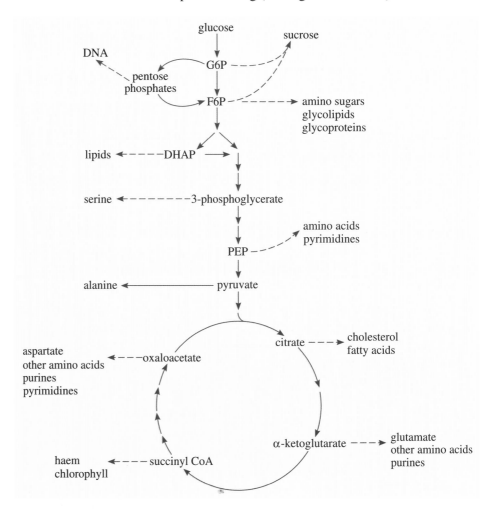

Figure 4.32 Many biosynthetic pathways use glucose oxidation intermediates as their starting point.

Some of the end products of biosynthesis are needed in only tiny amounts (e.g. the steroid hormones), but what happens if large quantities of one product are needed, so there is a run on a particularly important precursor, e.g. a TCA cycle intermediate?

○   Which TCA intermediate must be available if acetyl CoA is to enter the TCA cycle?

●   Oxaloacetate (OAA). Acetyl CoA reacts with this compound in reaction T1 (see Figure 4.20).

Without OAA, the first reaction of the TCA cycle cannot take place. So acetyl CoA accumulates from the link reaction, and particularly from fatty acid oxidation, and neither sugar nor fat can be further oxidized. In vertebrates, dangerous levels of ketone bodies may arise. To avoid such situations, key intermediates can be replenished from other sources by 'topping up' routes that are not strictly biosynthetic; but without them, central intermediates could not be diverted into specialized end products. In this section we describe only two biosyntheses — of polysaccharide and fat — and then only briefly. However, we indicate (1) how the oxidation pathway described in the previous section provides the *precursors* for biosynthesis and (2) how oxidation pathway intermediates can be *replenished* from other sources when necessary.

Rather than concentrate on the details of these routes, we look particularly at the interconversions they make possible, i.e. the beginning and end products. The metabolic map should be treated like a road map, where you can find whether or not there is a route from A to B, but need not memorize the towns in-between. Indeed, not all routes are 'open' in all cells all the time. Some are permanently closed because the relevant enzymes are never synthesized, while others are controlled by allosteric inhibitors, etc. (see Section 4.7 later).

We begin with a pathway very important in biosynthesis and replenishing routes, which we shall call **reverse-glycolysis** (also known as gluconeogenesis or glyconeogenesis, because it replenishes glucose — or its polymer glycogen, the form in which it is stored in animals).

4.6.2   REVERSING GLYCOLYSIS

The glycolytic pathway is like a railway line, whose many stations (carbon intermediates) act as junctions with other lines. To make full use of it for biosynthesis, the entire glucose-to-pyruvate sequence must be reversible. Seven of the glycolytic reactions are indeed reversible, the same enzymes catalysing reactions in both directions. But some steps are irreversible under physiological conditions, and here different enzymes are needed, to catalyse various 'bypass' reactions, as shown in Figure 4.33 overleaf.

Figure 4.33 Overview of glycolysis and reverse-glycolysis. Glycolytic reactions that cannot be reversed *in vivo* are catalysed by the regulatory enzymes in red-shaded ovals. Bypass reactions of reverse-glycolysis are catalysed by the regulatory enzymes in pink-shaded ovals.

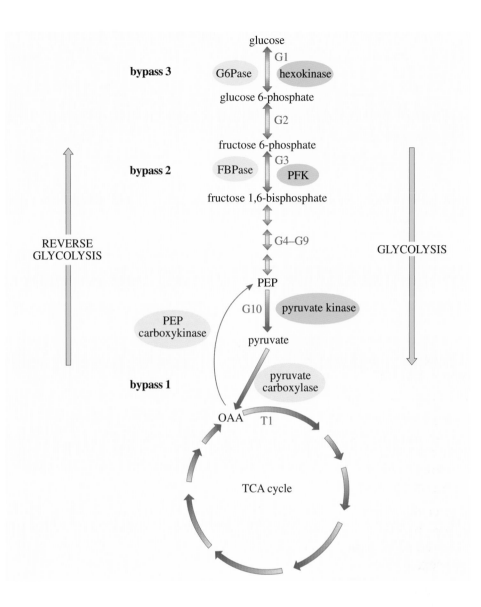

○ Can you think of an advantage of having glycolysis and reverse-glycolysis catalysed at certain points by different enzymes?

● The different enzymes are different proteins, and can therefore have different allosteric effectors and be subject to different *controls*.

Details of the bypass reactions are shown in Figure 4.34. The first bypass reverses the pyruvate kinase reaction (G10 at the end of glycolysis) and has two steps.

$$\text{pyruvate} \xrightarrow{\ \ 1\ \ } \text{OAA} \xrightarrow{\ \ 2\ \ } \text{PEP}$$

Step 1 of this bypass is catalysed by an important regulatory enzyme *pyruvate carboxylase*. (Carboxylase enzymes add CO_2 to carbon intermediates). The OAA product of Step 1 could be used for reaction T1 of the TCA cycle. But in reverse-

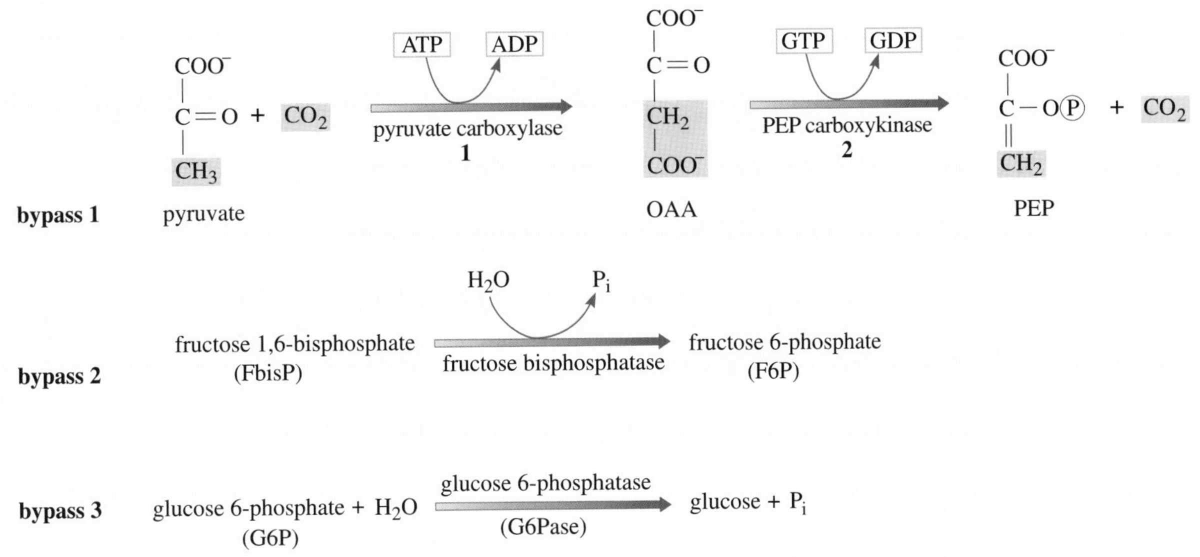

bypass 1 pyruvate   OAA   PEP

bypass 2 fructose 1,6-bisphosphate (FbisP) → fructose bisphosphatase → fructose 6-phosphate (F6P)

bypass 3 glucose 6-phosphate + H₂O (G6P) → glucose 6-phosphatase (G6Pase) → glucose + Pᵢ

Figure 4.34 Bypass reactions in reverse-glycolysis.

glycolysis it is now transported to the cytosol for step 2, which converts it into PEP thus completing the first bypass. (The relevant enzyme is PEP carboxykinase.)

From here, reverse-glycolysis can go as far as FbisP (fructose 1, 6-bisphosphate) simply by reversing glycolytic reactions G9–G4. Here a second bypass uses the enzyme *fructose bisphosphatase* (FBPase) to reverse the PFK reaction, G3. Both these catalysts are regulatory enzymes, subject to separate controls. Finally the hexokinase reaction is reversed by *glucose 6-phosphatase* (G6Pase), forming another enzyme pair with separate controls.

When G6Pase is absent, as in vertebrate muscle, reverse-glycolysis cannot release glucose into the blood for other needy tissues, but stops at G6P. This product, however, is the starting point for converting glucose into glycogen for storage (see next section).

We finish with two examples where the ability to reverse glycolysis is vital — one in plants and one in vertebrates. In plants, the first carbohydrate product of photosynthesis is 3-phosphoglycerate (3PG). Before it can be stored as starch or transported out of the leaf as sucrose, it must be converted into G6P.

○ Which of the reverse-glycolysis bypass enzymes must be present for 3PG to be converted into G6P?

● The enzyme fructose bisphosphatase of the second bypass. The first bypass is not needed, because 3PG feeds into glycolysis before this point. The third bypass is not needed because glycolysis needs reversing only as far as G6P, not glucose.

Our animal example concerns brain and heavily working vertebrate muscle. To produce the ATP to fuel contraction, muscle converts pyruvate into lactate (via the anaerobic LDH reaction in Figure 4.22). Lactate pours out of muscle into the blood, and is taken up by the liver and converted back into pyruvate. By now, however, there may be a crisis, in that blood glucose levels are low (during heavy exercise) and the brain is running out of glucose. Apart from the small supply of ketone bodies, the brain cannot use any other fuel, so coma and death can be averted only by replenishing blood glucose.

○ Which of the reverse-glycolysis bypass enzymes are needed for liver to convert its lactate-derived pyruvate into glucose, in order to top up blood glucose levels?

● All of them i.e. the enzymes catalysing steps 1 and 2 in the first bypass, as well as enzymes fructose bisphosphatase and glucose 6-phosphatase (FBPase and G6Pase).

4.6.3 SYNTHESIS OF STORAGE POLYSACCHARIDES

Higher organisms need not rely entirely on reverse-glycolysis for supplies of glucose in a crisis. They can *store* glucose in its polymerized form, as polysaccharide. The glucose derivative at the top of reverse-glycolysis is G6P, which can be converted to G1P (glucose 1-phosphate) and hence into insoluble storage polysaccharides, *starch* in plants and *glycogen* in animals (see Figure 4.35). In each case the glucose from G1P must first be covalently attached to a nucleotide (ADP for starch and UDP (Table 4.1) for glycogen). The glucose thus activated is then added, one molecule at a time, to a pre-existing glucose chain, forming glycogen or starch. When needed, glucose can then be released from the storage polymer as G1P again, e.g. through the activity of glycogen phosphorylase. (This last enzyme is activated by adrenalin, and features in the CD-ROM.)

These storage polysaccharides are formed solely from glucose. More exotic biosyntheses may need different sugars, some of which can be provided by the pentose phosphate pathway.

Figure 4.35 Synthesis of storage polysaccharides. Phosphorylases catalyse the removal of coenzymes ADP and UDP by hydrolysis.

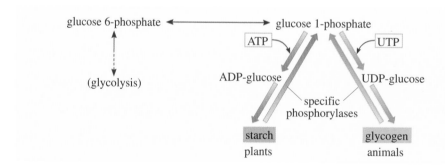

4.6.4 PENTOSE PHOSPHATE PATHWAY, PPP

The **pentose phosphate pathway** is a specialized route for glucose breakdown, in tissues that need NADP.2H or unusual sugar phosphates for biosynthesis. The reduced coenzyme NADP.2H, unlike its close relative NAD.2H, is not fed into the ETC for energy production, but used to provide H atoms in several biosynthetic reactions, notably those involving fatty acids. Hence in mammals, the PPP is particularly active in actively secreting mammary glands and adipose tissue.

The PPP can be viewed simplistically as a loop in glycolysis, diverging from it at G6P and rejoining it at F6P (see top left of Figure 4.32). In the loop between G6P and F6P are many useful sugar phosphate intermediates, including several *pentoses* (5C sugars), hence the name of the pathway. These pentoses include ribulose bisphosphate (an intermediate of the dark reactions of photosynthesis), and ribose 5-phosphate (needed for making nucleic acids).

4.6.5 GLYOXYLATE CYCLE

The **glyoxylate cycle** enables plants and microbes to convert fat into carbohydrate, by increasing the amount of acetyl CoA that can be turned into OAA. It can be viewed as a modified TCA cycle with some steps omitted and two new enzyme-catalysed steps added (see Figure 4.36). Animals lack these two enzymes, and therefore cannot use the glyoxylate cycle to turn fat into carbohydrate.

Figure 4.36 The glyoxylate cycle.

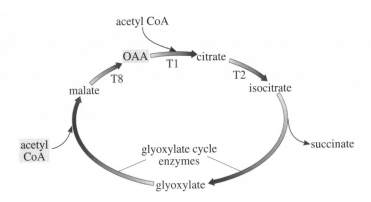

In plants, genes encoding the two extra enzymes are switched on when, for example, oil-rich seeds start to germinate. They can then convert oil reserves into structural carbohydrate, in what we may think of as two stages. First, the glyoxylate cycle is used to convert acetyl CoA from the breakdown of oil (TAG) into OAA.

○ What is the second stage?

● The conversion of OAA to the glycolytic intermediate PEP, and thence by reverse-glycolysis to glucose. (The OAA to PEP reaction you met earlier, as part of the first bypass in reverse-glycolysis.)

4.6.6 CENTRAL ROLE OF ACETYL CoA

Clearly acetyl CoA is a key intermediate in metabolism. As a product of the link reaction, it passes 2C units from pyruvate to the TCA cycle, and we have just seen how in plants and microbes it passes on 2C units from fatty acids. The alternative route to the TCA cycle from fatty acids — and the only one open to animals — is via fatty acid activation and oxidation as described in Section 4.5.3.

Apart from the glyoxylate cycle, these reactions take place in the mitochondria. But acetyl CoA can also be exported into the cytosol for *fatty acid synthesis*. Two highly regulated enzymes (acetyl CoA carboxylase and fatty acid synthase) then recombine its 2C acetyl units into fatty acid. *Fatty acid synthase* is another example of a multienzyme complex, even bigger than PDC of the link reaction. Its seven different types of protein catalyse consecutive steps in the reaction, using NADP.2H (largely from the pentose phosphate pathway) to provide the H atoms needed for reduction steps.

Fatty acid synthesis via acetyl CoA allows organisms to produce fat from a variety of sources, e.g. amino acids in carnivores, glucose in rodents. Most animals eat no more than necessary for their immediate needs. But fat synthesis via acetyl CoA may be important in particular circumstances, e.g. in preparing for hibernation or for migration, during lactation in female mammals, and gross overeating in humans.

It used to be thought that humans should 'slim' by avoiding excess dietary carbohydrate — cutting down on cakes and sweets, etc. However, it is now clear that except in extreme cases, overindulgent humans put on weight by directing dietary fat into adipose tissue stores, rather than by converting dietary carbohydrate into fat. On a normal diet, dietary fat would have been oxidized — along with any dietary carbohydrate — to provide energy. On an excessive diet, the extra carbohydrate is oxidized instead, and most of the dietary fat is laid down as 'fat'. This is why slimmers should concentrate on low-fat diets, rather than on reducing carbohydrate. (In prolonged, gross over-eating of carbohydrate, or in those unfortunate people with metabolic defects, carbohydrates are converted into fats, and stored in adipose tissue.)

SUMMARY OF SECTION 4.6

1 Intermediates of the oxidation pathways may be precursors (starting compounds) for biosynthetic pathways.

2 Replenishing or 'topping up' routes may be needed to supply key intermediates from alternative sources.

3 Reverse-glycolysis can convert pyruvate into glucose, bypassing irreversible reactions with different, non-glycolytic enzymes. This arrangement has the advantage of allowing separate control mechanisms. In bypass 1, the PK (pyruvate kinase) reaction is replaced by a two-step reaction: pyruvate $\longrightarrow$ OAA $\longrightarrow$ PEP. In bypass 2, fructose bisphosphatase replaces PFK (phosphofructokinase) and in bypass 3, glucose 6-phosphatase replaces HK (hexokinase).

4 Glucose storage polymers, starch and glycogen, can be synthesized from G6P via G1P (glucose 1-phosphate) after activation by ATP or UTP; glucose is released again as G1P by the action of phosphorylase enzymes.

5 The PPP (pentose phosphate pathway) operates as a loop between glycolytic intermediates G6P and F6P, in tissues where reduced NADP and specialized sugars (e.g. ribose phosphate) are needed for biosynthesis.

6 The glyoxylate cycle allows plants and microbes to convert extra acetyl CoA into OAA, by a modified version of the TCA cycle involving two new enzymes.

7   Acetyl CoA is a key metabolic intermediate in the oxidation of both glucose and fatty acid, and in the synthesis of fatty acid as catalysed by fatty acid synthase, a highly regulated cytosolic enzyme that uses NADP.2H.

4.7   CONTROL OF METABOLISM

4.7.1   OVERVIEW

The rate of glucose oxidation in the cell is carefully tuned to its current needs, since there is clearly no point, for example, in breaking down valuable fuel compounds if the cell is already able to meet all demands for ATP. The same is true of all metabolic pathways; there has to be a balance between catabolism and biosynthesis, tuned to the changing needs of each part of the organism. There are two aspects to metabolic control, first the basic mechanisms that control **metabolic flux**, the rate at which materials flow through a particular pathway. How, for example, is flux through the oxidation pathways tailored to meet the need for ATP at different times — in rest, exercise, rapid growth, etc?

The second, broader aspect of metabolic control concerns the *balance between different pathways* in particular tissues and particular physiological circumstances, e.g. in plants when laying down seed reserves or in germination, and in animals during starvation or preparation for hibernation, lactation, etc.

Although all tissues in an organism have the same genes, different metabolic pathways may predominate depending on tissue function. Hormonal control of the expression of metabolic enzymes is one, relatively long-term control mechanism while in the short term, metabolism is controlled by basic mechanisms common to all cells — substrate availability, allostery, covalent modification, compartmentation and hormones. We consider each of these regulators in turn, before looking in Section 4.8 at some individual tissues in vertebrates.

4.7.2   SUBSTRATE AVAILABILITY

Any reaction, e.g. $A \longrightarrow B$ has a natural balance point where the ratio of product concentration to reactant concentration ($[B]/[A]$) is such that the forward reaction ($A \longrightarrow B$) proceeds at the same rate as the back reaction ($B \longrightarrow A$). The equilibrium constant K is the ratio of product to reactant concentration ($[B]/[A]$) at this *equilibrium point*.

However, the cell is not at equilibrium but in a **steady state** where A is constantly being regenerated from precursor a, and B is constantly being turned into C and hence removed. As reactants are continually being supplied and products removed, the concentration of intermediates between them remains the same. It is like a bath with taps on and plug pulled out, always filling and always emptying. At a certain flow rate, the level of bath water stays the same, even though individual water molecules are being replaced. So if substrate availability drops, flux through the whole pathway drops. This happens when supplies of the first reactant dwindle, or when an intermediate is tapped off into a branching pathway.

In a steady state, some enzymes are operating nearer their equilibrium positions than others. For those where substrate and product levels ([S] and [P]) are nearly at equilibrium, little can be achieved by changing the *rate* at which equilibrium is reached. However, for an enzyme whose substrate/product levels are far from equilibrium, even small increases in catalytic activity can have a major influence on flux through the pathway as a whole. Such an enzyme may be catalysing the *rate-determining step* in a pathway. An example may make this type of regulation clearer.

○ At cellular concentrations, the ratio of product concentration, [P], to substrate concentration, [S], is 0.03 for the glycolytic enzyme PFK, and 0.24 for the enzyme catalysing the previous reaction, G3. The respective equilibrium constants are 1200 and 0.4. Which enzyme will have the greatest effect on glycolytic flux, if its catalytic activity is increased by an activator? (Note: the equilibrium constant is the ratio of product to substrate when the reaction is at equilibrium.)

● The relative levels of S and P are very far from equilibrium for the PFK enzyme (0.03 compared with 1200) but almost at equilibrium for the G3 enzyme (0.24 compared with 0.4). Hence *changes in the activity of PFK* will have the greatest effect on glycolytic flux.

It used to be thought that 'far-from-equilibrium' enzymes were the major control points in glucose oxidation, because they catalysed rate-determining steps in the pathway. This view has now been modified, partly to take account of metabolic channelling (see below) where groups of closely linked enzymes operate as a unit. However, it has also become clear that control is, to a certain extent, shared between all the enzymes in a pathway. While certain far-from-equilibrium **regulatory enzymes** do take a major share, there is usually no single control point as was once thought.

Calculations described as *metabolic control analysis* attempt to quantify the contributions of different enzymes to overall flux rate under different conditions within the cell, and hence identify the rate-determining steps.

4.7.3 ALLOSTERY

Regulatory enzymes are usually allosteric proteins (Chapter 2), and their catalytic activity can be controlled by compounds structurally unrelated to the substrate. This can be very useful for coordinating different pathways, or different parts of the same pathway for example, by inhibiting the early reactions of glycolysis when products of later reactions are beginning to build up — the phenomenon known as **feedback inhibition**. Compounds known as allosteric effectors bind specifically to a separate *regulatory site* on the enzyme protein, and from here a conformational change can be relayed through the tertiary structure to the catalytic site, altering V_{max} or more usually, K_M. As we shall see in the examples in Section 4.8, some *carbon intermediates* can act as allosteric inhibitors of key glucose oxidation enzymes, while the most important activators are *adenine nucleotides* (notably AMP) and *calcium ions*.

You have frequently met the two common adenine nucleotides, ATP and ADP. The third one, AMP or adenosine monophosphate, can be formed from ADP in a reversible reaction catalysed by the enzyme **adenylate kinase**.

$$2\text{ ADP} \rightleftharpoons \text{ATP} + \text{AMP} \qquad\qquad (4.7)$$

This very active enzyme is found in all tissues, and helps to ensure a steady supply of ATP via glycolysis, even when energy needs are fluctuating widely. *In vivo* ATP levels in the cytosol are remarkably constant at around 3 mmol l^{-1}, but small changes are *amplified* by the action of adenylate kinase. The extra ATP produced in reaction 4.7 adds little to the 3 mmol l^{-1} already present. However resting AMP levels are only around 0.01 mmol l^{-1}, and can be boosted several hundred-fold by this reaction. Since AMP is a powerful activator of phosphorylase and PFK, glycolytic flux increases and ATP levels are automatically restored. This amplification mechanism makes the cell extremely sensitive to small fluctuations in ATP levels.

4.7.4 COVALENT MODIFICATION

Allostery is a rapid low-cost control mechanism, involving only non-covalent interactions between effector and enzyme protein. Covalent modification is energetically more expensive, because a small group of atoms is *covalently* linked to a particular amino acid in the protein. This addition alters the packing of nearby groups and relays a conformational change to the catalytic site of the protein — just as in allostery. *Phosphorylation* adds a phosphate from ATP, and is the commonest such modification. It is catalysed by *protein kinase* enzymes specific for the protein being modified. An example is phosphorylase kinase, as in Figure 4.37. The phosphate group is then removed by a specific *phosphatase*.

A big advantage of this system is the built-in amplification, since one molecule of a kinase can activate (or inhibit) many molecules of its substrate protein — which itself is often an enzyme with its own substrate. So the effect on this second substrate of the original kinase activity is greatly amplified. Linking enzyme activations in this way is aptly called a *cascade*.

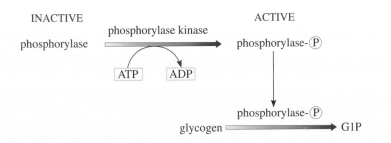

Figure 4.37 Activation of the enzyme phosphorylase, by its kinase, phosphorylase kinase, has a cascade effect on levels of G1P.

4.7.5 HORMONES

Hormones and growth factors may exert their effects by activating a protein kinase by covalent modification and so changing metabolic flux. An example is adrenalin, which binds to cell surface receptors, that in turn activate the kinase

Figure 4.38 Effect of hormones on glucose availability. The mechanisms whereby hormones affect their targets is outlined only. In reality, other proteins (receptors) are involved.

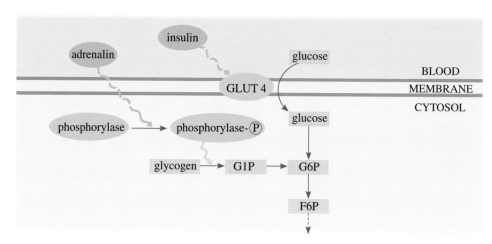

that phosphorylates the enzyme glycogen phosphorylase. Once phosphorylated, this enzyme is far more active in breaking down glycogen (Figure 4.37). Hence adrenalin indirectly makes more G6P available for glycolysis (see Figure 4.38). You will learn more about this in Chapter 6.

More usually, however, hormones affect *gene expression* rather than covalent modification, thereby altering the levels of metabolic enzymes by protein synthesis. A third method of hormonal control is seen in the case of *insulin*, which raises the availability of existing molecules of **GLUT 4**, the specific glucose transporter in the outer membranes of skeletal muscle (see Figure 4.38). Without insulin, GLUT 4 is not available and glucose in the blood cannot get into the muscle.

4.7.6 COMPARTMENTATION AND METABOLIC CHANNELLING

Transport proteins play a big part in metabolism since without them, most cell and organelle membranes are impermeable to carbon intermediates, nucleotides and ions. A pyruvate transporter, for example, is needed to move pyruvate across the inner mitochondrial membrane for further oxidation. Specific transporters are also needed for phosphate and calcium ions, and for equilibrating the pools of NAD/NAD.2H and ATP/ADP between the mitochondria and the cytosol. The adenine nucleotide transporter, however, does not carry AMP.

○ Since adenylate kinase is a cytosolic enzyme, what are the implications for AMP as a control molecule?

● Its effects are confined to the cytosol. (In fact as we shall see shortly, ADP not AMP is the control nucleotide for ATP synthesis within the mitochondrion.)

One advantage of **compartmentation** is that soluble reactants — substrates and most enzymes — are confined to smaller spaces, and are hence more concentrated than if they were free to diffuse throughout the cell. Intermediates of the TCA cycle, for example, remain within the mitochondrial matrix (although specific transporters allow some of them to participate in metabolic pathways elsewhere in the cell).

Metabolic channelling confines soluble intermediates even further. Some enzymes are so closely linked that the product of one immediately becomes the substrate of another, passing directly between the two active sites without dissolving in the surrounding medium at all. Metabolic channelling is particularly advanced in the pyruvate dehydrogenase complex (PDC), which has three different types of protein subunit, each catalysing a different step in the overall reaction. Similarly, there appears to be a loose non-covalent connection between certain glycolytic enzyme-pairs, G4/G6 and G6/G7, allowing carbon intermediates to pass rapidly between them. The electron transfer chain is another example of metabolic channelling, where electron carriers are embedded in the inner mitochondrial membrane in order of their electron affinity. Electrons are channelled rapidly from one to another without passing into the surrounding medium.

SUMMARY OF SECTION 4.7

1 Metabolic flux rates can be controlled by substrate availability.

2 Substrate levels within the cell are not at equilibrium but in a steady state. So factors affecting one step alter flux through the pathway as a whole.

3 Allosteric effectors bind to regulatory (allosteric) sites on enzymes, and alter catalytic activity at the active site. They provide fine control by compounds not directly involved in the reaction, and may allow feedback inhibition.

4 Phosphorylation is one example of a covalent change to enzyme structure that alters catalytic activity at the active site. It may be indirectly under hormonal control (e.g. adrenalin in the case of the phosphorylation of the enzyme glycogen phosphorylase).

4.8 INTEGRATING THE ENERGY NEEDS OF DIFFERENT TISSUES IN VERTEBRATES

4.8.1 OVERVIEW

In vertebrates, some tissues such as muscle make big demands on the energy supply of the body as a whole, while others are specialized for energy storage, e.g. glycogen in liver tissue and TAGs in adipose tissue (fat). We see first how these fuel resources are shared between different tissues via the blood, and how each tissue has its preferred source of energy. We then look at one tissue — skeletal muscle — in more detail, so that you can see how the molecular control mechanisms just described (Section 4.7) actually coordinate the pathways described earlier (Sections 4.4–4.6).

4.8.2 DIFFERENT VERTEBRATE TISSUES USE DIFFERENT FUELS

Perhaps surprisingly, only in brain is glucose the main fuel oxidized. The blood–brain barrier cannot be crossed by any of the alternative fuels except ketone bodies, which are used in starvation. Since life stops when the brain is deprived of energy, other tissues tend to conserve glucose, using non-glucose fuels for most of the time. For example, both heart and skeletal muscle preferentially oxidize fatty acids rather than glucose. These larger molecules are readily transported in the blood from either gut (dietary fat) or adipose tissue (fat stores).

The heart is another vital organ that cannot be allowed to stop working, but unlike the brain, it can oxidize lactate as well as fatty acids, ketone bodies or glucose.

○ Which tissue produces large quantities of lactate?

● Skeletal muscle produces large quantities of lactate during heavy exercise (see Section 4.4.5). The lactate is secreted into the blood, from where the heart takes it up.

○ Which reactions/pathways are involved in producing ATP from lactate, in oxidative conditions?

● Lactate is first converted into pyruvate, via the LDH reaction (see Figure 4.3a in Section 4.4.5), and then completely oxidized via the link reaction, TCA cycle and ETC.

Liver is unusual in that dietary amino acids reach it directly from the gut and they are its major fuel source for ATP production in people on a protein-rich diet.

○ Which enzyme-catalysed reactions and pathways produce ATP from amino acids (via oxidative phosphorylation) in liver?

● Specific transaminases convert certain amino acids directly into carbon intermediates of glycolysis or the TCA cycle. The link reaction and/or TCA cycle (and ETC) complete the oxidation process. (Many other amino acids are converted *indirectly* into carbon intermediates of the glucose oxidation pathway.)

In these ways, fuels are distributed round the vertebrate body, optimizing the use of available fuels for different tissues in different situations — rest, exercise and starvation.

4.8.3 METABOLIC CONTROL IN SKELETAL MUSCLE

Skeletal muscle that moves the limbs, etc. is specialized not for steady continuous contraction like the heart, but for periods of intense activity followed by rest. Heart muscle, of course, cannot rest without disastrous consequences, and structurally it is very different from skeletal muscle which has two main types of fibres. White 'glycolytic' fibres have very few mitochondria, and are specialized for making ATP by glycolysis under anaerobic conditions. In contrast, red 'oxidative' fibres make ATP via oxidative phosphorylation. The proportion of red to white fibres depends on what the muscle does. The flight muscle of a ground-based bird such as the pheasant has mostly white fibres, so is specialized for coping with the short intense activity of flying into a tree to roost. Sprinters and weight-lifters also expend energy in short intensive bursts, and also have predominantly white fibres in the appropriate muscle. In such athletes, intensive training can increase the proportion of white fibres till they constitute up to 75% of all fibres. In contrast, marathon runners and migratory birds need to sustain moderate activity for long periods, and their leg or flight muscles are largely made up of oxidative, red fibres.

Energy production in both fibre types is controlled by the molecular mechanisms described in Section 4.7, and varies in different circumstances. We now describe skeletal muscle in three different circumstances.

A AFTER A MEAL WHICH CONTAINS CARBOHYDRATE

Levels of blood glucose rise after such a meal, so skeletal muscle has the opportunity of replenishing its glycogen stores (see Figure 4.35).

○ Why does the first step in this process involve the hormone insulin?

● Muscle cell membrane is impermeable to glucose unless the specific glucose transporter GLUT 4 is available. Insulin promotes the transport of glucose from blood to cytosol, by increasing the availability of this membrane-bound protein (see Section 4.7.5).

○ Once in the cytosol, glucose can be converted into glycogen. What is the sequence of intermediates involved?

● Glucose $\longrightarrow$ G6P $\longrightarrow$ G1P $\longrightarrow$ UDP-glucose $\longrightarrow$ glycogen (see Figure 4.35)

Normally skeletal muscle has enough stored glycogen to maintain ATP supplies via glycolysis for only 20 seconds. Athletes who indulge themselves at pasta parties before a competitive endurance event can store large quantities of starch-derived glucose as glycogen.

B AT REST

Skeletal muscle at rest oxidizes TAGs, first hydrolysing them to fatty acids and glycerol which automatically saves glucose for the brain, by switching off glycolysis. The shut-down mechanism involves three allosteric proteins, and is initiated directly and indirectly by the rise in fatty acid levels (see Figure 4.39a).

1   As fatty acids feed into the TCA cycle, citrate levels rise (see **1** in Figure 4.39a). Citrate is an inhibitor of the allosteric enzyme PFK (phosphofructokinase). Inhibiting PFK leads to a build-up of its substrate F6P (see **2** in Figure 4.39a) which in turn raises the level of G6P (by reversing the G2 reaction).

2   G6P is an allosteric inhibitor of glycogen phosphorylase (see **3** in Figure 4.39a), which catalyses the release of G1P from glycogen. This is the key rate-determining step in the whole sequence of reactions leading to the oxidation of stored glucose. Hence as fatty acid levels rise, glycogen phosphorylase is automatically switched off and glycolysis is deprived of glycogen-derived glucose. Note the efficiency of this feedback inhibition, which minimizes wastage by blocking the first step in the pathway.

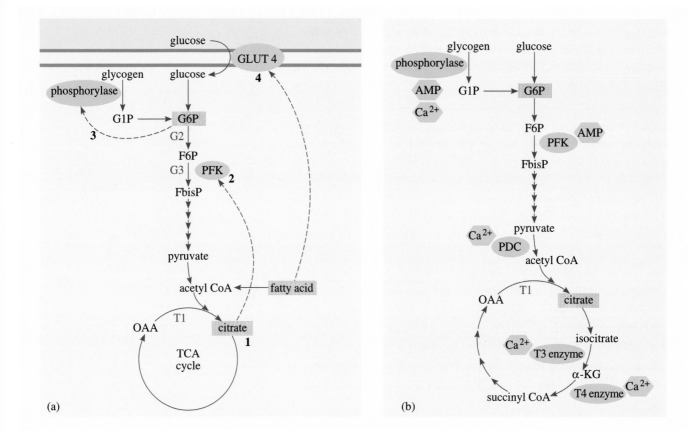

Figure 4.39 Allosteric proteins in the control of glucose oxidation in skeletal muscle. Allosteric proteins are in red ovals, inhibitors in grey boxes, activators in orange hexagons. (a) Effect of carbon intermediates. Citrate levels rise as fatty acid levels rise (see **1**); citrate inhibits allosteric enzyme PFK (see **2**); the resulting build-up of G6P (see text) inhibits the allosteric enzyme glycogen phosphorylase (see **3**). Blood glucose uptake is inhibited by the direct action of fatty acid on the allosteric protein GLUT4 (see **4**). (b) Effect of calcium ions and AMP.

3   Although glycolysis can now no longer be fuelled from glycogen, blood glucose is still available. This loophole is also closed by fatty acid, this time acting directly. Fatty acid binds to a regulatory site on a third allosteric protein GLUT 4, the glucose transport protein, thereby blocking its glucose-binding site. Hence blood glucose cannot enter the cell (see **4** in Figure 4.39a).

C   DURING EXERCISE

Our final scenario is skeletal muscle in exercise, when both glycogen stores and — in prolonged exercise — blood glucose are broken down anaerobically (by white fibres) and aerobically (by red fibres). Glycolytic flux responds to the small drop in ATP concentration via AMP (see Section 4.7.3). Since AMP is a potent activator of both PFK and glycogen phosphorylase, the overall effect is to speed up the oxidation of glycogen-derived glucose (see Figure 4.39b) which automatically restores ATP levels.

This effect is reinforced by calcium ions, which are released into the cytosol of contracting fibres, and boost the activity of both glycogen phosphorylase and its kinase. Since phosphorylase activation is via a cascade, the Ca^{2+} effect is greatly amplified. In red fibres, Ca^{2+} also stimulates each stage of aerobic oxidation by acting as allosteric activator for PDC (link reaction), and isocitrate dehydrogenase and α-ketoglutarate dehydrogenase (the T3 and T4 enzymes of the TCA cycle).

Thus in exercise, extra energy is provided via the actions of AMP and Ca^{2+}, both of which increase the output of ATP. A hormonal mechanism may also come into play. Any sudden switch from rest to intense activity can stimulate the release of adrenalin, the 'flight or fight' hormone that prepares vertebrates to cope with emergency. It overrides the 'stop signal' posted on glycolysis by the presence of fatty acids, and via cell surface receptors activates phosphorylase kinase by covalent modification.

SUMMARY OF SECTION 4.8

1   Vertebrate tissues are specialized to oxidize different fuels, which are distributed between them via the blood.

2   Skeletal muscle is structurally specialized for the anaerobic or aerobic oxidation of glucose, depending on its content of white or red fibres.

3   Hormonal control is exerted through substrate availability after a meal (insulin/GLUT 4) and covalent modification in emergency (adrenalin/ phosphorylase cascade).

4   Calcium ions released during muscle contraction are allosteric activators for protein kinase in the phosphorylase cascade, thereby increasing glycolytic flux. Aerobic oxidation is similarly stimulated by calcium ions, via the allosteric activation of PDC, and the T3 and T4 enzymes.

5   At rest, skeletal muscle oxidizes fatty acid, and glycolysis is shut down by allosteric inhibition of PFK, phosphorylase and GLUT 4.

6   In exercise, glycolytic flux in skeletal muscle is increased by the activation of both glycogen phosphorylase and PFK. The relevant activators are calcium ions (which also activate PDC and the T3/T4 enzymes), and AMP.

FURTHER READING

Stryer, L. (1995) *Biochemistry* (4th edn), W. H. Freeman and Company, New York.

Zubay G. L (1998) *Biochemistry* (4th edn), Wm. C. Brown Publishers (McGraw-Hill), Dubuque, USA.

[Comprehensive biochemistry texts for those who wish to read about biochemistry in more detail.]

MAKING ATP

5.1   INTRODUCTION

5.1.1   DIFFERENT WAYS OF MAKING ATP FROM THE OXIDATION OF NUTRIENTS

In the last chapter we saw how complex food molecules are broken down to provide building blocks for biosynthesis, and to release energy for this and other processes. We now see how this energy is converted into ATP, the all-important molecule that acts both as a coenzyme and as a short-term energy store. (Because the breakdown of ATP to ADP has a large negative ΔG, it can drive many energy-requiring reactions; see coupled reactions in Section 4.2.3.) So far we have said little about ATP and just discussed the formation of reduced coenzymes. One of the commonest ways of making ATP from nutrients is to reoxidize these coenzymes via the mitochondrial electron transport chain. This involves the high ATP-yielding process of oxidative phosphorylation which, like photo-phosphorylation in chloroplasts, takes place on specialized energy-exchange membranes (e.g. the inner mitochondrial membrane). It uses a proton gradient to link the energy of electron transport to ATP synthesis. Oxidative phosphorylation was outlined in Chapter 3. Quite different is the low-yield synthesis of ATP by substrate-level phosphorylation, which takes place in solution, in the cytosol.

This chapter describes these different mechanisms of ATP synthesis, starting with substrate-level phosphorylation (Section 5.1.2). We then set the scene for photo- and oxidative phosphorylation by describing energy-exchange membranes and chemiosmosis, and the membrane-bound ATP synthase (Section 5.2). We then show how these principles apply to making ATP by oxidative phosphorylation in mitochondria (Section 5.3) and in microbes (Section 5.4), before turning to photophosphorylation (Sections 5.5 and 5.6).

5.1.2   SUBSTRATE-LEVEL PHOSPHORYLATION

Substrate-level phosphorylation is an enzyme-catalysed process in which ATP is made by transferring a phosphate group directly to ADP from a phosphorylated carbon intermediate in the cytosol. To get the necessary energy, substrate-level phosphorylation is always coupled to an enzyme-catalysed, energy-releasing oxidation. An example is the G6/G7 pair of glycolytic reactions which link ADP phosphorylation in reaction G7 to the oxidation of G3P in reaction G6 (see Figure 5.1, overleaf). The 2H atoms removed in the oxidation are picked up by coenzyme NAD. The problem with making ATP in this way is that the NAD.2H so formed must be reoxidized before NAD is once again available for the G6 step. (Remember this pathway is anaerobic, and no electron transport chain is involved in substrate-level phosphorylation.) The right side of Figure 5.1 shows how the reoxidation problem may be solved in a second coenzyme-requiring reaction where another carbon intermediate is reduced, taking the 2H package from NAD.2H and leaving NAD. You have already met this particular reduction — it is the LDH reaction in heavily exercising skeletal muscle of vertebrates (Chapter 4).

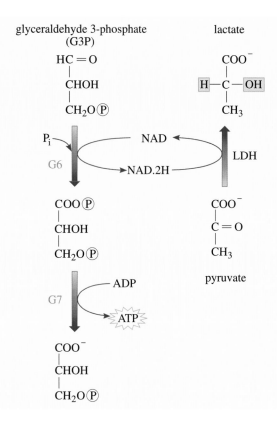

Figure 5.1 Linked coenzyme-requiring reactions in the regeneration of NAD from NAD.2H. The left side of the figure shows how NAD is reduced to NAD.2H in the oxidation reaction G6. The right side of the figure shows how NAD is regenerated in the reaction catalysed by lactate dehydrogenase (LDH).

Because no specialized membrane-rich organelles are needed, substrate-level phosphorylation is the only way of making ATP in cells that have no mitochondria, such as red blood cells and in eye lens (where mitochondria would disrupt the passage of light). It is also a major source of ATP in cells that need a lot of energy for biosynthesis, e.g. in tumours and in the immune system.

However, this anaerobic process is a very inefficient way of generating energy from nutrients, since the carbon skeleton is not completely broken down. The TCA cycle can increase the recovery of nutrient energy by splitting glucose-derived intermediates right down to CO_2, and attaching all that is left — the H atoms — to coenzymes. These reactions produce large quantities of reduced coenzymes, key compounds which can then be reoxidized by molecular oxygen, in the high-yield ATP-synthesizing process known as oxidative phosphorylation; here the oxidation (of reduced coenzymes) is coupled to the phosphorylation of ADP to ATP. Coupling takes place in the mitochondria and, like the similar process of photophosphorylation in chloroplasts, it depends on the unique properties of proteins embedded in energy-exchange membranes.

5.2   ENERGY-EXCHANGE MEMBRANES

5.2.1   STORING ENERGY IN TRANSMEMBRANE ION GRADIENTS

We now come to this totally different way of making ATP which depends upon specialized proteins embedded in a phospholipid membrane enclosing a small space; the membrane must be impermeable to ions except via specific protein channels. Just such an arrangement is seen in the two energy-exchange organelles — mitochondria and chloroplasts — which channel the chemical energy of metabolism or the light energy of photosynthesis, into the chemical energy of ATP. In each case, the energy source (metabolism or light) is used to *create a proton gradient across the membrane*, i.e. to transport H^+ ions through the membrane so that there is an excess on one side. This imbalance can be used to store energy. In mitochondria and chloroplasts, there is said to be an *electrochemical* gradient rather than a simple concentration gradient, because the accumulated ions give an imbalance of charge as well as concentration. However, the net effect of the transmembrane gradient is the same; when the protons are allowed to move back down the gradient, the energy released can be used to do work.

In the energy-exchange organelles we are describing, this downhill movement is directed through the proton channel of a membrane-bound enzyme, **ATP synthase**, a large complex molecule that makes up 15% of the protein in the inner mitochondrial membrane. Its structure is shown in Figure 5.2a (overleaf). It catalyses the synthesis of ATP (ADP + $P_i \longrightarrow$ ATP). The catalytic 'head' of the enzyme is known as the F_1 subunit and can be clearly seen in electron micrographs as small knobs protruding from the membrane into the mitochondrial matrix. As shown in Figure 5.2b, the F_1 subunits can be sheared off the membrane by artificial means *in vitro*, forming a solution that can hydrolyse ATP. This reaction, of course, is the opposite of ATP synthesis, and releases energy rather than using it up. Only when F_1 is attached to the proton channel — known as the F_0 subunit — can it perform the energy-requiring reverse reaction and synthesize ATP. The F_1 subunit can be re-attached to a mitochondrial membrane, even if this has been damaged so that it is freely permeable to protons.

○   Why can such a preparation no longer make ATP, even though electron transport is still taking place?

●   Although electron transport energy is still being used to create a transmembrane proton gradient, the energy stored in this gradient is largely dissipated, as protons flood back through numerous nonspecific 'holes' in the membrane, rather than through the F_0 channel.

It was many years before scientists accepted that this temporary energy store — the transmembrane proton gradient — was the long-sought missing link between electron transport and ATP synthesis. It is now accepted, however, that the inner mitochondrial membrane is one example of an energy-exchange membrane that operates by **chemiosmotic coupling**. Here, electron transport energy is converted into proton gradient energy, which is then converted into chemical bond energy.

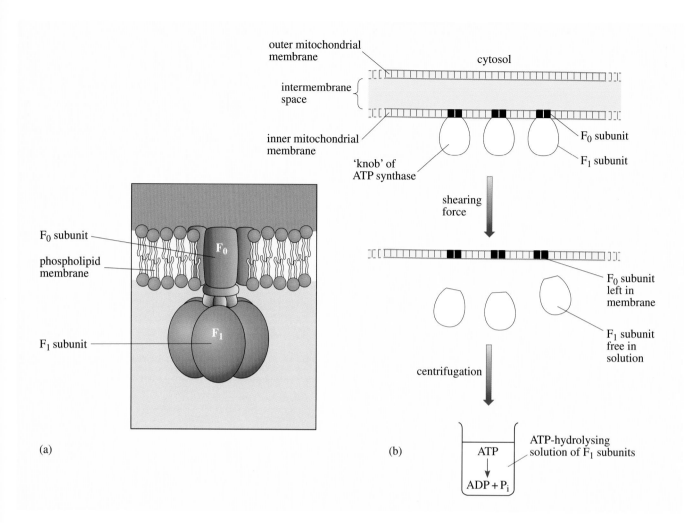

Figure 5.2 (a) Diagram of intact ATP synthase. (b) Separating F_0 and F_1 subunits of the ATP synthase protein by mechanical agitation followed by centrifugation.

Chemiosmotic coupling utilizing different ions occurs in a wide range of situations. In the chloroplast, for example, an energy-exchange membrane links electron transport to ATP synthesis in photophosphorylation, a chemiosmotic process where electrons are energized by light, not chemical energy. Some bacteria use Na^+ ions, not protons, in oxidative phosphorylation, driving their ATP synthase by a flood of Na^+ ions through the F_0 channel. There will be other examples of the enormous versatility of chemiosmotic coupling in what follows. All that is needed is a membrane impermeable to ions, with specialized proteins embedded in it. One such protein, which is central for ATP synthesis, is the F_0-F_1 ATP synthase.

5.2.2 THE F_0-F_1 ATP SYNTHASE

In vivo, this protein acts as an ATP synthase, using the energy of proton movement to synthesize ATP. However, *in vitro*, as we have already seen (Figure 5.2), it can act in reverse to hydrolyse ATP, and this ATPase activity has been a major tool in unravelling the reaction mechanism. The protein is made of eight different types of polypeptide chain, some with as many as 12 copies. The F_1 chains are labelled by Greek letters (α, β, etc.) and the F_0 chains by bold

Roman letters (**a**, **b**, **c**). Many different research groups have been asking the same question: how can a single protein convert electrical energy into chemical energy and vice versa? The answer, quite unexpectedly, points to an elastic go-between mechanism, a tiny rotating protein 'rod' that can be wound up in one direction by the electrical energy of proton movement and then released, using its wound-up elastic energy to drive ATP synthesis.

To visualize elastic energy, think of a rubber band with one end fixed and the other free to rotate (Figure 5.3). Imagine a pencil is inserted at the free end and rotated several times. The mechanical energy of rotation twists and stretches the rubber band which stores elastic energy, so that when the pencil is released it is immediately propelled across the room. The elastic energy has been converted into a third energy form, kinetic energy.

Studies on the ATP synthase point to a similar series of energy interconversions, not mechanical $\longrightarrow$ elastic $\longrightarrow$ kinetic (as for the rubber band) but electric $\longrightarrow$ elastic $\longrightarrow$ chemical.

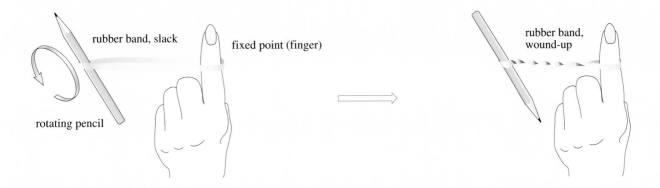

Figure 5.3 Elastic energy from stretching being stored in a rubber band.

The F_1 subunit of the ATP synthase uses chemical energy which, as we shall see, is derived from elastic energy. It has three identical catalytic sites which operate sequentially, making ATP molecules one after the other. The catalytic sites are arranged as a hollow ring of $\alpha\beta$ polypeptide chains with a rod made up of gamma (γ) chains in the centre (see Figure 5.4, overleaf). This gamma rod connects with another ring made of **c** chains, which lies in the membrane as part of the F_0 subunit. This **c** ring controls the movement of protons in and out of the protein as a whole, which brings us to the big question: how does movement of protons through the **c** ring provide the energy for ATP synthesis in the $\alpha\beta$ ring?

The answer, which is still tentative, comes from studying the reverse reaction, the *hydrolysis* of ATP at the three $\alpha\beta$ catalytic sites. Hydrolysis energy can be used to *rotate* the central gamma rod within the circle of $\alpha\beta$ catalytic units — a remarkable event that can actually be seen in isolated F_1 subunits, by attaching a synthetic fluorescent label to each chain in the gamma rod, and bathing the preparation in a solution of ATP. Figure 5.5 (overleaf) shows one such arrangement in detail. There is some remarkable video footage showing the minute fluorescent tail whirring round at a speed dependent on ATP concentration.

Figure 5.4 Artist's view of ATP synthase (based on Junge *et al.*, 1997).

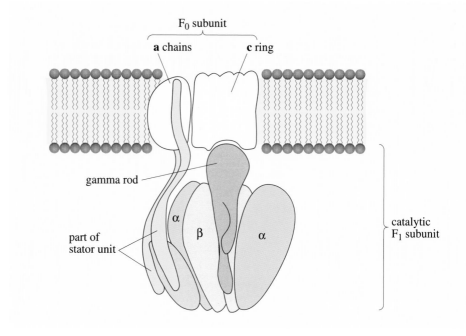

Figure 5.5 Arrangement for demonstrating rotation of the gamma rod of ATP synthase, when isolated F_1 subunits are bathed in a solution of ATP (based on Junge *et al.*, 1997).

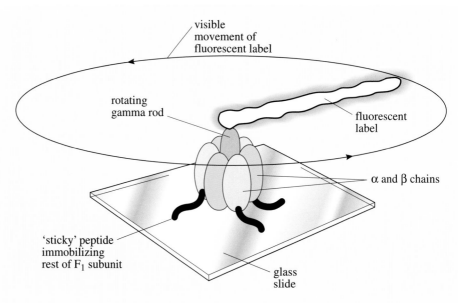

You might expect the $\alpha\beta$ ring to be dragged round by the gamma rod rotating inside it. But it is held firmly in place by polypeptide chains of the 'stator unit', some of which are embedded in the membrane (see Figure 5.4). As the gamma rod rotates, it also drags on the membrane-bound **c** ring connected to it. However, the **c** ring is constrained by electrostatic interactions with **a** chains lying next to it in the membrane. These electrostatic interactions, it is argued, can be relieved by the movement of protons. (For example, a proton binding to the R group of a negatively charged amino acid such as aspartate (Table 2.2) in a **c** chain would reduce its affinity for the positively charged R group of arginine on an **a** chain. This is turn would reduce the restraints on rotation.)

Though details of the link between proton movement and rotation remain to be worked out, this much seems clear: when the ATP synthase works in reverse, the chemical energy of ATP hydrolysis can be converted into elastic energy by rotating the gamma rod, and this energy is somehow converted into electric energy for proton movement. Conversely *in vivo* it is argued, proton movement in the other direction (as protons flood back down the gradient) rotates the gamma rod in the opposite direction, generating elastic energy which is now used to drive the synthesis of ATP.

Thus to summarize, the ATP synthase is a tiny electrically driven motor (the **c** ring) with a central rotating crankshaft (the gamma rod) that conveys the energy for ATP synthesis to each $\alpha\beta$ catalytic site in turn.

SUMMARY OF SECTIONS 5.1 AND 5.2

1   In substrate-level phosphorylation, ATP is made anaerobically, by transferring phosphate from a carbon intermediate to ADP. This reaction is linked to an enzyme-catalysed, energy-releasing oxidation; molecular oxygen is not required.

2   Oxidative phosphorylation and photophosphorylation take place on energy-exchange membranes by chemiosmotic coupling. Both require an electron transport chain, and oxidative phosphorylation also requires aerobic conditions.

3   Chemiosmotic coupling can use the energy of electron transfer to drive ATP synthesis, via a transmembrane ion gradient.

4   In oxidative phosphorylation and photophosphorylation, protons provide the ion gradient. Protons moving down their concentration gradient, through the F_0 channel of an F_0-F_1 ATP synthase, can drive the synthesis of ATP at the catalytic site of the F_1 subunit.

5   The ATP synthase converts the electrical energy of the proton gradient into elastic energy, by using it to rotate a molecular 'crankshaft'. When released, the crankshaft 'unwinds', delivering energy to three separate catalytic sites for ATP synthesis.

5.3   OXIDATIVE PHOSPHORYLATION IN MITOCHONDRIA

5.3.1   OVERVIEW

Having described in general terms how ATP is made on energy-exchange membranes by chemiosmotic coupling, we can now study a particular example — oxidative phosphorylation in mitochondria. The inner mitochondrial membrane is a very efficient energy-exchange system, synthesizing ATP by using energy extracted during the oxidation of fuel compounds. You will remember that both the link reaction and the TCA cycle produce NAD.2H and FAD.2H (see Chapter 4). Figure 5.6 (overleaf) shows diagrammatically how reoxidation of these reduced coenzymes is linked to ATP synthesis by chemiosmotic coupling. Three sets of membrane-embedded proteins are needed — electron carriers, proton pumps and ATP synthase. We examine the first two, and then go on to describe how chemiosmotic coupling can be controlled (Section 5.3.4) and investigated experimentally (Section 5.3.5).

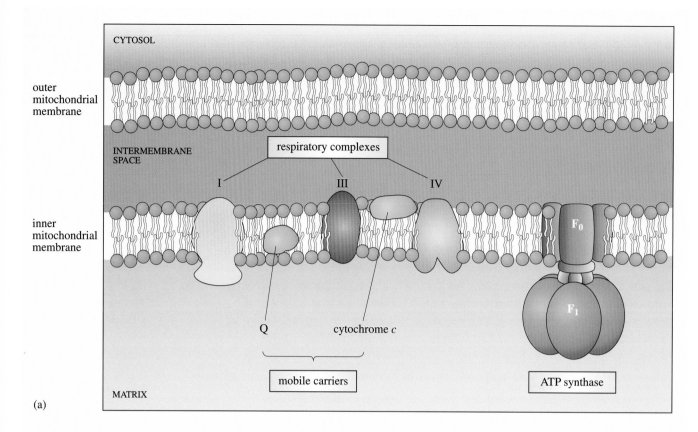

CYTOSOL

outer mitochondrial membrane

INTERMEMBRANE SPACE

respiratory complexes

I   III   IV

inner mitochondrial membrane

F₀

F₁

Q   cytochrome *c*

mobile carriers   ATP synthase

MATRIX

(a)

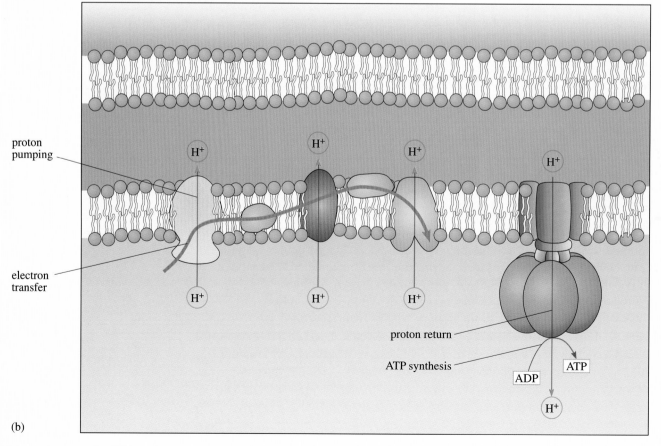

proton pumping

H⁺   H⁺   H⁺   H⁺

electron transfer

H⁺   H⁺   H⁺

proton return

ATP synthesis

ADP   ATP

H⁺

(b)

Figure 5.6   (a) Electron carriers in the inner mitochondrial membrane. Note that respiratory complexes I, III and IV also act as proton pumps. (b) Chemiosmotic coupling links electron transfer, proton pumping and ATP synthase. When electron transport begins (see brown arrow), energy becomes available for proton pumping (see red arrows). Some of these protons return via the F_0 channel, providing energy for ATP synthesis.

5.3.2   ELECTRON CARRIERS

Most **electron carrier** proteins have one or more metal atoms as part of their structure, each capable of temporarily accommodating an extra electron. The commonest such metal is iron (Fe) which can exist in two oxidation states, Fe^{2+} and Fe^{3+}. The higher oxidation state, Fe^{3+}, is seen when iron metal rusts, i.e. when it loses three electrons per atom. (All Fe^{3+} compounds have the red-orange colour of rust.) The oxidation of Fe^{2+} to Fe^{3+} (Equation 5.1) is readily reversible, which is very useful in the electron transport chain, where Fe-containing electron carriers can easily accept an electron from one neighbour and pass it on to the next. In passing the electron on, the Fe^{2+} reverts to the higher oxidation state, Fe^{3+}. In fact there is a constant switch between the two states, as shown in Equation 5.1.

$$Fe^{2+} \rightleftharpoons Fe^{3+} + e^- \qquad (5.1)$$

Iron can be incorporated into protein in different ways. In the group of small, reddish proteins known as cytochromes, the iron is part of the haem group, found also in haemoglobin. In the iron-sulfur or Fe-S proteins, up to four Fe atoms are linked together through the SH groups of several cysteine amino acids.

In the membrane, electron carriers are arranged in order of their electron affinity or *redox potential*. This allows electrons to pass spontaneously from one to another (see Box 5.1, overleaf, which you should read now). Carriers are also bunched together into four **respiratory complexes** (see Figure 5.6a). If phospholipids in the membrane are gently disrupted by detergent, the components of each complex remain together as a unit. Components of each unit can still pass electrons between them. In the intact membrane, electrons are carried between complexes — about one every 10 milliseconds — by two **mobile carriers**, the small lipid-soluble molecule ubiquinone (or Q), and the protein cytochrome *c* (shown in Figure 5.6).

Here we consider just respiratory complexes I, III and IV, which are involved in passing electrons from NAD.2H to O_2. (Complex II is involved in passing electrons into the ETC from FAD.2H.) Complex I contains the protein NADH dehydrogenase, which removes electrons from NAD.2H and passes them on via at least five Fe-S proteins, to the mobile carrier Q. Each of the five carriers is just the right distance from its electron-receiving partner, so that electrons follow an ordered pathway through the complex. The last carrier in complex I has a binding site for mobile carrier Q, which can also bind to the first member of complex III.

BOX 5.1 REDOX POTENTIAL

After a preliminary read through of the important but difficult material in this Box, you might like to look at the animated account of 'Redox Potentials' in the CD-ROM *Making ATP* (see section entitled 'ETC').

Whether or not a particular electron carrier can accept electrons from its neighbour, depends upon its electron affinity or **redox potential** (its potential to be **red**uced or **ox**idized). In mitochondria, for example, the mobile carrier Q in Figure 5.6 has a higher redox potential (RP) than carriers in the first respiratory complex, but a lower RP than those in the third complex. It therefore readily accepts electrons from the first and passes them on to the third. The point to remember is that low RP indicates low electron affinity, so *electrons flow towards compounds with high RP.*

The precise difference in RP between two compounds is important, because all electron transfer releases free energy which can do work (e.g. proton pumping). The free energy released is proportional to the RP difference ΔE, according to the following equation:

$$\Delta G = nF\Delta E \qquad\qquad (5.2)$$

where G is free energy (see Box 4.1), n represents the number of electrons transferred (usually one or two) and F is known as the Faraday constant. Electrons flow spontaneously towards compounds with a higher RP or lower free energy.

Figure 5.7 shows diagrammatically the RP values of the main electron carriers in the mitochondrial ETC. A large drop in RP — as between Q and cyt c, or between cyt c and oxygen — releases much free energy, which is shown in Figure 5.7 as three near-vertical arrows.

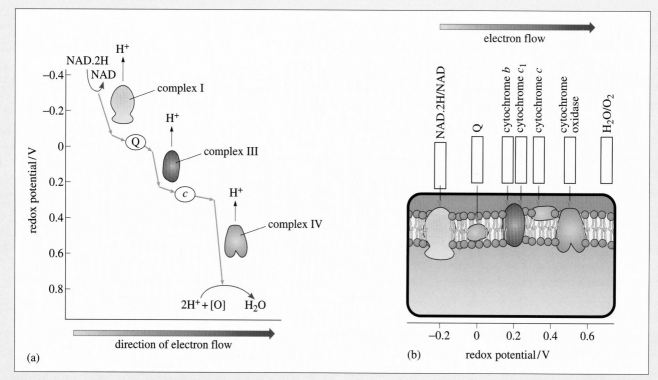

Figure 5.7 Redox potentials (RP) of mitochondrial electron carriers. (a) Graph showing RP on the vertical axis. Note how large RP differences release enough energy to pump protons. (b) Diagram of carriers *in situ* in membrane, with the RP axis horizontal (from the CD-ROM *Making ATP*).

The two forms — oxidized and reduced — of a substance that can readily exist in either form, are known as a **redox pair**, and can be represented as A_{red}/A_{ox}. Each *redox reaction* involves electron transfer between two such redox pairs, as in this equation:

$$A_{red} + B_{ox} \longrightarrow A_{ox} + B_{red} \tag{5.3}$$

Sometimes this equation is shown as two half-reactions, so that the separate redox pairs are clearer (see Figure 5.8). Either representation is a shorthand way of combining the oxidation of A ($A_{red} \longrightarrow A_{ox} + e^-$) with the simultaneous reduction of B ($B_{ox} + e^- \longrightarrow B_{red}$).

To measure the RP of a redox pair A_{red}/A_{ox}, for example, a half-reduced solution of compound A is compared with a half-reduced 1 mol l^{-1} solution of a reference redox pair $H_2/2H^+$. Electrodes are placed in each solution, so that electrons can pass from one to the other; the direction of flow depends of course on which solution has the strongest electron affinity, i.e. the highest RP. Under certain standard conditions (e.g. at 1 mol l^{-1} concentration) the reference redox pair is said to have an RP value of zero. So redox pairs with lower electron affinity *donate* their electrons to the standard; their RP values are negative. Conversely, redox pairs with high electron affinity *receive* electrons from the standard. Their RP values are positive. The direction of flow, and the precise RP value can be seen from the voltage registered on a voltmeter in the circuit. Hence RP values are expressed in volts (V) or millivolts (mV). In biological systems, they range from around −0.4 V to 0.8 V. Some examples are given in Table 5.1.

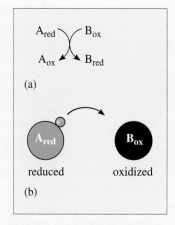

Figure 5.8   Ways of depicting a redox pair: (a) as two half-reactions; (b) as in the CD-ROM, where the small red sphere represents an electron.

Table 5.1   Standard redox potentials at pH 7 of redox pairs found in biology. (*Note*: the reduced form of each redox pair is shown in red.)

Redox pair	Redox potential/V
CO/CO_2	−0.54
$H_2/2H^+$	−0.42
$NADP.2H/NADP$	−0.32
$NAD.2H/NAD$	−0.32
H_2S/S^{2-}	−0.23
$Q_{(red)}/Q_{(ox)}$	+0.04
cyt $b_{(red)}$/cyt $b_{(ox)}$	+0.07
cyt $c_{1(red)}$/cyt $c_{1(ox)}$	+0.23
cyt $c_{(red)}$/cyt $c_{(ox)}$	+0.25
cyt $a_{(red)}$/cyt $a_{(ox)}$	+0.29
cyt $a_{3(red)}$/cyt $a_{3(ox)}$	+0.55
Fe^{2+}/Fe^{3+}	+0.78
H_2O/O_2	+0.82

From Q, electrons pass to this next complex which contains at least eight different proteins, among them cytochromes b and c_1 and another Fe-S protein. From here electrons pass out of complex III to the second mobile carrier, cytochrome c and finally to complex IV. Here they are received by cytochrome a_3, a protein which catalyses the final step in electron transfer.

$$2H^+ + 2e^- + [O] \longrightarrow H_2O \tag{5.4}$$

(The square brackets around oxygen indicate that only half an oxygen molecule is needed for each pair of electrons. The protons H^+ are drawn from the solution bathing the matrix side of the membrane, thus contributing to the proton gradient.)

Cytochrome a together with cytochrome a_3 are often referred to together as cytochrome oxidase. With cytochrome oxidase, we come at last to the oxygen that forms part of the overall equation for glucose oxidation (see Equation 4.7 earlier). The active site of cytochrome oxidase can bind molecular oxygen. Unfortunately it also binds certain other small molecules including cyanide, irreversibly blocking electron transport. So swallowing or inhaling cyanide can be fatal.

For a light-hearted look at respiratory complexes, see Figure 5.9 which has an extract from the *Biochemists' Songbook* by Harold Baum (1982).

THE BATTLE HYMN OF THE AEROBES

(*Tune: 'The Battle Hymn of the Republic'*)

Mine eyes have seen the glory of respiratory chains
In every mitochondrion, intrinsic to membranes,
Functionally organised in complex sub-domains
Where electrons flow along.
Glory, glory, respiration! (*three times*)
Where electrons flow along.

Each chain is a mosaic of Complexes I to IV
Embedded in the lipid (which is what the lipid's for)
But that is not sufficient, there are *two* components more
Where electrons, *etc.*

The first is a small cytochrome that rolls around the place
That's easily extractable from cytoplasmic face
That restores respiration if you just add back a trace,
Where electrons, *etc.*

The other's a [benzo]quinone that is ubiquitous,
It floats around the lipid phase with hardly any fuss,
For mobile pooling function it's become synonymous,
Where electrons, *etc.*

Figure 5.9 Respiratory complexes as featured in the *Biochemists' Songbook* by Harold Baum (1982, Pergamon Press).

5.3.3 PROTON PUMPS

Each respiratory complex in the mitochondrion can use the energy of electron transport to 'pump' protons against a concentration gradient, probably by an allosteric mechanism in which one of these membrane-embedded proteins flips from a high-affinity conformation to a low-affinity conformation. In the first state, a proton is picked up from the mitochondrial matrix, and moved across the protein to the edge of the intermembrane space (Figure 5.10). Simultaneously, electron transfer drives the conformational change to low affinity, and the proton is released.

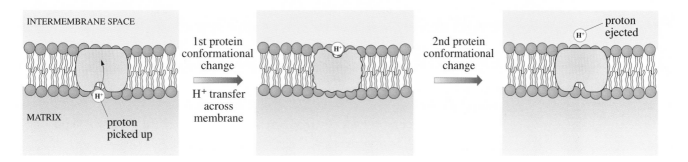

Figure 5.10 Possible role of allosteric proteins in proton pumping. In mitochondria, the conformational change would be powered by the energy of electron transfer.

5.3.4 RESPIRATORY CONTROL

The rate at which an organism oxidizes its fuel supply is carefully linked to its energy needs. Some of the control mechanisms for this were described in Chapter 4. However, in mitochondria, there is a further extremely important control point — the coupling of electron transport to ATP synthesis. So long as the inner mitochondrial membrane is impermeable to protons — except through the proton pump and F_0 channels described earlier — then neither electron flow nor ATP synthesis can operate independently of one another. It is as though electron carriers sense the activity of ATP synthase; when ATP synthesis slows down because ATP supplies are fully topped up, then the electron carriers slow down too. This phenomenon is known as **respiratory control**. It is very beneficial in the energy economy of the cell.

○　How does the coupling of electron transport to ATP synthesis prevent the wasteful breakdown of fuel compounds?

●　When ATP needs are satisfied and ATP synthase activity slows down, good respiratory control ensures that electron transport also slows, which leads to an accumulation of reduced coenzymes. Until they are reoxidized, the NAD- and FAD-dependent reactions of the TCA cycle, etc. cannot proceed.

Hence in so-called 'tightly coupled' mitochondria, where electron transport and ATP synthesis are strongly linked, there is an automatic feedback mechanism that conserves fuel when ATP is plentiful.

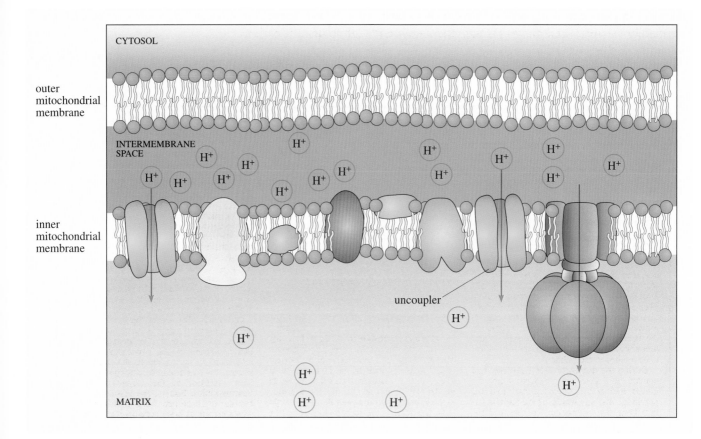

Figure 5.11   Uncouplers provide alternative, non-ATP-generating routes for protons returning to the mitochondrial matrix.

In terms of chemiosmotic coupling, the link between electron transport and ATP synthesis is clearly the proton gradient. As this builds up and more 'proton power' is available for the ATP synthase, then electron transport becomes increasingly difficult. However, this tight coupling between electron transport and ATP synthesis can be loosened — sometimes crudely as by accidental damage to the inner membrane of isolated mitochondria in cell homogenates — and sometimes more subtly as *in vivo*. An **uncoupler** is any compound that increases the proton permeability of the inner mitochondrial membrane and hence severs the link between electron transport and ATP synthesis. The energy is instead released as heat. The hormone thyroxine is one such compound. Another is the uncoupling protein of brown adipose tissue (BAT), a specialized thermogenic tissue found in mammals. The inner membranes of its many, rather large mitochondria contain an uncoupler protein with a specific proton channel (see Figure 5.11). Protons returning by this route rather than through the F_0 channel do not contribute energy for ATP synthesis. Thus the proton gradient is dissipated without making ATP, and the energy is released as heat instead.

Poisons such as 2,4-dinitrophenol and compounds previously marketed as related 'slimming' drugs also act as uncouplers — sometimes with disastrous consequences, as recorded in Figure 5.12. Only very small amounts are needed because each uncoupler molecule is regenerated. One molecule picks up a proton from the intermembrane space and moves through the membrane with it, depositing it in the matrix. It then returns through the membrane for another proton.

DRUGS USED FOR SLIMMING

REFERENCE was made at the monthly meeting of the Pharmaceutical Society, held at its Bloomsbury Square headquarters yesterday, to the recent case in which a girl dancer was found to have died through an overdose of drugs taken for slimming purposes.

A letter had been received from the Home Office, stating that the Home Secretary was of the opinion that if, as he was informed, drugs of the nitrophenol group were highly poisonous, they should be placed under the utmost restriction possible pending the coming into force of the Pharmacy and Poisons Act, 1933. The letter inquired whether the council of the Pharmaceutical Society was prepared to initiate the steps necessary to add to Part I of the Poison Schedule such nitrophenols and preparations containing them as were likely to be retailed to the public.

During the discussion Mr Beardsley had pointed out that the chemist from whom the tablets had been purchased had told the purchaser that she would be well advised to take them only under doctor's orders, and that the Coroner, at the inquest, had made it clear that the chemist had taken all reasonable precautions.

ON THIS DAY

April 5, 1934

Sixty-five years ago, a dancer died after taking an overdose of a drug in order to reduce her weight; a few months later the Pharmaceutical Society, prompted by the Home Secretary, took action to prevent it from being on general sale.

On the proposal of the Vice-President (Mr S. Peck), seconded by Mr. Hardy, a resolution to add these substances to Part I of the Schedule of Poisons was passed as follows: That by virtue and in exercise of the powers vested in the council of the Pharmaceutical Society of Great Britain, the said council doth hereby resolve and declare that the Schedule to the Poisons and Pharmacy Act, 1908, ought to be amended by the addition to Part I of the following words: Dinitrophenols, dinitrocresols, preparations or admixtures containing dinitrophenols; preparations or admix-

tures containing dinitrocresols; and that a copy of this resolution be sealed with the corporate seal of the council.

It was stated that the resolution would be sent to the Privy Council for consideration and approval.

At an inquest at Paddington last month on a young woman cabaret artist, who died through an overdose of a drug which she had taken to reduce her weight, it was stated by a witness on behalf of the makers of the drug that in September, 1933, his company suggested that this preparation should be placed on the Poisons List so that it could not be bought except as a result of medical prescription. The company had no reply to the first letter, the witness said, and a second was sent and the reply received was that the matter was having consideration.

On March 22 the Home Secretary stated in the House of Commons that the Poisons Board, set up under the Pharmacy and Poisons Act of last year, was considering the restrictions to be applied to that and other poisons. He was also in consultation with the Lord President of the Council and the Pharmaceutical Society, the responsible authorities until the new Act comes into force, with a view to its being scheduled as a poison at the earliest possible date, and he was taking up the matter with the manufacturers with a view to the adoption of further precautions.

Figure 5.12 Dangers of using uncouplers as slimming drugs: a report from *The Times* newspaper (reproduced on 5/4/99).

5.3.5 THE OXYGEN ELECTRODE

The discovery of uncouplers, and indeed of respiratory control, would not have been possible without some device for measuring the rate of oxygen uptake by cell homogenates and by isolated mitochondria.

○ Why does a mitochondrial suspension use up oxygen when a TCA-cycle acid (say, citrate) is added to it?

● The citrate is oxidized via the TCA cycle, producing reduced coenzymes that feed electrons into the ETC, passing them eventually to cytochrome oxidase, which reduces oxygen to water (see Section 5.3.2).

The uptake of oxygen can be seen in appropriate apparatus as a reduction in the volume of gas above the suspension. This volume can be quantified directly using the classic Warburg manometer, a cumbersome but ingenious piece of glassware that played a big part in unravelling the glucose oxidation pathways in the 1930s. Nowadays, the oxygen electrode is used (see Box 5.2, overleaf, which you should now read).

Box 5.2 The oxygen electrode

The **oxygen electrode** can measure the change in concentration of oxygen in a mitochondrial suspension, simply from the current produced when dissolved oxygen reacts with two electrodes (see Figure 5.13; *note*: only one electrode can be seen in this figure.). With the stopper firmly in place, oxygen supplies are limited to what is already dissolved, so the mitochondria slowly use up oxygen in the suspension and in the electrode-bathing solution below it. (Note the oxygen-permeable membrane in Figure 5.13.)

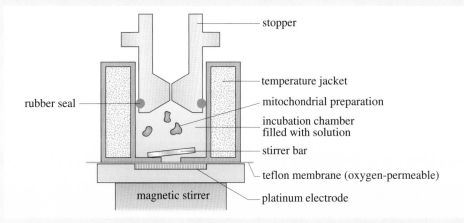

- stopper
- temperature jacket
- mitochondrial preparation
- incubation chamber filled with solution
- stirrer bar
- teflon membrane (oxygen-permeable)
- platinum electrode

rubber seal

magnetic stirrer

Figure 5.13 Oxygen electrode.

Figure 5.14 shows the *traces* drawn by a recorder connected to the electrodes. Here, oxygen uptake is plotted against time. The dashed line in Figure 5.14a shows what happens when a TCA intermediate such as malate or succinate is added as a source of electrons to a suspension of *uncoupled* mitochondria. Reduced coenzymes are rapidly produced (through increased activity of the TCA cycle) and oxygen levels fall as these

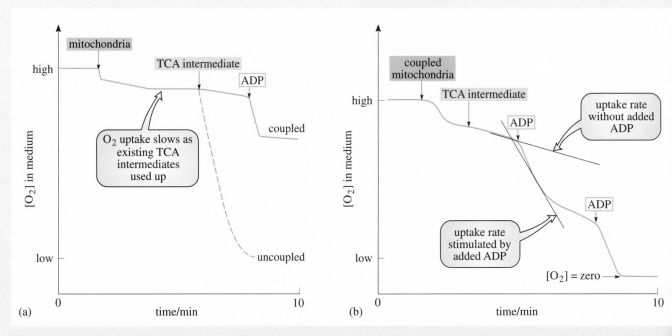

Figure 5.14 Oxygen electrode traces. (a) Comparison of coupled and uncoupled mitochondria. Note how oxygen-uptake rates are identical when ADP is added to the coupled preparation. (b) Respiratory control demonstrated by adding ADP to boost oxygen uptake in coupled mitochondria.

reduced coenzymes are oxidized by the ETC. Even though ADP supplies are long gone, electron transport (oxygen uptake) continues unabated because proton return is no longer linked to ATP synthesis. However, in *tightly coupled* mitochondria (where electron transport is restrained by the rate of ATP synthesis), oxygen uptake is very slow. It speeds up only on addition of ADP as well as the TCA intermediate. The solid line in Figure 5.14a shows how this rapid rate of oxygen uptake slows to its previous level as soon as ADP supplies have been depleted because electron transport is once again restrained by the rate of ATP synthesis.

Just how far oxygen consumption rates can be stimulated by adding ADP is expressed in terms of the respiratory control ratio, the ratio of oxygen uptake rates in the presence and absence of ADP (Figure 5.14b). In uncoupled mitochondria, where ADP is not stimulatory, the ratio is 1. In coupled mitochondria, ratios of 3–6 are common.

The oxygen electrode can be used to deduce the order of electron carriers in the ETC. This needs two types of compound. The first is *inhibitors that block electron transport* by inactivating specific carrier proteins. An example is rotenone, which inhibits electron flow through complex I, preventing electrons being passed to cytochrome *b* and on down the ETC. Similarly, the fungal poison antimycin blocks between cytochromes *b* and c_1 (see Figures 5.6 and 5.7).

The second type of compound needed for these experiments is the *alternative electron source*. Electrons need not be supplied to the ETC in the form of reduced coenzyme or TCA intermediate. For example, oxygen electrode studies show that there is a rapid uptake of oxygen when a particular artificial electron source is added to the antimycin-inhibited system just described. This source donates electrons directly to cytochrome *c*, thereby side-stepping the block between cytochrome *b* and cytochrome c_1. Other such alternative electron sources may donate directly to other ETC components.

SUMMARY OF SECTION 5.3

1   The electron transport chain in mitochondria carries electrons from NAD.2H to O_2. It contains three respiratory complexes, whose components are arranged in order of electron affinity. Electrons pass from complex I to IV and finally to molecular oxygen, via two mobile carriers Q and cytochrome *c*.

2   In each of complexes I, III and IV is a proton pump, an allosteric protein able to use the energy of electron transport to move protons into the intermembrane space, against a concentration gradient.

3   Respiratory control of tightly coupled mitochondria conserves fuel supplies by linking electron transport to ATP synthesis.

4   Uncouplers allow protons to leak back into the matrix, bypassing the ATP synthase, and producing heat, which can be physiologically useful.

5   The oxygen electrode measures oxygen uptake in isolated mitochondria, and can be used to demonstrate respiratory control and, with specific inhibitors and alternative electron sources, to unravel the order of carriers in the ETC.

5.4 OXIDATIVE PHOSPHORYLATION IN MICROBES

The strategy of using an electron transport chain to generate energy for making ATP is seen in many different life forms. The underlying principles are the same, only the electron carriers involved differ.

5.4.1 HETEROTROPHIC MICROBES

All heterotrophs obtain energy by oxidizing organic compounds but microbes, unlike animals, can metabolize a wide range of different carbon compounds, not just carbohydrate, fat and protein as described in Chapter 4. Between them, microbes can metabolize virtually any organic compound, depending on their genetic make-up. Some have the necessary enzymes for growing on dicarboxylic acids like succinate, phenols (the acidic components of coal tar) and many other compounds unpalatable to us. Most of these microbes produce NAD.2H by feeding their particular nutrient into the appropriate point in glycolysis, link reaction or TCA cycle. However, some reduce different coenzymes such as FAD, which feeds directly into ubiquinone (see Q in Figure 5.6 earlier). The microbial ETC can be viewed as three units: a dehydrogenase complex (with different components depending on the nutrients available), a lipid-soluble quinone (usually Q), and an oxidase complex (see Figure 5.15). Microbial ETCs are much more variable than those of mitochondria, which are virtually the same in all eukaryotes. The electron carriers are still Fe-S proteins, cytochromes or quinones, but their precise structures reflect the need for different redox potentials (see Box 5.1) when accepting electrons from different sources. Indeed this variability underpins microbial versatility, allowing them to colonize different environments with different nutrients and still make ATP by chemiosmotic coupling.

Figure 5.15 Simplified diagram of a microbial electron transport chain.

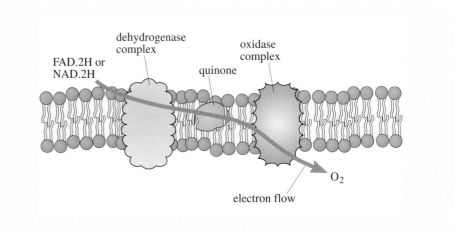

Remarkably, some microbes continue to make ATP in this way even in the absence of oxygen. They are the *anaerobic* heterotrophs, whose specialized cytochrome oxidase proteins allow them to use alternatives to oxygen as the **terminal electron acceptor**. For example, the denitrifying bacteria (prominent in the nitrogen cycle) pass electrons to nitrate rather than oxygen, while some sulfate reducers (important in the sulfur cycle) pass electrons to sulfate ions (SO_4^{2-}) instead of oxygen.

In terms of ATP yield, using such alternative terminal electron acceptors is a better way of dealing with anaerobic conditions than the strategy described earlier.

○   What was the name of this strategy?

●   Substrate-level phosphorylation (see Section 5.1).

○   Can you recall a major disadvantage of this way of making ATP?

●   The energy for phosphorylating ADP has to come from coupling it to an energy-releasing oxidation reaction (reaction G6 of glycolysis — see Figure 4.16 earlier). This reaction produces NAD.2H which has to be reoxidized to NAD ready for the next substrate-level phosphorylation. It cannot be reoxidized by the ETC because of the anaerobic conditions, so alternative, enzyme-catalysed reactions are needed.

Some microbes generate all their fuel-derived ATP by substrate-level phosphorylation, and then solve the problem of regenerating NAD by redox reactions that do not need molecular oxygen, as seen in the alcohol-producing yeast featured in the CD-ROM. They have no ETC under these anaerobic conditions.

5.4.2   CHEMOAUTOTROPHIC MICROBES

These very interesting bacteria have specialized electron transport chains that allow them to accept electrons from *inorganic* compounds. They still make ATP by oxidative phosphorylation, but they have no need for organic molecules to provide reduced coenzymes to feed into the ETC. Indeed some remarkable chemoautotrophs can grow on just an inorganic salt solution, with CO_2 as sole carbon source. Inorganic electron sources may include Fe^{2+}, and sulfide (S^{2-}) ions as well as ammonia (NH_3), H_2 or even carbon monoxide (CO) gas.

Several chemoautotrophs are economically important. By oxidizing nitrogen or sulfur compounds, some play a big part in the nitrogen and sulfur cycles. Others oxidize metal ions like Fe^{2+}, and so can detoxify mining waste and reclaim useful metals as soluble salts. Another useful group is the methanogens, anaerobic Archaea that generate methane (as in North Sea gas) by reduction of CO_2 by H_2 gas.

$$CO_2 + 4H_2 \longrightarrow CH_4 + 2H_2O \qquad\qquad (5.5)$$

(Methanogens also generate methane 'wind' in the gut of humans and other animals, especially ruminants.)

When using these various inorganic sources of electrons, specialized electron carriers are needed for the first oxidation step. These proteins pass the electrons on to an ETC similar to that in mitochondria, although there are usually fewer than three proton pumping sites. Hence in chemoautotrophs, ATP yields (per pair of electrons) tend to be lower than in mitochondria. Exceptions are those using H_2 or CO as the inorganic electron source; their strongly negative RP values mean there is a large free energy drop when electrons are passed from them, via the ETC, to oxygen as the terminal electron acceptor (see Box 5.1).

Anaerobic chemoautotrophs that do not use oxygen as their terminal electron acceptor also have low ATP yields because the various alternative acceptors (e.g. nitrate) have less positive RP values than oxygen. Hence the total drop in RP during electron transport is lower, so according to Equation 5.2, less energy is released.

However, despite these disadvantages, chemoautotrophs are an important group, able to produce ATP by oxidative phosphorylation under unusual conditions.

5.4.3 WHERE DID OXIDATIVE PHOSPHORYLATION BEGIN?

Making ATP is so basic to life, it is hardly surprising that the high-yield chemiosmotic method (oxidative phosphorylation) has been adopted by both eukaryotes and prokaryotes. The prokaryotes evolved first, of course, and most people now accept that mitochondria evolved from them. Indeed the ETC components of *Paracoccus* are so similar to those of mitochondria, that this heterotrophic bacterium has been likened to a free-living mitochondrion; it could be the original symbiotic microbe that colonized primitive eukaryotic organisms, and from which all of today's mitochondria have evolved.

SUMMARY OF SECTION 5.4

1 Many non-photosynthesizing heterotrophic microbes make ATP by oxidative phosphorylation.

2 Those growing anaerobically use alternative terminal electron acceptors (e.g. nitrate not O_2) and specialized cytochrome oxidases.

3 Reduced coenzymes for oxidative phosphorylation are produced from oxidation of a wide range of organic compounds (heterotrophs) or inorganic compounds (chemoautotrophs) and fed into specialized ETCs that produce ATP by chemiosmotic coupling, but may have fewer than three proton pumps, and correspondingly reduced ATP yields.

> This is a good point at which to complete your study of the *Making ATP* CD-ROM, by working through the final section entitled 'ETC'.

5.5 USING LIGHT ENERGY TO MAKE ATP

5.5.1 PHOTOPHOSPHORYLATION

Plants and microbes with light-absorbing pigments can make ATP by a rather different, membrane-based mechanism, **photophosphorylation**.

The simplest organism to use light to make ATP is the purple-membrane archaeon, *Halobacterium halobium* (Chapter 3). Purple patches in its cell membrane contain a molecular complex that includes a light-absorbing pigment and a proton pump. The energy of absorbed light is used to power structural rearrangements within the complex, and as a result protons accumulate in the enclosed space between the cell membrane and the outer wall of the microbe, forming a transmembrane proton gradient. The ATP is made as protons flow back into the cytoplasm, through a membrane-bound ATP synthase.

Despite its ingenuity, this simple system has a major problem — ATP cannot be synthesized in the dark. In fact, purple patches are made only when oxygen levels are low, as a survival mechanism in adverse conditions. More sophisticated photophosphorylating organisms can also carry out photosynthesis, storing the light energy as carbohydrate.

5.5.2 PHOTOSYNTHESIS

Photosynthesizing organisms can use light energy to reduce carbon dioxide, converting it into carbohydrate $(CH_2O)_n$. As we saw for glucose earlier, carbohydrate can then be oxidized to release energy whether or not the sun is shining.

In photosynthesizing organisms, only part of the light energy goes to make ATP. The rest is used to form the reduced coenzyme NADP.2H. Coenzyme NADP is very similar to NAD (see Chapter 4) and acts as the final electron acceptor in the ETC of photosynthesizing organisms. Its reduction to NADP.2H is then completed by picking up H^+ ions from the surrounding medium. Thus the immediate source of H atoms for CO_2 reduction is NADP.2H. But what provides the electrons that are excited by light at the beginning of the ETC?

The **electron donor** for this first step has changed during the course of evolution. The most abundant electron donor in today's world is H_2O, but a great deal of energy is needed for it to reduce NADP, as you can see from the redox potential graph in Figure 5.16a.

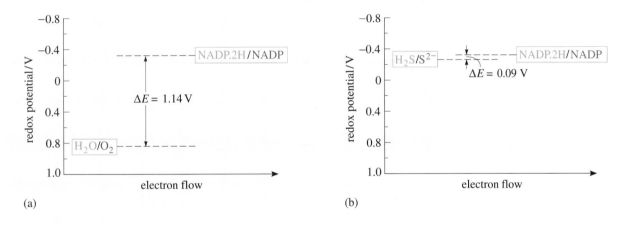

Figure 5.16 (a) H_2O or (b) H_2S as electron donor for the reduction of NADP in photosynthesis. (*Note*: the reduced form of each redox pair is shown in red.)

○   Use Table 5.1 to calculate the difference in redox potential (ΔE) between redox pairs H_2O/O_2 and NADP.2H/NADP.

●   The redox potentials of H_2O/O_2 and NADP.2H/NADP are 0.82 V and −0.32 V, respectively. Therefore, $\Delta E = 0.82 - (-0.32) = 1.14$ V.

Light energy is absorbed in discrete packets known as **photons**, and more than one photon of light energy would be needed to energize the electrons of H_2O by this huge amount. However, a different electron donor H_2S (hydrogen sulfide) looks more promising. This evil-smelling gas (a good source is rotten eggs) forms part of the redox pair H_2S/S^{2-}, which has an RP value of only -0.23 V. So there is less of a jump when electrons pass from H_2S to NADP than from H_2O (see Figure 5.16b). H_2S is indeed the electron donor in more primitive photosynthetic organisms such as the green sulfur bacteria.

The chloroplasts of higher plants do, however, use H_2O as their electron donor in photosynthesis. They achieve this by having *two* sets of light-absorbing pigments, allowing electrons to be energized by two photons of light energy. We now look in more detail at photosynthesis in chloroplasts.

5.6 PHOTOSYNTHESIS IN CHLOROPLASTS

5.6.1 CHLOROPLASTS HAVE LARGE AREAS OF INTERNAL MEMBRANE

In higher plants, photosynthesis takes place in specialized organelles, the chloroplasts (Section 1.4.5). Like the much smaller mitochondria, the chloroplasts lie in the cytosol, each surrounded by a double membrane. There is nothing equivalent to the mitochondrial cristae, but inside the chloroplast, the matrix or stroma contains an enormous network of internal 'energy-exchange' membranes, the lamellae. Most of these are arranged as stacks of little flattened bags or thylakoids, each like a hollow pancake (or pitta bread). When viewed from the side, all that can be seen of these thylakoid stacks (grana) is a pile of membranes (Figure 5.17). This enormous surface area of membrane is very important in photosynthesis, since the light reactions involve both membrane-bound proteins and pigments that are tethered to the lamellar membrane by their hydrophobic tails. The single (unstacked) stromal lamellae that connect the grana also add to this membrane network.

Figure 5.17 Diagram of chloroplast showing internal 'energy-exchange' membranes — the thylakoids and stromal lamellae.

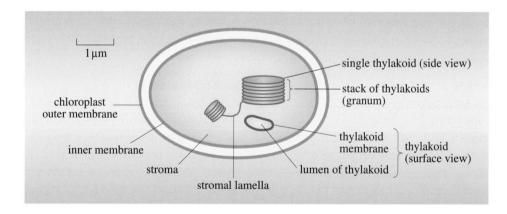

5.6.2 OVERVIEW OF PHOTOSYNTHESIS

Photosynthesis can be simply represented by the equation:

$$6CO_2 + 6H_2O \xrightarrow[\text{chlorophyll}]{\text{sunlight}} C_6H_{12}O_6 + 6O_2 \qquad (5.6)$$

There are two stages to photosynthesis, the light reactions, followed by the dark reactions. The **light reactions** take place on the lamellae and use the energy of sunlight to synthesize *ATP* and *reduced NADP*. Neither of these molecules appear in the overall equation of course, because they are intermediates produced in the light reactions that are immediately used up in the dark reactions. In fact, it can be said that the products of the light reactions drive the dark reactions. Most of the **dark reactions** take place in the chloroplast matrix (stroma) with some reactions in the cytosol. They are not directly dependent on light, and can continue for a short while in darkness, till stocks of ATP and reduced NADP are exhausted. They use this ATP and reduced NADP for the 'fixation' of CO_2, which is reduced and converted into glucose. Sugars other than glucose may also be formed.

5.6.3 LIGHT HARVESTING AND THE PHOTOCHEMICAL REACTION

The pigment chlorophyll has a light-absorbing 'head' centred on an atom of magnesium (an element vital for plant growth) and a hydrophobic 'tail' attached to a membrane-bound protein and embedded in the lamellar membrane (Figure 5.18, overleaf). It appears green because it absorbs visible light of all wavelengths except those in the green part of the spectrum (which are reflected). In moderate shade, light is absorbed as packets of energy or photons, at the rate of about one photon per chlorophyll molecule per second. Atoms have several discrete energy levels for accommodating electrons, and their lowest 'ground state' energy level is where an electron is most likely to be found. However, an electron can be boosted to a higher energy level by absorbing a photon of light energy. Such an 'excited' electron is highly reactive.

To use this energy effectively, chlorophyll molecules are arranged on the lamellar membrane in *antennae*, groups of several hundred radiating out from a common centre. In this way, energy from excited electrons can be harvested, by passing from one chlorophyll molecule to another, towards the two chlorophylls in the *reaction centre* (Figure 5.19, overleaf). This last is where the actual photochemical, light-powered reaction takes place, and a high-energy electron is ejected from the chlorophyll molecule altogether.

Antennae and reaction centre together form a **photosystem**. In the reaction centre, excited electrons in the last pair of chlorophylls, pass out of the pigment molecules, into a pair of electron acceptor molecules (pheophytin) which are also embedded in the lamellar membrane. This first electron transfer leaves a 'hole' in each of the reaction centre chlorophylls which is filled by electrons from the weak but abundant electron donor — water. Since chlorophyll is now returned to its resting state, it shows no net change. So the overall result of the photochemical reaction can be written as:

$$H_2O + \text{light energy} \longrightarrow 2H^+ + 2e^- + [O] \tag{5.7}$$

The equation can be made to balance by considering the reaction powered by absorbing exactly four photons of light energy.

$$2H_2O + 4 \text{ photons} \longrightarrow 4H^+ + 4e^- + O_2 \tag{5.8}$$

Figure 5.18 Chemical structure of a chlorophyll molecule.

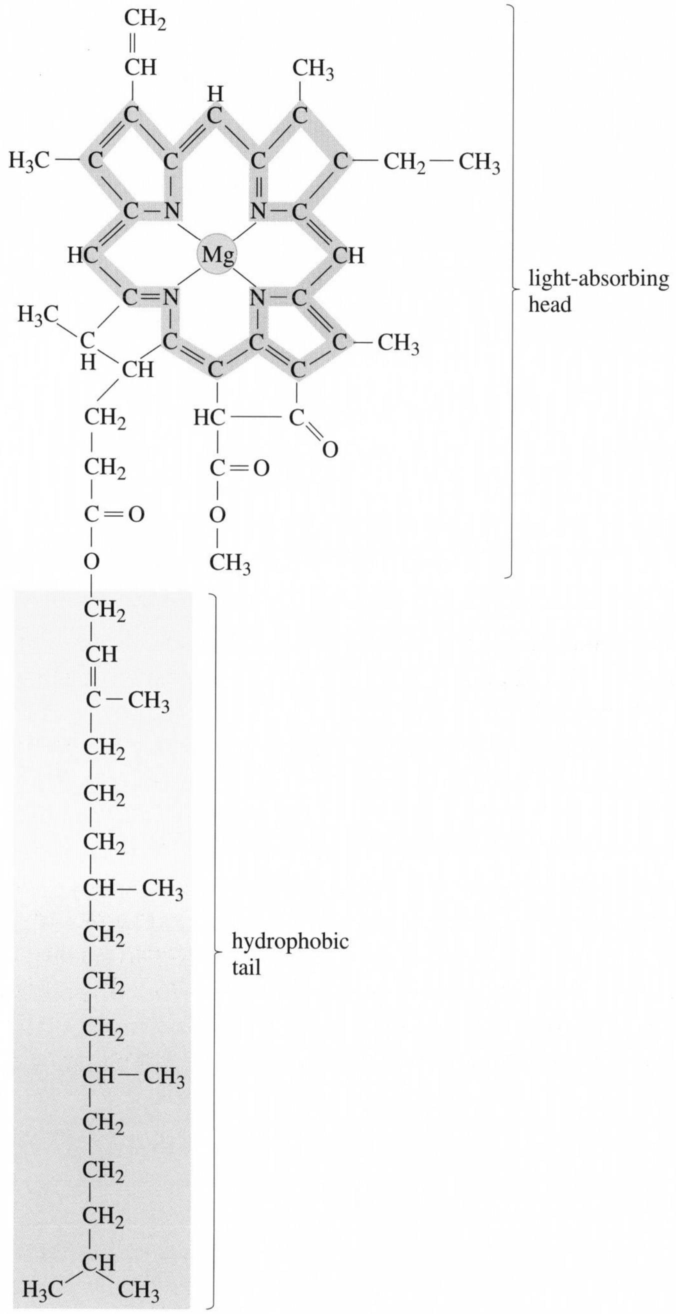

Oxygen is of course one of the products in the overall reaction of photosynthesis (Equation 5.6). Although neither electrons nor H+ ions from Equation 5.8 appear in this overall equation, they are vital intermediates for forming ATP and reduced NADP in the next stage of the light reactions.

Light energy can be absorbed only in discrete packets (photons), and there is not enough energy in one photon to empower electrons from a weak donor such as water to combine with a weak acceptor, i.e. a compound of low electron affinity

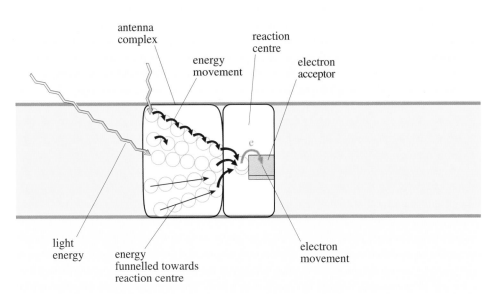

Figure 5.19 Movement of energy and electrons from antennae to reaction centre. The pale green spheres represent chlorophyll molecules.

such as NADP; the gap in redox potential is too big, being the difference between +0.82 V for water and −0.32 V for NADP (see Figure 5.16a earlier). So green plants have two linked photosystems, each with their own antennae and reaction centre. For historical reasons the photosystem (PS) we have just described is known as PSII (PS-two), and a second photosystem (known paradoxically as PSI or PS-one) gives the electrons a further boost of light energy. The two photosystems absorb at slightly different wavelengths, and are located in different areas of the chloroplast lamellar system. Since the electrons received by PSI are still partially excited by the first photochemical reaction, they — or, more correctly, the protein-pigment carriers to which they are attached — start with a redox potential of around +0.5 V (see Figure 5.20) which is considerably nearer the required RP than that of water (+0.82 V) with which they started. So the second energy boost in PSI is enough to raise the RP to −1.0 V, which is sufficiently negative for electrons to reduce NADP (whose RP is only −0.32 V).

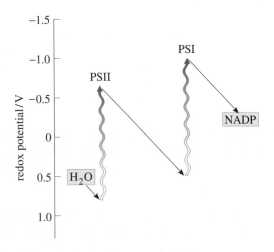

Figure 5.20 Two linked photosystems are needed to bridge the redox potential gap between H_2O and NADP.

Put simply, the electrons have now had two energy boosts. The first takes place within PSII, where an O_2-releasing complex catalyses the reaction shown in Equation 5.7. The second energy boost takes place within PSI. Electrons are now reactive enough to pass along an ETC to NADP which picks up protons from the surrounding medium and is reduced to NADP.2H. We now describe this ETC.

5.6.4 ELECTRON TRANSPORT AND NADP REDUCTION

As in mitochondria, the energy of excited electrons is dissipated slowly, and high-energy electrons from the first photochemical reaction pass down an ETC in much the same way as those from reduced coenzymes pass along the mitochondrial ETC. In fact, ETC components are chemically similar in the two organelles (Figure 5.21).

Figure 5.21 Electron carriers in mitochondria and chloroplasts. Note that, for comparison, the mitochondrial matrix is shown above the membrane, not below as in Figure 5.6, etc.

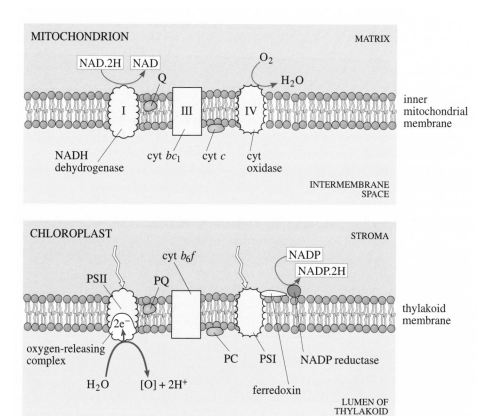

Figure 5.22 shows the strongly negative redox potential (low electron affinity) of the first acceptor, pheophytin. From here electrons continue along a series of carriers, moving spontaneously towards those with greater electron affinity (more positive redox potential). As in mitochondria, small mobile carriers move between large protein complexes (Figure 5.21). Plastoquinone (PQ) is similar to ubiquinone in the mitochondria, and transports electrons from pheophytin in PSII to cytochrome b_6f, a protein complex very similar to the cytochrome bc_1 complex in mitochondria (except that it has no proton pump). From here, a second mobile carrier plastocyanin (PC) moves electrons to PSI. PC is a small protein, equivalent to cytochrome c in mitochondria.

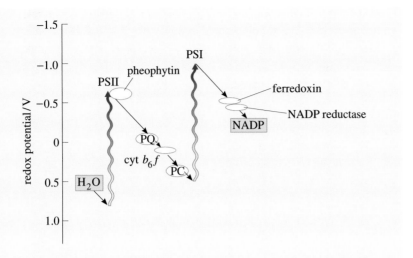

Figure 5.22 Electron transport chain in chloroplasts.

○ What is the role of cytochrome *c* in mitochondria?

● Cytochrome *c* carries electrons from cytochrome bc_1 (in respiratory complex III) to cytochrome oxidase (respiratory complex IV). See Figures 5.6 and 5.7.

In PSI, electrons receive their second energy boost. Now at last they have enough energy to reduce NADP. They pass along a second short limb of the ETC to *ferredoxin* (a small water-soluble protein with no equivalent in mitochondria), and finally to another large membrane-bound protein with a binding site for NADP. This last is NADP reductase; it catalyses the reaction NADP $\longrightarrow$ NADP.2H, drawing H$^+$ ions from the chloroplast stroma.

Because of its shape, the diagram relating electron flow and energy levels in the chloroplast lamellae is known as the **Z-scheme** (see the Z on its side, in Figures 5.20 and 5.22). It shows how chloroplasts use two photosystems to boost the energy of an electron from water high enough to reduce NADP. The resulting NADP.2H provides H atoms for synthesizing carbohydrate in a series of reactions that do not need light. However, these 'dark reactions' do need ATP, and we now see how supplies are provided by the light reactions.

5.6.5 ATP SYNTHESIS

As in mitochondria, ATP synthesis is driven by chemiosmotic coupling, using the energy released as protons flow spontaneously down an electrochemical gradient. A key feature is again the building of the transmembrane proton gradient.

○ What device is used in mitochondria to build a transmembrane proton gradient by moving protons to one side of the membrane?

● Each of the three respiratory complexes has a *proton pump* that moves protons out of the matrix into the intermembrane space (see Figure 5.6).

○ Where do proton pumps get the energy needed to 'pump' protons against an electrochemical gradient?

● From electron transport. Energy is released in proportion to the redox potential difference between adjacent carriers in the electron transport chain (see Box 5.1 and Figure 5.7).

The chloroplast has no proton pumps as such, but a transmembrane gradient is built up in the thylakoids in three steps, each allowing protons to accumulate preferentially on one side of the lamellar membrane. First, the photochemical reaction in PSII takes place at a particular site, namely the *inner* edge of the thylakoid membrane. This reaction releases H⁺ ions into the interior of the thylakoid (Figure 5.23) by the reaction $H_2O + \text{light energy} \longrightarrow 2H^+ + 2e^- + [O]$ (Equation 5.7). The final reaction of the ETC also has a directional quality. It is catalysed by NADP reductase, a protein lying on the *outer* edge of the thylakoid lamella. Written in full this reduction reaction is:

$$NADP + 2H^+ + 2e^- \longrightarrow NADP.2H \tag{5.9}$$

○ Are protons *released* during this reaction, or *taken up*?

● Protons are taken up, since H⁺ is needed for the reaction. These protons come from the surroundings — here the chloroplast matrix or stroma (see Figure 5.23).

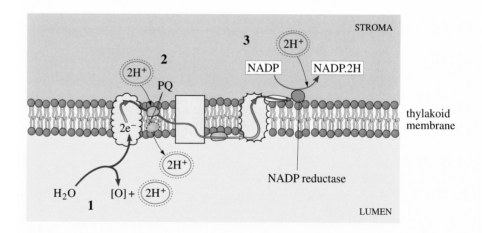

Figure 5.23 Build-up of proton gradient across thylakoid membrane. Step 1: 2H⁺ released from H_2O into lumen. Step 2: Plastoquinone withdraws 2H⁺ from the stroma and releases them into the lumen. Step 3: 2H⁺ withdrawn from stroma during reaction catalysed by NADP reductase.

Thus far, electron transport in the chloroplast has effectively released protons into the thylakoid lumen, and removed them from the surrounding stroma. A third mechanism for directing protons out of the stroma into the thylakoid lumen involves one of the mobile electron carriers that you met earlier — plastoquinone. As this molecule shuttles between PSII and cytochrome b_6f (carrying electrons) it takes a circular route, collecting a proton from the stroma and releasing it into the thylakoid lumen (Figure 5.23). So to summarize, for every light-energized electron passing down the ETC in the thylakoid lamella, there are three opportunities for directing protons into the thylakoid lumen, making it distinctly acid compared to the stroma. In strong light, the differences may be as great as pH 5 (thylakoid interior) and pH 8 (stroma).

○ Why is light needed?

● To energize electrons and hence start electron flow which provides the energy for accumulating protons in the thylakoid lumen, against their electrochemical gradient.

In this way, electron transport energy is briefly stored as a transmembrane proton gradient. So long as the lamellar membrane remains intact, this gradient can be used to power ATP synthesis.

○ By analogy with ATP synthesis in mitochondria, how is this gradient used?

● Protons flow back into the stroma through a special protein, the ATP synthase.

Chloroplast and mitochondrial synthases are structurally very similar, with the chloroplast subunits known as CF_0 (proton channel) and CF_1 (catalytic site) by analogy with the homologous structures in ATP synthase (Figure 5.2).

○ By comparing H^+ flow in chloroplasts and mitochondria, and the orientation of ATP synthase 'knobs' (Figure 5.21 and Figure 5.24), describe how ATP synthesis is powered in chloroplasts.

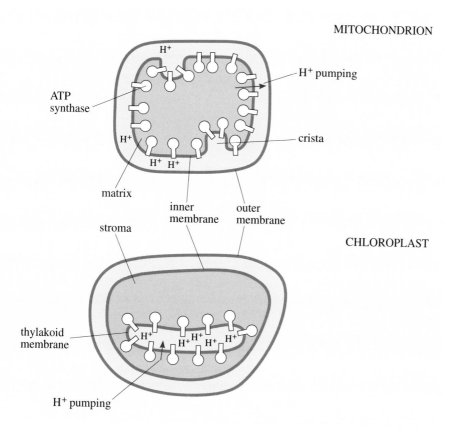

Figure 5.24 Proton pumping in mitochondrion and chloroplast. *Note*: these diagrams are drawn to the same size although mitochondria are much smaller.

● Protons flow back, out of the thylakoid lumen into the stroma, through the CF_0 channel of ATP synthase molecules in the thylakoid membrane. Since flow is down the H^+ concentration gradient, it is an energy-releasing activity and can drive the energy-consuming reaction of ATP synthesis, which is catalysed by the CF_1 'knobs' projecting into the chloroplast stroma.

So to recap, ATP, the first product of the light reactions, is formed when light energy excites chlorophyll electrons; this energy is channelled through a series of chlorophyll molecules to the reaction centre, where an excited electron passes from chlorophyll to an electron acceptor, which is the first member of the chloroplast ETC. Electron transport down this ETC is linked to ATP synthesis via a concentration gradient of H^+ ions across the thylakoid membrane.

5.6.6 CYCLIC ELECTRON FLOW

Some plants can boost ATP yields by recycling electrons from PSI that would otherwise have gone on to reduce NADP. The recycling electrons pass from ferredoxin back to plastoquinone as shown in Figure 5.25. The pathway allows PQ to continue its proton transporting activity, increasing the transmembrane proton gradient — and hence powering ATP synthesis — without the need for excited electrons from PSII. Only PSI is involved in cyclic electron flow. This system is used to make extra ATP without producing more NADP.2H at the same time.

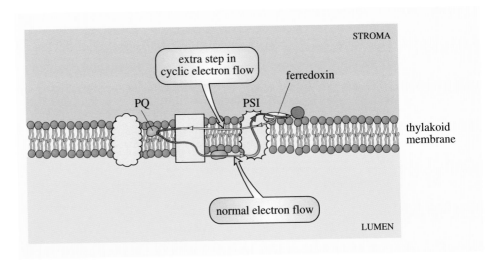

Figure 5.25 Cyclic electron flow.

5.6.7 HERBICIDES

Many synthetic herbicides (weedkillers) are often directed at the electron transport chain. For example, DCMU (dichlorophenyldimethylurea) prevents plastoquinone from carrying electrons between PSII and cytochrome b_6f, while paraquat accepts electrons from ferredoxin, thus preventing them being used to reduce NADP (Figure 5.26). Worse still, the reduced paraquat then reacts with oxygen to form superoxide, a highly reactive lipid-damaging free radical.

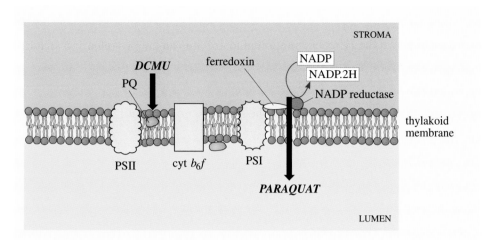

Figure 5.26 Sites of herbicide action on the electron transport chain.

○ What would you expect to happen to supplies of NADP.2H, in green leaves treated with DCMU?

● The NADP.2H supply would dry up, since no electrons could pass down the ETC beyond plastoquinone.

○ If an alternative electron supply were fed directly to cytochrome b_6f, what would happen to NADP.2H levels?

● They would rise, since the block in the electron transport chain is now effectively bypassed.

○ Would this rise in NADP.2H levels be dependent on light?

● Yes, since the artificially supplied electrons need an energy boost from the PSI photochemical reaction before they can reduce NADP.

SUMMARY OF SECTIONS 5.5 AND 5.6

1 Photophosphorylation is a form of chemiosmotic coupling in which incoming electrons are energized by light rather than by metabolism.

2 The purple-membrane archaeon *Halobacterium halobium* has a light-powered proton pump, able to make ATP by chemiosmotic coupling, but unable to store energy as carbohydrate.

3 Photosynthetic organisms use light energy to make both ATP and reduced coenzyme (NADP.2H) which are used in the dark reaction, to reduce CO_2 and make carbohydrate.

4 In chloroplasts, light energy is absorbed at two linked photosystems; this gives two energy boosts to electrons from the weak donor water, enabling them to reduce NADP.

5　In chloroplasts, energized electrons pass from the first photochemical reaction (in PSII) down an ETC to plastocyanin, from where a second photochemical reaction (in PSI) gives them a second energy boost, enabling them to pass down another short ETC through ferredoxin to NADP reductase. The plot of electron flow against energy levels is known as the Z-scheme.

6　ATP is made during the light reactions, by the catalytic subunit (CF_1) of chloroplast ATP synthase, using the energy released as protons flow through the CF_0 subunit down their electrochemical gradient.

7　The necessary transmembrane proton gradient is set up in three steps: the directional nature of the reactions $H_2O + light\ energy \longrightarrow 2H^+ + 2e^- + [O]$ and $NADP + 2H^+ + 2e^- \longrightarrow NADP.2H$, and by the transmembrane cycling of proton-carrying plastoquinone. These steps are all energized by electron flow.

8　Many common herbicides act by blocking the chloroplast ETC.

REFERENCES

Junge, W., Lill, H. and Engelbrecht, S. (1997) ATP synthase: an electrochemical transducer with rotary mechanics, *Trends in Biochemical Sciences* **22**, pp. 420–423.

FURTHER READING

Stryer, L. (1995) *Biochemistry* (4th edn), W. H. Freeman and Company, New York.

Zubay G. L (1998) *Biochemistry* (4th edn), Wm. C. Brown Publishers (McGraw-Hill), Dubuque, USA.

[Comprehensive biochemistry texts for those who wish to read about biochemistry in more detail.]

ACKNOWLEDGEMENTS

Grateful acknowledgement is made to the following sources for permission to reproduce material in this book:

CHAPTER 1

FIGURES

Figures 1.3, 1.4a, 1.5a, 1.6b,c, 1.7a, 1.17, 1.18, 1.22, 1.33b, d: Courtesy of Jill Saffrey, Department of Biological Sciences, The Open University; *Figure 1.8a*: Courtesy of Department of Biological Sciences, The Open University; *Figure 1.11*: The Nobel Foundation; *Figure 1.12*: Reprinted from *Trends in Cell Biology*, **8**, 1998, p. 3, with permission from Elsevier Science; *Figure 1.15*: Courtesy of Susan Van Noorden; *Figure 1.16, 1.19*: Courtesy of Heather Davies, Department of Biological Sciences, The Open University; *Figures 1.24a, 1.27a, 1.28a, 1.31a, 1.32a*: Courtesy of Professor Mike Stewart, Department of Biological Sciences, The Open University; *Figure 1.25*: Adapted from Purves, W. K. *et al.* (1998) *Life, the Science of Biology'*, 5th edn, Sinauer Associates Inc.; *Figure 1.30a*: CNRI/ Science Photo Library; *Figure 1.30b*: Dr Don Fawcett/Science Photo Library.

CHAPTER 2

FIGURES

Figure 2.7: Courtesy of Christine Lancashire; *Figure 2.11*: Laboratory of Molecular Biology, Cambridge; *Figure 2.13*: Thomas Hollyman/SPL; *Figure 2.15*: Banks, R. D. *et al.* (1979) 'Sequence, structure and activity of phosphoglycerate kinase: a possible hinge-bending enzyme', *Nature*, **279**, p. 775; *Figures 2.18, 2.19*: Stryer, L. (1988) 'Part 1, molecular design of life', *Biochemistry*, 3rd edn, W. H. Freeman and Company; *Figure 2.20*: E. E. Kim, R. Varadarajan, H. W. Wyckoff and F. M. Richards (1992), 'Refinement of the crystal structure of Ribonuclease S. Comparison with and between the various Ribonuclease A structures', *Biochemistry*, **31**, p. 12 304; *Figure 2.21*: I. Andersson, Oxford Molecular Biophysics Lab/SPL; *Figures 2.25, 2.30*: Alberts, B. *et al.* (1983) *Molecular Biology of the Cell*, 3rd edn, Garland Publishing Inc., reprinted by permission of Hodder Headlines plc; *Figures 2.27, 2.28*: Alberts, B. *et al.* (1998) 'Chapter 5, Protein structure and function', *Essential Cell Biology*, Garland Publishing Inc., reprinted by permission of Hodder Headlines plc; *Figure 2.29*: Greer, J. (1980) 'Model for haptoglobin heavy chain based upon structural homology', *Proc. Natl. Acad. Sci, USA, Biological Sciences*, **77**; *Figure 2.54a*: Krause, K. L., Volz, K. W. and Lipscomb, W. N. (1985) 'Structure of 2.9 Å resolution of aspartate carbamoyltransferase complexed with the bisubstrate analogue N-(phosphoacetyl)-L-aspartate', *Proc. Natl. Acad. Sci.*, **82**, pp. 1643–7. *Figure 2.47*: Reprinted with permission from Elsevier Science from Johnson *et al.* 'David Phillips and the origin of structural enzymology', *Trends in Biochemical Sciences*, **24** (7), pp. 287–289.

CHAPTER 3

FIGURES

Figure 3.1b–e: Alberts, B. *et al.* (1983) 'Chapter 4, How cells are studied', *Molecular Biology of the Cell*, 3rd edn, Garland Publishing Inc., reprinted by permission of Hodder Headlines plc; *Figure 3.1f*: Copyright Professor L. A. Staehelin in Alberts, B. *et al.* (1983) 'Chapter 4, How cells are studied', *Molecular Biology of the Cell*, 3rd edn, Garland Publishing Inc., reprinted by permission of Hodder Headlines plc/ Taylor & Francis, Inc., http://www.routledge-ny.com; *Figures 3.10*: Adapted from Alberts, B. *et al.* (1983) 'Chapter 10, Membrane structure', *Molecular Biology of the Cell*, 3rd edn, Garland Publishing Inc., reprinted by permission of Hodder Headlines plc; *Figures 3.12b, 3.13a, b*: Alberts, B. *et al.* (1983) 'Chapter 10, Membrane structure', *Molecular Biology of the Cell*, 3rd edn, Garland Publishing Inc., reprinted by permission of Hodder Headlines plc; *Figure 3.15b*: Courtesy of Professor Mike Stewart; *Figure 3.17*: Alberts, B. *et al.* (1983) 'Chapter 19, Cell junctions, cell adhesion, and the extracellular matrix', *Molecular Biology of the Cell*, 3rd edn, Garland Publishing Inc., reprinted by permission of Hodder Headlines plc; *Figure 3.25*: Godfrey Argent; *Figure 3.28a*: Eye of Science/ Science Photo Library; *Figure 3.31, 3.34*: Alberts, B. *et al.* (1983) 'Chapter 12, Intracellular compartments and protein sorting', *Molecular Biology of the Cell*, 3rd edn, Garland Publishing Inc., reprinted by permission of Hodder Headlines plc; *Figure 3.37*: Adapted from Alberts, B. *et al.* (1983) 'Chapter 13, Vesicular traffic in the secretory and endocytic pathways', *Molecular Biology of the Cell*, 3rd edn, Garland Publishing Inc., reprinted by permission of Hodder Headlines plc; *Figure 3.38, 3.40a, 3.44*: Alberts, B. *et al.* (1983) 'Chapter 13, Vesicular traffic in the secretory and endocytic pathways', *Molecular Biology of the Cell*, 3rd edn, Garland Publishing Inc., reprinted by permission of Hodder Headlines plc; *Figure 3.39a, b*: Perry, M. M. and Gilbert, A. B. (1979) 'Yolk transport in the ovarian follicle of the hen...', *Journal of Cell Science*, **39**, pp. 257–272, Company of Biologists Limited; *Figure 3.40b*: Reprinted from Roitt, I. *et al.* (1998) *Immunology*, 4th edn, fig.15.6, Courtesy of Dr A. F. Rowley by permission of Mosby, an imprint of Times International Publishers Ltd; *Figure 3.43*: Anderson *et al.* 'Caveolae on the plasma-membrane of a human fibroblast', *Cell*, **68**, pp. 673–682, with permission of Elsevier Science.

TABLES

Tables 3.1 and 3.2: Adapted from Alberts, B. *et al.* (1983), *Molecular Biology of the Cell*, 3rd edn, Garland Publishing Inc., reprinted by permission of Hodder Headlines plc.

CHAPTER 4

FIGURES

Figure 4.1: Adapted from Copyright © Alberts, B. *et al.* (1983), *Molecular Biology of the Cell*, 3rd edn, Garland Publishing Inc., reprinted by permission of Hodder Headlines plc.

CHAPTER 5

FIGURES

Figures 5.4, 5.5: Adapted from Junge, W. *et al.* (1997), 'ATP synthase: an electrochemical transducer with rotatory mechanics', *Trends in Biochemical Sciences*, pp. 420–423, with permission from Elsevier Science Limited; *Figure 5.9*: Baum, H. (1982) *The Biochemists' Songbook*, 1st edn, Pergamon Press Ltd, reprinted by permission of Taylor and Francis Books Limited; *Figure 5.12*: 'Drugs used for slimming', © Times Newspapers Limited, 5th April 1934.

INDEX

Note: Entries in **bold** are key terms. Page numbers referring to information that is given only in a figure or caption are printed in *italics*.